Intermediate
Mathematical Analysis

Intermediate
Mathematical Analysis

ANTHONY E. LABARRE, JR.
Fresno State College

HOLT, RINEHART AND WINSTON, INC.
New York · Chicago · San Francisco · Atlanta
Dallas · Montreal · Toronto · London

To the memory of Mary Amelia Le Marchand Labarre

Preface

This book is an outgrowth of a set of notes that the author
wrote for a course designed to bridge the gap between the
elementary calculus and the advanced calculus as given at
Fresno State College for the past six years. Experience had
taught that some advanced calculus courses were too difficult for students just completing the typical freshman
analytic geometry and calculus sequence. Although a con-
siderable amount of the topology of the real numbers can
be readily generalized (by a mature mathematician) to
n-dimensional Euclidean space, evidently it is too much to
ask a student with only an elementary calculus background
to learn some topology of the real numbers, to immediately
generalize this to Euclidean n-space, and then to study functions with domain and range lying in such spaces. In order

to prepare the student for the level of abstraction necessary to accomplish a transition from "one-space" to "n-space" calculus, this book emphasizes basic theorems in their simplest setting, that is, it deals primarily with real-valued functions of a real variable, and, in supplements to certain chapters, indicates the situation encountered for complex numbers. It is only in Chapters 8 and 9 that functions of two variables will be found to be indispensable; except for these two chapters, supplements may be omitted without loss of continuity.

The basic assumption underlying the text is that the student has completed an elementary calculus course. Since emphasis is placed on concepts, as opposed to techniques, it is not essential, for example, that the student have at his fingertips a stock of tricks for integrating combinations of elementary functions. It is hoped, therefore, that the book will serve as a steppingstone for individuals who completed a course sequence in elementary calculus sometime ago and plan to study more advanced mathematics. It should be unnecessary for such students to take a refresher course in elementary calculus before studying this book.

For several years now, baccalaureate mathematics curricula have included a course in "modern abstract algebra," which is usually the first rigorous course in algebra (frequently the first rigorous course in mathematics) that the student encounters. Such a course paves the way to all subsequent study in the area of algebra. It is hoped that this text will serve a similar purpose in the area of analysis.

This text has been prepared with the advice and assistance of many individuals. The author is especially indebted to Edwin Hewitt, Editorial Consultant in Mathematics for the publisher. Dr. Hewitt made numerous helpful suggestions concerning the contents and exposition of the book and called my attention to the recent contribution to the theory of Fourier series by L. Carleson. My wife Gloria, beside showing understanding by living through it all, caught many errors in the proofreading task and helped with the preparation of the index. Finally, the staff of Holt, Rinehart and Winston, and especially Mrs. Elaine Wetterau, Senior Copy Editor in Mathematics, are to be complimented for their outstanding role in the production of the book.

A. E. L.

FRESNO, CALIFORNIA
FEBRUARY 1968

Contents

Intermediate
Mathematical Analysis

1

Sets, Relations, and Functions

INTRODUCTION

We make no attempt here to give an axiomatic treatment of set theory and the dependent concepts of relations and functions; our purpose is merely to review some results from this area which will be used subsequently.

Roughly speaking, a *set* is a collection of objects, a *relation* is a set whose members are ordered pairs, and a *function* is a special kind of relation. The main theme of this chapter is to elaborate on this statement. At the end of the chapter a basic theorem regarding *equivalence relations* is proved. This result finds widespread application in various fields of mathematics. Extensive use of it will be made in Chapter 4.

In illustrating some of the set-theoretic concepts, we assume the reader to know that if a and b are real numbers, then $|a - b|$ is the distance between a and b. In particular, $|x + 3| = |x - (-3)|$ is the distance between the points corresponding to the real numbers x and -3. Analytically, $|x + 3| \leq 5$ if and only if $-5 \leq x + 3 \leq 5$, that is, $-8 \leq x \leq 2$.

It is convenient to introduce some basic notation and terminology to be used throughout the text:

The symbol $\in$ means "belongs to" and $\notin$ means "does not belong to" when used in set-theoretic connotation.

The abbreviation iff means "if and only if."

The notation $\{x \mid P\}$ is used for "the set of all x having the property P."

The symbol $\exists$ means "there exists."

The symbol $\ni$ means "such that."

The symbol $\forall$ means "for every."

The symbol $\blacksquare$ is used to signal the end of a proof of a theorem.

The symbol $\Rightarrow$ means "implies." If $S \Rightarrow T$, we say that S is *sufficient* for T; alternatively, we say that T is *necessary* for S. The statement $S \Leftrightarrow T$ means $S \Rightarrow T$ and $T \Rightarrow S$. The *contrapositive* of $S \Rightarrow T$ is the statement not $T \Rightarrow$ not S. We assume that the reader knows that a statement and its contrapositive are equivalent; that is, either one implies the other.

1.1   SETS

In mathematics we single out certain objects for study. For example, in elementary algebra we study the set of all polynomials with integer coefficients. In plane analytic geometry we introduce the set of all points in the plane, that is, the set of all ordered pairs of real numbers. In solid analytic geometry we direct our attention to the set of all ordered triples of real numbers. Without committing ourselves as to the nature of the objects, let us single out some set X for study with the understanding that all objects under investigation belong to the basic set or *universe* X.

Definition 1.1.   Let A and B be sets. *A is a subset of B* (written $A \subset B$) iff
$$x \in A \Rightarrow x \in B.$$
We say *A is a proper subset of B* ($A \subsetneq B$) iff $A \subset B$ and $\exists\, x \in B \ni x \notin A$.

Example 1.1.   Let X be the set of all natural numbers: $X = \{1, 2, 3, \cdots\}$. The set $P = \{2, 3, 5, 7, \cdots\}$ of primes is a proper subset of X. The set A of all natural multiples of 6, that is,
$$A = \{x \mid x \in X \quad \text{and} \quad x = 6n, n \in X\}$$
is a proper subset of the set of all even natural numbers B where
$$B = \{x \mid x \in X \quad \text{and} \quad x = 2n, n \in X\}.$$

Definition 1.2.   Let A and B be sets. We say A *is equal to* B $(A = B)$ iff

$$A \subset B \quad \text{and} \quad B \subset A.$$

Therefore to prove two sets A, B equal, it is necessary and sufficient to show that

$$x \in A \Rightarrow x \in B$$

and

$$x \in B \Rightarrow x \in A.$$

From two given sets A and B, there are several useful ways to construct new sets. First, we can form the *union* of A and B.

Definition 1.3.   By the *union of A and B* is meant the set

$$A \cup B = \{x \mid x \text{ belongs to at least one (perhaps both) of } A \text{ or } B\}.$$

Thus, in Example 1.1 above, we have $A \cup B = B$.

We may also form the *intersection* of A and B by taking the elements common to A and B.

Definition 1.4.   By the *intersection of A and B* is meant the set

$$A \cap B = \{x \mid x \in A \quad \text{and} \quad x \in B\}.$$

In particular, if A and B have no elements in common, we write $A \cap B = \varnothing$ (the *empty set* or *null set*) and say that A and B are *disjoint*. Thus, in Example 1.1 we have $A \cap P = \varnothing$ and $A \cap B = A$.

A useful convention to which we adhere is that for all sets A we have $\varnothing \subset A$. The reasonableness of the convention becomes apparent when one considers the alternative: There exists a set A such that $\varnothing \not\subset A$. This is clearly unacceptable.

Also useful is the *complement of A with respect to B*, or, put another way, the *difference* $(B - A)$.

Definition 1.5.   By the *complement of A with respect to B* is meant the set

$$B - A = \{x \mid x \in B \quad \text{and} \quad x \notin A\}.$$

In particular, if we take B to be the space X, we usually call $X - A$ the *complement of A* (omitting the phrase "with respect to X") and give this set the special symbol cA. Thus

$$cA = \{x \mid x \in X \quad \text{and} \quad x \notin A\}.$$

There is an important connection involving complements, unions, and intersections. We have reference to "De Morgan's laws": $c(A \cup B) = cA \cap cB$, $c(A \cap B) = cA \cup cB$. (See Section 1.2, Exercise 3(d).)

Finally, we need the *Cartesian product* of A and B $(A \times B)$ which is the set of all ordered pairs (x, y) where $x \in A$ and $y \in B$. Formally, we have the following.

Definition 1.6. By the *Cartesian product of A and B* is meant the set
$$A \times B = \{(x, y) \mid x \in A \quad \text{and} \quad y \in B\}.$$

(NOTE: $A \times B$ makes sense even in case A and B are subsets of two entirely different sets of objects X and Y, say. On the other hand, in the special case where each of X and Y consists of all real numbers, then $X \times Y$ can be interpreted as the set of all points in the Cartesian plane.)

Example 1.2. The concept of Cartesian product simplifies many counting problems found, for example, in elementary combinatorics. To illustrate, suppose that we can travel from San Francisco to New York by plane, train, or car, and from New York to Le Havre, France, by plane or steamer. In how many ways can the trip from San Francisco to Le Havre via New York be made? Let
$$A = \{P, T, C\}$$

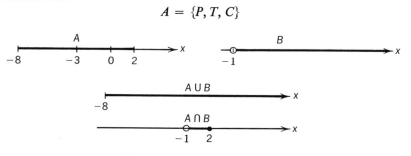

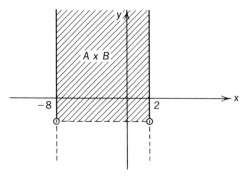

Fig. 1.1 Note: Broken lines denote sets of points excluded from the graph and small circles are used to signify that their centers are excluded from the graph.

(we have in mind that A is the set of modes of travel from San Francisco to New York—P for "plane," T for "train," and so forth). Let

$$B = \{P, S\}.$$

A trip from San Francisco to Le Havre via New York can be represented by an ordered pair of elements—the first entry from A and the second from B. Thus, (T, S) represents selection of train for the journey from San Francisco to New York, and steamer for the second leg of the journey. The problem can then be interpreted as counting the number of elements in the Cartesian product $A \times B$. Of course, there are six elements since

$$A \times B = \{(P, P), (P, S), (T, P), (T, S), (C, P), (C, S)\}.$$

It is true in general that if A has n elements and B has m elements, then $A \times B$ has nm elements. In elementary counting theory, this statement is referred to as "the fundamental counting principle."

Example 1.3. Let X be the set of all real numbers. If $x \in X$ and

$$A = \{x \mid |x + 3| \leq 5\}$$

and if

$$B = \{x \mid x > -1\},$$

then (see Fig. 1.1)

$$A \cup B = \{x \mid x \geq -8\}$$
$$A \cap B = \{x \mid -1 < x \leq 2\}$$
$$A \times B = \{(x, y) \mid -8 \leq x \leq 2 \text{ and } y > -1\}$$
$$B \times A = \{(x, y) \mid x > -1 \text{ and } -8 \leq y \leq 2\}$$
$$B - A = \{x \mid x > 2\}$$
$$A - B = \{x \mid -8 \leq x \leq -1\}$$
$$cA = \{x \mid x > 2 \text{ or } x < -8\}$$
$$cB = \{x \mid x \leq -1\}.$$

1.2 EXERCISES

Remember: If you are to prove that the sets C, D are equal, it is enough to do both of the following:
(1) Assume $x \in C$ and show that $x \in D$.
(2) Assume $x \in D$ and show that $x \in C$.

1. Show that union and intersection of sets have the following properties:

(a) $A \cup B = B \cup A$ (a') $A \cap B = B \cap A$

(b) $A \cup (B \cup C) = (A \cup B) \cup C$ (b') $A \cap (B \cap C) = (A \cap B) \cap C$

(c) $A \cup A = A$ (c') $A \cap A = A$

(d) $A \cup \varnothing = A$ (d') $A \cap X = A$, where $A \subset X$

(e) $A \cup X = X$, where $A \subset X$ (e') $A \cap \varnothing = \varnothing$

(f) $A \cap (B \cup C) = (A \cap B) \cup (A \cap C)$

(g) $A \cup (B \cap C) = (A \cup B) \cap (A \cup C)$.

2. Show that $A \subset B \Leftrightarrow A \cap B = A$.

3. Show that complementation of sets has the following properties:

(a) $A \cup cA = X$, $A \cap cA = \varnothing$

(b) $c\varnothing = X$, $cX = \varnothing$

(c) $c(cA) = A$

(d) $c(A \cup B) = cA \cap cB$ $\left.\right\}$ (De Morgan's laws)
    $c(A \cap B) = cA \cup cB$

(e) $A \subset B \Rightarrow cA \supset cB$

(f) $A - B = A \cap cB$

(g) $A \cap B = A - (A - B)$.

[HINT: Use 3(f).]

4. Define $A \triangle B = (A \cup B) - (A \cap B)$. (See Fig. 1.2.) $A \triangle B$ is called the *symmetric difference* of A and B. Show that with the operations

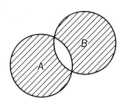

$A \triangle B$ is shaded.

Fig. 1.2   Symmetric difference of two sets.

$A \cap B$ and $A \triangle B$ the following are valid:

(a) $A \triangle B = B \triangle A$ ($\triangle$ is a commutative operation)

(b) $(A \triangle B) \triangle C = A \triangle (B \triangle C)$ ($\triangle$ is associative)

[HINT: Show that

$A \triangle B = (A \cap cB) \cup (B \cap cA)$,
making use of 3(f) and 3(d). Using

this, show that $(A \triangle B) \triangle C =$
$(A \cap cB \cap cC) \cup (cA \cap B \cap cC) \cup$
$(A \cap B \cap C) \cup (cA \cap cB \cap C)$.
From this last identity interchange A
and C to show that $(C \triangle B) \triangle A =$
$(A \triangle B) \triangle C$. Then invoke commutativity of $\triangle$ twice in the left member
of this equality to get $(C \triangle B) \triangle A =$
$A \triangle (C \triangle B) = A \triangle (B \triangle C)$.]

(c) $A \triangle \varnothing = A$ for all A ($\varnothing$ is the identity under $\triangle$)

(d) $A \cap (B \triangle C) = (A \cap B) \triangle (A \cap C)$ ($\cap$ is distributive with respect to $\triangle$)

(e) Show that if A, B are given, the equation $A \triangle Y = B$ has a solution Y.

[HINT: $A \triangle (A \triangle B) = ?$]

5. If A, B are given sets, does the equation $A \cup Y = B$ always have a solution Y? How about $A \cap Y = B$?

1.3 RELATIONS

It is instructive to begin with some examples.

Example 1.4. Let X be the set of all real numbers. Define

$$S = \{(x, y) \mid x \in X, y \in X, x < y\}.$$

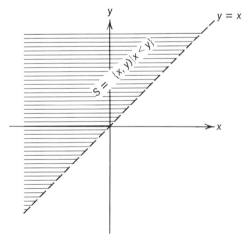

Fig. 1.3 Graph of the relation "less than."

Then the relation of "less than" for real numbers is completely specified by S in the sense that if $x < y$, then $(x, y) \in S$ and if $x \nless y$, then $(x, y) \notin S$. From the definition of S above, we see that S is a certain subset of the Cartesian product of the reals with themselves. The set of all $(x, y) \in S$ is called the *graph* of S. A geometric interpretation of S is shown in Fig. 1.3. Here it is understood that points in the shaded region belong to S since their coordinates satisfy the condition $x < y$ while points on the line $y = x$ or below it do not belong to S since, for them, $x \nless y$.

Example 1.5. The relation of congruence modulo 3 is important in the study of divisibility of integers by the integer 3. We say, of two integers x and y, that they are *congruent mod 3* [written $x \equiv y(3)$] iff their difference $x - y$ is divisible by 3, that is, iff there exists an integer k such that $x - y = 3k$. Thus, $17 \equiv 5(3)$ since $17 - 5 = 3 \cdot 4$, while $17 \not\equiv 6(3)$ since $17 - 6$ is not divisible by 3. Let us define

$$S = \{(x, y) \mid x, y \text{ integers}, x - y = 3k, k \text{ an integer}\}.$$

It is easy to see that S is then the set of all those lattice points of the plane (that is, points with integral coordinates) which belong to some member of the one-parameter family $x - y = 3k$ (k an integer) of straight lines with slope 1 and having a y intercept which is a multiple of 3 (see Fig. 1.4.).

———————————

Both of these examples—and many more—may be treated from a unified viewpoint by defining a *relation* to be any set of ordered pairs.

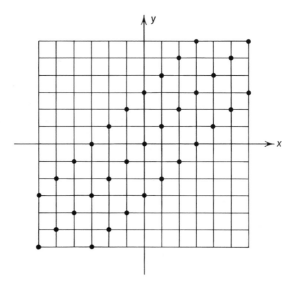

Fig. 1.4   Graph of the relation "congruence mod 3."

Definition 1.7. A *relation* is any subset S of $X \times Y$, that is, any set of ordered pairs. We say x *is S-related to y* (and write $x \, S \, y$) iff the ordered pair (x, y) belongs to S. We define the *domain* of the relation S to be the set of all first coordinates of members of S and the *range* of the relation S to be the set of all second coordinates of members of S. The set of all $(x, y) \in S$ is called the *graph* of S.

Remark

From a logical viewpoint we do not distinguish between a relation and its graph. In many instances, however, geometric interpretations can be given to a relation and this accounts for the choice of the word "graph."

Example 1.6. Let $S = \{(x, y) \mid |x - 1| \leq 2, |y| > 1\}$.

A geometric interpretation of S (the graph of S) is shown in Fig. 1.5. The broken lines denote sets of points excluded from S, and the small circles are used to signify that their centers are excluded from S.

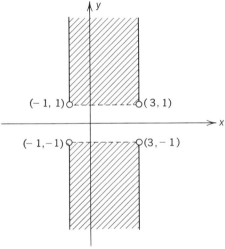

Fig. 1.5 Graph of $S = \{(x, y) \mid |x - 1| \leq 2, |y| > 1\}$.

Here, domain of $S = \{x \mid -1 \leq x \leq 3\}$, range of $S = \{y \mid y > 1$ or $y < -1\}$. We write $x \, S \, y$ if and only if (x, y) is a point in the shaded region of Fig. 1.5.

Definition 1.8. If S is the relation defined by a certain subset S of the Cartesian product $X \times Y$, then the *inverse of S*, denoted by S^{-1}, is the set

$$S^{-1} = \{(y, x) \mid (x, y) \in S\}.$$

Thus, to obtain the inverse relation to S one simply interchanges the coordinates in the ordered pairs belonging to S.

(NOTE: If S is a relation, the inverse relation S^{-1} always exists.)

Example 1.7.   If
$$S = \{(x, y) \mid x, y \text{ real}, x < y\}$$
then
$$S^{-1} = \{(x, y) \mid x, y \text{ real}, (y, x) \in S\}$$
$$= \{(x, y) \mid x, y \text{ real}, y < x\}.$$
Geometrically interpreted, S^{-1} would consist of the set of points *below* the line $y = x$. This example shows that the inverse S^{-1} of a relation S is not the same thing as the complement cS, for here $cS = \{(x, y) \mid x, y \text{ real}, x \geq y\}$.

Many of the relations that we shall consider can be interpreted as subsets of the xy plane. In this connection, it is useful to keep in mind that *an arbitrary subset S of the plane defines a relation, namely, the set of points belonging to S. One obtains the domain of S by projecting the points of S on the x axis and taking the collection of x coordinates of such points. Similarly, the range of S consists of the y coordinates of the projections of points of S on the y axis.*

1.4 EXERCISES

1. Define
$$S = \{(x, y) \mid x, y \text{ real}, x^2 + y^2 \leq 1\}.$$
Draw the graph of S and give its domain and range.

2. Let
$$S = \{(x, y) \mid x, y \text{ real}, ax + by + c > 0, a^2 + b^2 \neq 0\}.$$
(The condition $a^2 + b^2 \neq 0$ disallows the simultaneous vanishing of a and b. Why?)
Discuss the graph of S for the following situations:
   (a) $a = 0$
   (b) $b = 0$
   (c) $a \neq 0$ and $b \neq 0$.

3. (a) Show that a necessary and sufficient condition that
$$S = \{(x, y) \mid Ax^2 + Bxy + Cy^2 + Dx + Ey + F = 0,$$
$$B^2 - 4AC > 0, A^2 + C^2 \neq 0\}$$

have two straight lines as its graph is that the determinant

$$\begin{vmatrix} 2A & B & D \\ B & 2C & E \\ D & E & 2F \end{vmatrix} = 0.$$

[Solve the quadratic for x or y and examine the discriminant, requiring that it be a perfect square. (Why?)]

(b) Assuming the above condition to hold, describe the graph of

$$T = \{(x, y) \mid Ax^2 + Bxy + Cy^2 + Dx + Ey \geq 0\}.$$

4. Draw the graphs of the relations:

   (a) $M_2 = \{(x, y) \mid (x^2 + y^2)^{1/2} \leq 1\}$

   (b) $M_1 = \{(x, y) \mid |x| + |y| \leq 1\}$

   (c) $M_{3/2} = \{(x, y) \mid |x|^{2/3} + |y|^{2/3} \leq 1\}$

   (d) $M_\infty = \{(x, y) \mid \max(|x|, |y|) \leq 1\}.$

(NOTE: If a and b are real numbers, max (a, b) denotes the greater of a and b.) More precisely,

$$\max(a, b) = \begin{cases} a, & \text{if } a \geq b \\ b, & \text{if } b \geq a. \end{cases}$$

An alternative definition is this:

$$\max(a, b) = \frac{a + b}{2} + \frac{|a - b|}{2}.$$

Show that these definitions of max (a, b) are equivalent.

[HINT: $(a + b)/2$ is the midpoint of the segment joining a and b; $|a - b|/2$ is half the distance between a and b. These observations make the above equality plausible, but the student should give an analytic proof.]

1.5   FUNCTIONS

Now we come to the most important kind of relation—a function. Those special relations F with the property that for each x in the domain of F there is a unique y such that $(x, y) \in F$ are called *functions*. Stated analytically, we have:

Definition 1.9.   A relation F is a *function* iff

$$(x, y) \in F \quad \text{and} \quad (x, z) \in F \Rightarrow y = z.$$

The *domain D* of *F* is the set

$$D = \{x \mid \exists y \ni (x, y) \in F\}.$$

The *range R* of *F* is the set

$$R = \{y \mid \exists x \ni (x, y) \in F\}.$$

We say that *F* is a function *on D onto R*. If $(x, y) \in F$, we say *y* is the *image of x under the function F* and we write $y = F(x)$.

Thus the relation

$$S = \{(x, y) \mid x, y \text{ real}, x < y\}$$

is *not* a function since $(2, 3) \in S$ and $(2, 4) \in S$, but $3 \neq 4$. As a matter of fact, if the graph of a relation *S* consists of a subset of the Cartesian plane, we see that *S* will be a function iff whenever *x* belongs to the domain of *S*, the vertical line through $(x, 0)$ contains *one and only one* point belonging to the graph of *S*. The gist of the matter is this: In the case of a function we insist that for each *x* in the domain there is associated one and only one *y* in the range. In practice, a function is often specified by giving its domain and telling how, for each *x* in the domain, the function value $F(x)$ is obtained. Accordingly, we write $F(x)$ when we have a rule which associates with each *x* of a given set, exactly one member $F(x)$ of another set.

Example 1.8.   Consider the relation

$$S = \{(x, y) \mid x, y \text{ real}, y = x^3\}.$$

Its graph is shown in Fig. 1.6. In this case, *S* is indeed a function since for

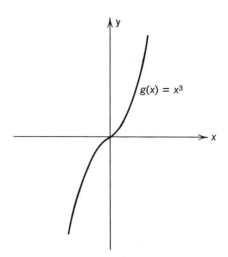

Fig. 1.6   Graph of the function $S = \{(x, g(x)) \mid g(x) = x^3\}$.

each real number x there is associated a unique $y = x^3$. Introducing notation, we write $g(x) = x^3$. Thus we have

$$g = \{(x, g(x)) \mid x \text{ real}, g(x) = x^3\}.$$

Note, however, that the relation

$$\{(x, y) \mid x, y \text{ real}, y \leq x^3\}$$

is *not* a function.

Example 1.9.   The relation

$$T = \{(x, y) \mid x, y \text{ real}, y = x^2\}$$

defines a well-known function. Its graph is shown in Fig. 1.7. The domain

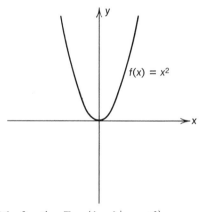

Fig. 1.7   Graph of the function $T = \{(x, y) \mid y = x^2\}$.

of T consists of all real numbers and its range consists of all nonnegative numbers.

While both $g = \{(x, g(x)) \mid g(x) = x^3, x \text{ real}\}$ and $f = \{(x, f(x)) \mid f(x) = x^2,$ $x \text{ real}\}$ are functions (and hence certainly both are relations), there is an important distinction here. The inverse of the first relation g is also a function while the inverse relation to f is *not* a function. The latter stems from the fact that given that $f(x)$ is the square of some real number, such a real number is not always uniquely determined (for example, if we are told that $f(x) = x^2 = 4$, we cannot say whether $x = +2$ or $x = -2$). On the other hand, if we are given the cube of some number, the number is uniquely determined (for example, $g(x) = x^3 = -8 \Rightarrow x = -2$). Here is another way of looking at it: In Fig. 1.7, if we pick an arbitrary number x in the domain of

$$T = \{(x, y) \mid x, y \text{ real}, y = x^2\}$$

and draw the corresponding vertical line through $(x, 0)$, this line will intersect the graph in one and only one point, namely, (x, x^2): Thus T is a function and we write

$$T = \{(x, f(x)) \mid x, f(x) \text{ real}, f(x) = x^2\}.$$

On the other hand, we cannot pick an arbitrary number in the domain of

$$T^{-1} = \{(x, y) \mid x, y \text{ real}, (y, x) \in T\}$$
$$= \{(x, y) \mid x, y \text{ real}, x = y^2\}$$

(the graph of T^{-1} is shown in Fig. 1.8), draw the corresponding vertical line

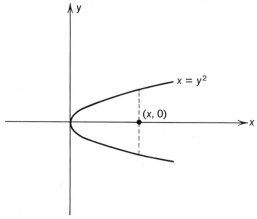

Fig. 1.8   The relation $T^{-1} = \{(x, y) \mid x = y^2\}$ is *not* a function.

through $(x, 0)$, and guarantee that this line will intersect the graph in one and only one point. With

$$S = \{(x, y) \mid x, y \text{ real}, y = x^3\},$$

however, we have

$$S^{-1} = \{(x, y) \mid x, y \text{ real}, x = y^3\}$$

and both S and S^{-1} are functions.

When a function has an inverse function, we say that the function establishes a *one-to-one correspondence* between the elements of its domain and its range since the function associates with element x in the domain exactly one element in its range, and the existence of the inverse function guarantees that no more than one element of the domain is associated with a given element of the range. More precisely, we have:

Definition 1.10.   Let F be a relation with domain D and range R. We say that F is a *one-to-one correspondence* between D and R if both F and F^{-1}

are functions. We say that F is a function on D onto R, and that F^{-1} is the inverse function of F. Note that F^{-1} is on R onto D.

The set notation used above is very valuable in making the concept of a function and its inverse precise. In practice we need less elaborate notation and more concise criteria for the existence of the inverse function. The situation most frequently encountered is this: we have some rule which associates with each object x of a certain set D, a unique object f(x) of a second set R; that is, for an arbitrary element $x_1 \in D$, the condition

$$x_1 = x_2 \Rightarrow f(x_1) = f(x_2) \tag{1.1}$$

holds, meaning that the set $f = \{(x, f(x)) \mid x \in D\}$ is a function on D. Conversely, if for an arbitrary element $f(x_1) \in R$, the condition

$$f(x_1) = f(x_2) \Rightarrow x_1 = x_2 \tag{1.2}$$

holds, then f has an inverse function; that is, the set $f^{-1} = \{(f(x), x) \mid f(x) \in R\}$ is a function. If both (1.1) and (1.2) hold, then we say f is a one-to-one function on D onto R.

Example 1.10. Let $f(x) = |x|$, x a real number. Is $f = \{(x, |x|) \mid x \text{ real}\}$ a function, and if it is, does f have an inverse function?

Since $x_1 = x_2 \Rightarrow f(x_1) = |x_1| = |x_2| = f(x_2)$, f is indeed a function whose domain is all real numbers (which we describe by writing $\{x \mid -\infty < x < \infty\}$); the range of f is the set of all nonnegative reals. On the other hand, (1.2) above fails since

$$f(-1) = f(1) = 1, \quad \text{yet} \quad -1 \neq 1.$$

Therefore, the function f does not have an inverse function.

Example 1.11. Let $g(x) = \langle x \rangle$, where $\langle x \rangle$ denotes the distance between the real number x and the nearest integer to x.

(NOTE: If $x = 0.5$, the nearest integer may be taken to be either 0 or 1; in any event, $\langle 0.5 \rangle = 0.5$.)

Thus, $g(1) = 0$, $g(1.2) = 0.2$, $g(1.5) = 0.5$, $g(1.7) = 0.3$. We see that $g(x)$ defines a function, for

$$x_1 = x_2 \Rightarrow g(x_1) = \langle x_1 \rangle = \langle x_2 \rangle = g(x_2)$$

(the implication here being valid because of the uniqueness of the *distance* between x and the nearest integer). However, $0 = \langle 1 \rangle = \langle 2 \rangle$ does not imply $1 = 2$ and, consequently, g does not have an inverse function. We emphasize that the *relation*

$$S = \{(x, y) \mid x \text{ real}, y = \langle x \rangle\}$$

does have an inverse *relation*

$$S^{-1} = \{(x, y) \mid (y, x) \in S\}.$$

Example 1.12.   Consider the formula $f(x) = (x - 2)/(x + 3)$. The expression $(x - 2)/(x + 3)$ is meaningful for all real numbers x except $x = -3$, so we may form the set $f = \{(x, (x - 2)/(x + 3)) \mid x \text{ real}, x \neq -3\}$. For each real number $x \neq -3$ which is substituted into $(x - 2)/(x + 3)$ we obtain exactly one real number after carrying out the indicated operations. Analytically, $u = v \neq -3 \Rightarrow f(u) = (u - 2)/(u + 3) = f(v) = (v - 2)/(v + 3)$. We conclude, therefore, that f defines a function whose domain D is all real numbers except -3. We write

$$D = \{x \mid x \neq -3\}.$$

To determine the range of f, consider any fixed real number y and ask whether or not there exists an $x \in D$ such that

$$y = \frac{x - 2}{x + 3},$$

that is, is y the image under f of some real number x? This is equivalent to asking if we can solve the equation

$$y(x + 3) = x - 2$$

for x. This can be done iff we can solve

$$x(y - 1) = -2 - 3y \tag{1.3}$$

for x. Finally, (1.3) can be solved for x iff $y \neq 1$ (because we have to divide by $y - 1 \neq 0$), the solution being

$$x = \frac{2 + 3y}{1 - y}. \tag{1.4}$$

Thus the range of f consists of all real numbers except 1. The graph of this function is shown in Fig. 1.9. It is obvious on geometric grounds that f has an inverse function. Here is an analytic proof:

$$f(u) = f(v) \Rightarrow \frac{u - 2}{u + 3} = \frac{v - 2}{v + 3} \Rightarrow (u - 2)(v + 3) = (v - 2)(u + 3)$$

$$\Rightarrow uv - 2v + 3u - 6 = vu - 2u + 3v - 6$$
$$\Rightarrow -2v + 3u = -2u + 3v \Rightarrow 5(u - v) = 0 \Rightarrow u = v.$$

Thus the function f^{-1} exists. From (1.4) above we may write

$$f^{-1}(y) = \frac{2 + 3y}{1 - y}.$$

Of course the domain and range of f^{-1} are the range and domain, respectively, of f. Note that f is a one-to-one function on $D = \{x \mid x \neq -3\}$ onto $R = \{y \mid y \neq 1\}$.

Because of its importance in mathematics, we call attention to the special kind of function called a sequence.

Definition 1.11.   A *sequence* is a function whose domain consists of all natural numbers (that is, positive integers).

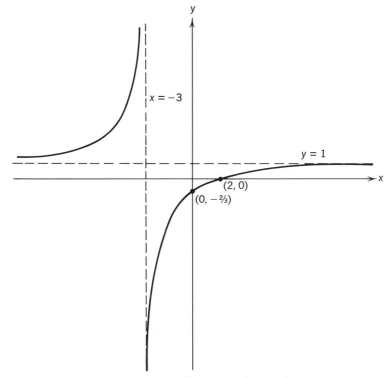

Fig. 1.9   Graph of the function $f = \{[x, (x - 2)/(x + 3)] \mid x \neq -3\}$.

By convention, a sequence $\{a_n\}$ is indicated by writing some of the elements of its range:

$$a_1, a_2, a_3, \cdots, a_n, \cdots.$$

If we wanted to be more precise, emphasizing that we have a function whose domain is the set of all natural numbers, we would write the elements of a sequence as the set

$$\{(1, a_1), (2, a_2), (3, a_3), \cdots, (n, a_n), \cdots\}.$$

We shall, however, use the abbreviated notation above, writing only the second entries of the ordered pairs.

As an example, we cite the sequence $\{p_n\}$ of prime numbers:

$$p_1 = 2, p_2 = 3, p_3 = 5, p_4 = 7, \cdots.$$

Example 1.13. Consider the sequence $\{a_n\}$ of real numbers defined by $a_n = 2^{-n}$. Its domain is, of course, the set of positive integers. Its range is the set $\{1/2, 1/2^2, 1/2^3, \cdots, 1/2^n, \cdots\}$ of all reciprocals of positive integral powers of 2.

Example 1.14. Let us define

$$A_n = \{x \mid |x| > n\}, \, n = 1, 2, 3, \cdots.$$

The sequence $\{A_n\}$ has all positive integers as its domain and its range is the set $\{A_1, A_2, A_3, \cdots, A_n, \cdots\}$ of sets, where we may also describe A_n by $A_n = \{x \mid x > n \text{ or } x < -n\}$.

Example 1.15. Put $a_1 = 1$, $a_2 = 2$, and $a_{n+1} = a_n + a_{n-1}$ if $n > 2$. The sequence defined in this way is the so-called Fibonnacci sequence. Its first few terms are 1, 2, 3, 5, 8, 13, 21, $\cdots$.

———————

We sometimes have occasion to consider the sequence $\{S_n\}$ constructed from a given sequence $\{a_k\}$ by summing the first n terms of $\{a_k\}$; that is,

$$S_n = a_1 + a_2 + a_3 + \cdots + a_n$$

or, more concisely,

$$S_n = \sum_{k=1}^{n} a_k.$$

This sequence is called a *series*. It is denoted by the symbol

$$\sum_{k=1}^{\infty} a_k = a_1 + a_2 + a_3 + \cdots.$$

1.6 EXERCISES

In Exercises 1 to 6 below consider the relations defined, sketch the graph, identify the domain and range, tell whether the relation is a function or not, and, if a function, determine whether the inverse function exists or not. Assume that x, y are real numbers.

1. $S = \{(x, y) \mid y = (x + |x|)/2\}$.

   [HINT: First show that if $T = \{(x, y) \mid y = \max(0, x)\}$, then $S = T$.]
2. $S = \{(x, y) \mid y = |x^2 - 1|\}$.
3. $S = \{(x, y) \mid y = 1 \text{ if } x \in [0, 1], y = 0 \text{ if } x \notin [0, 1]\}$.
4. $S = \{(x, y) \mid 0 \leq x \leq 1, y = \min[\sin x, \max(4x - 2, x - 1)]\}$ for each $x \in [0, 1]\}$.
5. $S = \{(x, y) \mid y = 3x/2 \text{ if } 0 \leq x \leq \frac{1}{2}; y = x/2 + \frac{3}{4}$
   if $\frac{1}{2} < x \leq 1\}$.
6. $S = \{(x, y) \mid y = x/(x + 2)\}$.
7. Let $S = \{(x, y) \mid x, y \text{ real}, |x| < y\}$. Compare S^{-1} with cS.

8. Given a sequence S_1, S_2, $\cdots$ of partial sums; that is, $S_n = x_1 + x_2 + \cdots + x_n$. Show how to recover the sequence x_1, x_2, $\cdots$ from which the partial sum sequence was constructed.

9. Prove, for the Fibonnacci sequence defined in Example 1.15, that $a_n < [(1 + \sqrt{5})/2]^n$ for $n \geq 1$.

1.7 SETS AGAIN

We have defined the union $A \cup B$ and intersection $A \cap B$ of two sets A, B. It is useful to extend our definitions of union and intersection to handle the case where more than two sets are given.

Definition 1.12. Let the n sets A_1, A_2, $\cdots$, A_n be given. We define the *union* of these sets to be the set

$$A_1 \cup A_2 \cup \cdots \cup A_n = \{x \mid x \in A_k \text{ for some } k = 1, 2, \cdots, n\}.$$

It is convenient to condense the notation, writing

$$\bigcup_{k=1}^{n} A_k = A_1 \cup A_2 \cup \cdots \cup A_n.$$

Thus, $x \in \bigcup_{k=1}^{n} A_k$ iff x belongs to at least one of the sets A_1, A_2, $\cdots$, A_n. We can go still further.

Definition 1.13. Let the sequence A_1, A_2, A_3, $\cdots$ of sets be given. By the *union* of this sequence of sets (written $A_1 \cup A_2 \cup A_3 \cup \cdots$ or simply $\bigcup_{k=1}^{\infty} A_k$) is meant the set

$$\bigcup_{k=1}^{\infty} A_k = \{x \mid x \in A_k \text{ for some } k = 1, 2, \cdots\}.$$

Example 1.16. Suppose $A_k = \left\{ x \mid -\dfrac{1}{k} < x \leq \dfrac{1}{k}, k = 1, 2, \cdots \right\}$. It is not difficult to see that

$$\bigcup_{k=1}^{5} A_k = (-1, 1].$$

[Recall that $(-1, 1] = \{x \mid -1 < x \leq 1\}$.] Also

$$\bigcup_{k=1}^{\infty} A_k = (-1, 1].$$

Analogously, we lay down the following definition.

Definition 1.14.   *The intersection of the sets A_1, A_2, $\cdots$, A_n is the set*

$$\bigcap_{k=1}^{n} A_k = \{x \mid x \in A_k \text{ for all } k = 1, 2, \cdots, n\}$$

and *the intersection of the sequence $\{A_n\}$ of sets is the set*

$$\bigcap_{k=1}^{\infty} A_k = \{x \mid x \in A_k \text{ for all } k = 1, 2, \cdots\}.$$

Example 1.17.   If $A_k = \left\{ x \mid -\dfrac{1}{k} < x < \dfrac{1}{k}, = 1, 2, \cdots \right\}$, then

$$\bigcap_{k=1}^{5} A_k = (-\tfrac{1}{5}, \tfrac{1}{5}); \qquad \bigcap_{k=1}^{\infty} A_k = \{0\}.$$

As a matter of fact, the definitions can be extended to more general situa-

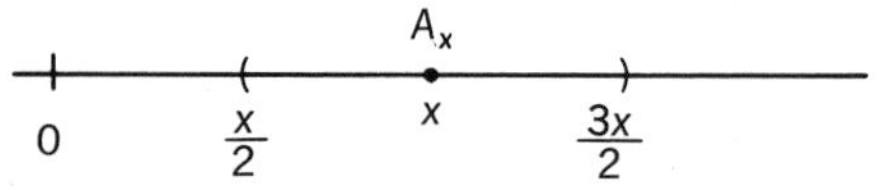

Fig. 1.10   A set A_x is associated with each $x > 0$.

tions. Thus, if we associate with each positive real number x the set A_x of real numbers defined by (see Fig. 1.10 for geometric interpretation)

$$A_x = \left\{ y \mid \frac{x}{2} < y < \frac{3x}{2} \right\},$$

that is, A_x is the open interval $(x/2, 3x/2)$, and if we define

$$\bigcup_{x \in (0,1)} A_x$$

to mean the set of all real numbers u such that u belongs to at least one of the A_x (for $0 < x < 1$), then

$$\bigcup_{x \in (0,1)} A_x = \left(0, \frac{3}{2} \right).$$

Similarly, we define

$$\bigcap_{x \in (0,1)} A_x = \{u \mid u \in A_x \text{ for every } x \in (0, 1)\}$$

and verify that

$$\bigcap_{x \in (0,1)} A_x = \varnothing.$$

If the idea is clear, the reader will have no difficulty in grasping the following more general situation: Suppose that for each element a of an arbitrary set A (called an "index" set), we have associated a set which we denote by

A_a. (In other words, we have a function whose domain is A and each element of the range is a set A_a where $a \in A$; the function is therefore the set of ordered pairs (a, A_a) with domain A). We may then introduce

Definition 1.15. Let $\{(a, A_a) \mid a \in A\}$ be a function with domain A and range a collection of sets A_a, $a \in A$. We define the *union*

$$\bigcup_{a \in A} A_a = \{x \mid x \in A_a \text{ for some } a \in A\}$$

and the *intersection*

$$\bigcap_{a \in A} A_a = \{x \mid x \in A_a \text{ for all } a \in A\}.$$

Example 1.18. Let A be the set of all integers—positive, negative, and 0. Put $A_k = \{x \mid x \text{ is real}, x \neq k\}$, $k = \cdots, -3, -2, -1, 0, 1, 2, 3, \cdots$. Then $\bigcup_{k \in A} A_k$ is the set of all real numbers and $\bigcap_{k \in A} A_k$ is the set of those real numbers which are not integers.

Even in the very general situation of Definition 1.15 De Morgan's laws hold (see Section 1.2, Exercise 3) and the proof is no more difficult than for the case $c(A \cup B) = cA \cap cB$; that is to say, we have that "the complement of a union is the intersection of the complements":

$$c\left(\bigcup_{a \in A} A_a\right) = \bigcap_{a \in A} cA_a.$$

Indeed, $x \in c(\bigcup_{a \in A} A_a) \Leftrightarrow x \notin \bigcup_{a \in A} A_a \Leftrightarrow x \notin A_a$ for every $a \in A \Leftrightarrow x \in cA_a$ for every $a \in A \Leftrightarrow x \in \bigcap_{a \in A} cA_a$.

1.8 EXERCISES

1. Let $A_n = \{x \mid x \text{ is real}, 1 - 1/n < x < 2 + 1/n\}$, $n = 1, 2, 3, \cdots$.

   (a) Interpret each of A_1, A_2, and A_3 geometrically.
   (b) Find $\bigcup_{n=1}^{3} A_n$.
   (c) Find $\bigcap_{n=1}^{3} A_n$.
   (d) Show that $A_1 \supset A_2 \supset A_3 \supset A_4 \supset \cdots$.
   (e) Find $\bigcup_{n=1}^{\infty} A_n$.
   (f) Find $\bigcap_{n=1}^{\infty} A_n$.

2. Let $A_n = \left\{x \mid x \text{ is real}, |x| \geq \dfrac{1}{n}\right\}$, $n = 1, 2, 3, \cdots$.

   (a) Interpret each of A_1, A_2, and A_3 geometrically.
   (b) Find $\bigcup_{n=1}^{3} A_n$.

(c) Find $\bigcap_{n=1}^{3} A_n$.

(d) Show that $A_1 \subset A_2 \subset A_3 \subset A_4 \subset \cdots$.

(e) Find $\bigcup_{n=1}^{\infty} A_n$.

(f) Find $\bigcap_{n=1}^{\infty} A_n$.

3. Let $A_n = \{x \mid x \text{ is real}, -n < x \leq 1/n\}, n = 1, 2, 3, \cdots$.

(a) Interpret each of A_1, A_2, and A_3 geometrically.

(b) Find $c\left(\bigcup_{n=1}^{3} A_n\right)$.

(c) Find $\bigcup_{n=1}^{3} (cA_n)$.

(d) Find $\bigcap_{n=1}^{\infty} (cA_n)$.

(e) Find $\bigcup_{n=1}^{\infty} (cA_n)$.

(f) Find $\bigcup_{n=1}^{\infty} \left(\bigcap_{k=1}^{n} A_k\right)$. Ans. $(-1, 1)$.

4. Define

$$A_n = \{(x, y) \mid \ |x| < 1/n, |y| \leq 1/n\}, n = 1, 2, 3, \cdots.$$

Find

$$\bigcup_{n=1}^{\infty} A_n, \ \bigcap_{n=1}^{\infty} A_n, \ c\left(\bigcup_{n=1}^{\infty} A_n\right), \ \bigcap_{n=1}^{\infty} (cA_n).$$

5. Let $\mathcal{A}$ be the unit square; that is,

$$\mathcal{A} = \{(x, y) \mid 0 \leq x \leq 1, 0 \leq y \leq 1\}.$$

Let $a = (x, y) \in \mathcal{A}$ and put $|a|^2 = x^2 + y^2$. Define

$$S_a = \{(u, v) \mid u^2 + v^2 < |a|^2\}.$$

Thus with each point a of the unit square we have associated a certain set S_a (draw the picture!).

(a) Find S_a if $a = (0, 0)$; if $a = (\frac{1}{4}, \frac{1}{2})$; if $a = (\frac{1}{2}, \frac{1}{2})$; if $a = (1, 1)$.

(b) Find $\bigcup_{a \in \mathcal{A}} S_a$.

(c) Find $\bigcap_{a \in \mathcal{A}} S_a$.

6. For each natural number $n = 1, 2, 3, \cdots$, define

$$A_n = \{(x, y) \mid \ |x + 3| > \frac{1}{n}, |y| < \frac{1}{n}, x, y \text{ real numbers}\}.$$

(a) Shade the set A_1 of points in the plane; shade A_2 also.

(b) Find $\bigcap_{n=1}^{\infty} A_n$.

(c) Find $\bigcup_{n=1}^{\infty} A_n$.

7. Let the sequence $A_1, A_2, \cdots$ of sets be given.

(a) By the *limit superior* of this sequence (written lim sup A_n) is meant the set of all points x such that x belongs to an infinite number of the sets; that is, lim sup $A_n = \{x \mid x \in A_k \text{ for infinitely many indices } k\}$. Show that

$$\limsup A_n = \bigcap_{n=1}^{\infty} \bigcup_{k=n}^{\infty} A_k.$$

(b) By the *limit inferior* of the sequence A_1, A_2, $\cdots$ of sets (written lim inf A_n) is meant the set of all points x such that x belongs to all of the terms of the sequence A_1, A_2, $\cdots$ from some index on; that is, x belongs to all but a finite number of the sets A_1, A_2, $\cdots$. To be precise,

$$\lim \inf A_n = \{x \mid \exists\, k(x) \ni x \in A_k, A_{k+1}, A_{k+2}, \cdots\}.$$

Prove

$$\lim \inf A_n = \bigcup_{n=1}^{\infty} \bigcap_{k=n}^{\infty} A_k.$$

(c) We say that the *limit* of the sequence A_1, A_2, $\cdots$ exists (and write lim A_n) iff lim inf A_n = lim sup A_n. Show that if $A_1 \subset A_2 \subset A_3 \subset \cdots$, then lim $A_n = \bigcup_{k=1}^{\infty} A_k$. Finally, show that if $A_1 \supset A_2 \supset A_3 \supset \cdots$, then lim $A_n = \bigcap_{k=1}^{\infty} A_k$.

(d) Find lim A_n for the sequences defined in Exercises 1, 2, and 3 above.

(e) Show that lim inf $A_n \subset$ lim sup A_n.

1.9 EQUIVALENCE RELATIONS

We want to prove a theorem which accounts for the importance of a special kind of relation known as an equivalence relation. We shall use the relation of congruence modulo 3 to provide a concrete example of a very general situation. Let Z be the set of all integers. We divide each element of Z by 3 and focus our attention on the remainder obtained.* We say that two integers x, y are *congruent modulo 3* [written $x \equiv y(3)$] provided the remainders obtained when x and y are divided by 3 are equal. This is the same as requiring that the difference $x - y$ be a multiple of 3; that is, $x - y = 3k$ where k is an integer. Thus

$$5 \equiv 8(3), \qquad \text{but } 5 \not\equiv 7(3).$$

It is a simple matter to check that the relation of congruence modulo 3 has the following properties:

(1) $x \equiv x(3)$ for all $x \in Z$ (reflexivity)
(2) If $x \equiv y(3)$, then $y \equiv x(3)$ (symmetry)
(3) If $x \equiv y(3)$ and if $y \equiv z(3)$, then $x \equiv z(3)$ (transitivity).

---

* We insist that the remainder be one of the numbers 0, 1, 2. Thus since $7 = 3 \times 2 + 1$, the quotient when 7 is divided by 3 is 2, the remainder is 1. Also $-8 = 3(-3) + 1$, so the quotient when -8 is divided by 3 is -3, the remainder is 1. These facts follow from a well-known theorem of algebra known as the "division algorithm": For given integers a, b, with $b > 0$, there exist unique integers q and r such that $a = bq + r$, $0 \leq r < b$.

Using our notation for a relation as a set of ordered pairs as introduced earlier, we can describe the relation of *congruence modulo 3* as the set M_3 defined by

$$M_3 = \{(x, y) \mid x, y \in Z \text{ and } x \equiv y(3)\}.$$

In this notation, the properties (1), (2), (3) enumerated above may be expressed by

(1) $(x, x) \in M_3$ for all $x \in Z$
(2) $(x, y) \in M_3 \Rightarrow (y, x) \in M_3$
(3) $(x, y) \in M_3$ and $(y, z) \in M_3 \Rightarrow (x, z) \in M_3$.

In general, we make the following definition.

Definition 1.16.   Any subset E of the Cartesian product $A \times A$ with the properties

(1) $(x, x) \in E$ for all $x \in A$ (reflexive property)
(2) $(x, y) \in E \Rightarrow (y, x) \in E$ (symmetric property)
(3) $(x, y) \in E$ and $(y, z) \in E \Rightarrow (x, z) \in E$ (transitive property)

is called an *equivalence relation on A.*

(NOTE: The domain of the equivalence relation E = range of E = A.)
For brevity, we sometimes write $x \sim y$ to denote that the ordered pair (x, y) belongs to the relation E. (In our present example where the "modulus" 3 is fixed, we use the symbol $\equiv$ instead of the symbol $\sim$.) In general, if we have a rule which specifies of every two elements x, y of a set A whether or not it is permissible to write $x \sim y$, then we see from the definition above that the collection of ordered pairs (x, y) for which $x \sim y$ holds is an equivalence relation iff

(1) $x \sim x$ for all $x \in A$ (the *reflexive* property)
(2) $x \sim y \Rightarrow y \sim x$ (the *symmetric* property)
(3) $x \sim y$ and $y \sim z \Rightarrow x \sim z$ (the *transitive* property).

Example 1.19.   Let the set A consist of all triangles in the plane. Let $x \sim y$ mean that triangle x is *similar* to triangle y. Then, clearly, the ordered pairs (x, y) for which we have $x \sim y$ constitute an equivalence relation since similarity of triangles has the reflexive, symmetric, and transitive properties.

Example 1.20.   Let A denote the set of all straight lines in the plane; that is,

$$A = \{ax + by + c = 0 \mid a, b, c \text{ real numbers}, a^2 + b^2 \neq 0\}.$$

Let $\ell_1, \ell_2 \in A$ where ℓ_i represents the linear equation $a_i x + b_i y + c_i = 0$. Define $\ell_1 \parallel \ell_2$ to mean that the following determinant vanishes:

$$\begin{vmatrix} a_1 & b_1 \\ a_2 & b_2 \end{vmatrix} = 0.$$

It is an interesting exercise to check that "parallelism" ($\ell_1, \parallel \ell_2$) has the three properties required for an equivalence relation. We leave this to the reader.

———

Let us now return to the relation of congruence modulo 3. Observing that any integer when divided by 3 must leave a remainder of 0, 1, or 2 (that is, must be congruent to one of the three integers 0, 1, or 2) we may use the relation to define three sets, A_0, A_1, A_2, placing a given integer x into the set A_0, A_1, or A_2 according as it is congruent modulo 3 to 0, 1, or 2, respectively. Thus we define

$$A_k = \{x \mid x \equiv k(3)\}, \; k = 0, 1, 2.$$

We call the sets A_k, $k = 0, 1, 2$ *equivalence classes*. In general, we have the following definition.

Definition 1.17.   If E is an equivalence relation $\sim$ whose domain is A, then the sets E_x, $x \in A$, defined by

$$E_x = \{y \mid y \sim x\}$$

or alternatively

$$E_x = \{y \mid (y, x) \in E\}$$

are called *equivalence classes*.

We see immediately that in the present example

(1) $A_0 \cup A_1 \cup A_2 = Z$

and

(2) $A_i \cap A_j = \emptyset$ if $A_i \neq A_j$.

In other words, (1) says that the union of the sets A_0, A_1, A_2 is the entire domain Z of the relation of congruence modulo 3, and (2) tells us that the sets A_0, A_1, A_2 are disjoint in pairs. Such a splitting of all of Z into pairwise disjoint sets is called a *partition* of Z. In general, we have the following definition.

Definition 1.18.   Let A be an arbitrary set. By a *partition of A* is meant a collection of nonempty pairwise disjoint subsets of A whose union is A.

The above example illustrates the following important theorem.

■ **Theorem 1.1.**   If E is an equivalence relation with domain A, then the corresponding equivalence classes form a partition of A.

Proof: We are to show that the equivalence classes, defined by

$$E_x = \{y \mid (y, x) \in E\},$$

where x ranges over A, form a partition of A. This means we must show that

(1) the union of all E_x's, as x varies over A, is equal to A, and
(2) distinct equivalence classes are disjoint.

The equality

$$\bigcup_{x \in A} E_x = A \tag{1.5}$$

can easily be checked: Let $y \in \bigcup_{x \in A} E_x$. Then, (by definition of union) y belongs to some E_x, meaning $(y, x) \in E$. This implies that $y \in A$ and therefore we have that

$$\bigcup_{x \in A} E_x \subset A.$$

On the other hand, if $u \in A$, then $(u, u) \in E$ and consequently $u \in E_u$, which in turn implies $u \in \bigcup_{x \in A} E_x$. Thus $A \subset \bigcup_{x \in A} E_x$, completing the proof of (1.5).

Now to show that distinct classes are pairwise disjoint, we are given that $E_x \neq E_y$ and are to conclude that $E_x \cap E_y = \varnothing$. We prove the contrapositive. If $E_x \cap E_y \neq \varnothing$, then there is an element $u \in E_x \cap E_y$. This leads to $(u, x) \in E$ and $(u, y) \in E$. By symmetry and transitivity of E we have that $(x, y) \in E$. We can use this fact to show that $E_x = E_y$. For, let $z \in E_x$. Then, by definition of E_x, $(z, x) \in E$. But we know that $(x, y) \in E$ and consequently $(z, y) \in E$, that is, $z \in E_y$. Thus $E_x \subset E_y$. The fact that $E_y \subset E_x$ is shown in a similar manner. ∎

Our theorem can be summarized by saying that every equivalence relation on a set A yields a partition of A. But the converse is also true, as we now show.

■ **Theorem 1.2.**   Every partition of a set A yields an equivalence relation on A.

Proof: We take a given set T of the partition (see Fig. 1.11) and form the Cartesian product $T \times T$. Do this for every set T of the partition. The union of the sets of ordered pairs formed in this manner is the equivalence relation we seek. To prove this, we write our hypotheses:

$$A = \bigcup_{\alpha \in \mathfrak{a}} T_\alpha \tag{1.6}$$

and

$$T_\alpha \neq T_\beta \Rightarrow T_\alpha \cap T_\beta = \varnothing. \tag{1.7}$$

We define

$$E = \{(x, y) \mid x \in T_\alpha \text{ and } y \in T_\alpha \text{ for some } \alpha\}. \tag{1.8}$$

Now we have to prove that E is an equivalence relation on A.

(1) $(x, x) \in E$ for all $x \in A$. For, $x \in A$ implies $x \in T_\alpha$ for some α [this follows from hypothesis (1.6) above], and therefore, by our construction (1.8) of E, $(x, x) \in E$.

(2) $(x, y) \in E \Rightarrow (y, x) \in E$ by our definition (1.8) of E.

Finally, to show

$$(3) \quad (x, y) \in E \quad \text{and} \quad (y, z) \in E \Rightarrow (x, z) \in E,$$

we first note that $x, y \in T_\alpha$ and $y, z \in T_\beta$, by assumption. It follows that $T_\alpha \cap T_\beta \neq \varnothing$ since y belongs to both T_α and T_β. By (1.7) above we conclude that $T_\alpha = T_\beta$. Thus, all three of x, y, z belong to T_α. In particular $x, z \in T_\alpha$ and this means that $(x, z) \in E$, by definition of E. ∎

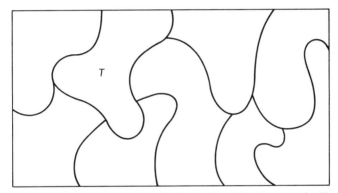

Fig. 1.11   A "partition" of the set A of points enclosed by the rectangle. The "pieces" of the "jigsaw puzzle" are the equivalence classes.

The last two theorems assert the existence of a one-to-one correspondence between equivalence relations with a given domain and partitions of that domain. Thus, Theorem 1.1 asserts the existence of a function which assigns to each equivalence relation on A a partition of A, and Theorem 1.2 asserts the existence of the inverse of that function.

Example 1.21.   Let (x, y), (u, v) be two points in the plane. Define $(x, y) \sim (u, v)$ iff $\exists$ positive integer n such that $n - 1 \leq |x| + |y| < n$ and $n - 1 \leq |u| + |v| < n$. Show that $\sim$ is an equivalence relation and describe the equivalence classes.

If (x, y) is any point in the plane, it is clear that $|x| + |y|$ is a nonnegative real number and hence there exists a positive integer n such that $n - 1 \leq |x| + |y| < n$, that is, $(x, y) \sim (x, y)$. The relation $\sim$ is reflexive.

Symmetry and transitivity of $\sim$ follow immediately from the definition. A typical equivalence class is shown in Fig. 1.12.

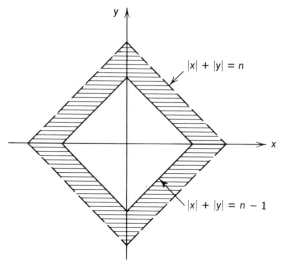

Fig. 1.12   A typical equivalence class in Example 1.21.

1.10 EXERCISES

In Exercises 1 to 5 consider the given relations. Determine whether each is reflexive, symmetric, or transitive. Which are equivalence relations?

1. $S = \{(A, B) \mid A, B$ are subsets of the real numbers and $A = B\}$.
2. $S = \{(A, B) \mid A, B$ are subsets of the real numbers and $A \subset B\}$.
3. $S = \{(x, y) \mid x, y$ real; $x \leq y\}$.
4. $S = \{(x, y) \mid x, y \in [-\frac{1}{2}, \frac{1}{2}], x - y$ is a rational number$\}$.
5. $S = \{(x, y) \mid x, y$ are real numbers and $x^2 + y^2 \leq 1\}$.
6. Prove that if S is an equivalence relation, then
   (a) $S^{-1} = S$,
   (b) cS is not an equivalence relation.
7. It is interesting to interpret geometrically the conditions for an equivalence relation in the special case where the relation is a subset of the xy plane. In doing this, it is convenient to refer to the straight line $y = x$ as "the diagonal"; that is, the diagonal is the set of points of the form (x, x). Prove that the conditions for an equivalence relation then become:
   (a) Over the domain of the equivalence relation S, the corresponding portion of the diagonal is contained in S (reflexivity).

(b) The graph of S is symmetric with respect to the diagonal (symmetry).

(c) If three consecutive vertices of a rectangle whose sides are parallel to the axes belong to the graph of S, and if the second vertex lies on the diagonal, then the remaining fourth vertex of the rectangle belongs to S (transitivity).

8. Prove that the only equivalence relations E which are functions are subsets of the diagonal (see Exercise 7).

9. Let S denote the set of all rational numbers. Define $a/b \sim c/d$ ($b \neq 0$, $d \neq 0$), to mean $ad = bc$. What are the resulting equivalence classes of rationals?

10. Let $S = \{a_1, a_2, \cdots, a_n\}$. Let $T \subset S$. By the *characteristic function* of T is meant the function χ_T defined by

$$\chi_T(x) = \begin{cases} 1, & \text{if } x \in T \\ 0, & \text{if } x \notin T. \end{cases}$$

(a) Show that χ_T is indeed a function with range $\subset \{0, 1\}$.

(b) Conversely, show that every function on S with range $\subset \{0, 1\}$ determines a unique subset of S.

(c) Use the facts above to determine how many subsets of S there are.

11. For each natural number $n = 1, 2, 3, \cdots$, define

$$S_n = \{(x, y) \mid n - 1 \leq x^2 + y^2 < n\}.$$

(a) Show that if $n \neq m$, then $S_n \cap S_m = \emptyset$.

(b) $\bigcup_{n=1}^{\infty} S_n = ?$

(c) According to (a) and (b), the class $\{S_n\}$, $n = 1, 2, 3, \cdots$, of sets partitions the plane. What is the equivalence relation corresponding to this partition?

12. Let f be an arbitrary function with domain S. Then f associates with each "point" $x \in S$, a unique point $f(x)$. Using this "point" function, we can define a "set" function in the following way: If $X \subset S$, define

$$f(X) = \{y \mid y = f(x) \text{ for some } x \in X\}.$$

Moreover, if Y is a subset of the range of f, define

$$f^{-1}(Y) = \{x \mid f(x) \in Y\}.$$

With these definitions prove:

(a) $A \subset B \subset S \Rightarrow f(A) \subset f(B)$

(b) $f(A \cup B) = f(A) \cup f(B)$

(c) $f(A \cap B) \subset f(A) \cap f(B)$. Show that equality here is not valid.

(d) $V \subset W \subset Y \Rightarrow f^{-1}(V) \subset f^{-1}(W)$

(e) $f^{-1}(V \cup W) = f^{-1}(V) \cup f^{-1}(W)$

(f) $f^{-1}(V \cap W) = f^{-1}(V) \cap f^{-1}(W)$

(g) $f^{-1}(cV) = cf^{-1}(V)$.

2

The Real Numbers

INTRODUCTION

Throughout our work we shall be speaking of real numbers. It is essential, therefore, that this concept be clear. The definition of a real number is concise but elusive: *A real number is an element of a complete ordered field.* Our present goal is to gain some idea of what this statement means and to develop some of the basic properties of the real numbers. The axioms for an ordered field will be found in the Appendix and should be studied along with this chapter.

We assume the reader to be familiar with the algebraic properties of the real-number system. To be precise, he should know that the real numbers satisfy the axioms required of a field. Roughly speaking, this means that one can add, subtract, multiply, and divide (except by zero) real numbers, the results always being real numbers. However, there are many other mathematical systems which form fields besides the real numbers. It is especially important for us to observe in this connection that the set of all *rational numbers* (numbers of the form a/b where a, b are integers,

$b \neq 0$) with the usual addition and multiplication also forms a field. Now since we are interested in characterizing the real numbers, that is, finding necessary and sufficient conditions for a system to be indistinguishable (apart from notation) from the real-number system, it is clear that further properties will be needed for this purpose. We eliminate some fields from consideration when we take into account the notion of order and introduce the concept of an *ordered field*.* Nevertheless, even in the presence of this concept we cannot distinguish the rational numbers from the real numbers; that is, both systems satisfy the axioms for an ordered field. Only the real numbers, however, form a *complete ordered field*. The reader is made to feel at home with this abstract concept when we indicate that, after all, a complete ordered field is simply the familiar collection of all decimals (finite and infinite) together with appropriate extensions of the usual rules of arithmetic for operating with these.

There is another important distinction between the rational and real numbers: It lies in the fact that in a precise mathematical sense there are *more* real numbers than there are rational numbers. Both sets, of course, contain an infinite number of elements, and since every rational number is at the same time a real number, it may seem that this is a trivial statement. Actually, the distinction is subtle as we shall see.

Finally, we prove a few "tool theorems" which provide a basis for techniques to which we shall resort frequently in the sequel.

2.1   THE COMPLETE ORDERED FIELD

First we need the notion of an upper bound for a subset A of an ordered field F.

Definition 2.1.   An element u of an ordered field F is said to be an *upper bound* for the subset A of F iff

$$u \geq x \quad \text{for all} \quad x \in A.$$

If no such element exists, then we say that A has no upper bound. A *lower bound* for A is defined by replacing $\geq$ by $\leq$.

———————————

Example 2.1.   (A set with neither an upper bound nor a lower bound.) Let F be the rational numbers, let A be the integers. Then no upper or lower bound exists for $A \subset F$.

———————————

* For example, the set of all complex numbers is eliminated since with the usual addition and multiplication the complex numbers form a field but not an ordered field. (See Sec. 2.3, Exercise 2.)

Example 2.2. (A set with a lower bound but no upper bound.) Let F be the rational numbers, let A be the natural numbers. Then A has no upper bound, but 1 or any rational number less than 1 will serve as a lower bound for A.

Example 2.3. (A set with both an upper bound and a lower bound.) Let F be the rational numbers. Define $A = \{x \mid x \in F, 1 \leq x < 3\}$. Then 3 or any rational number greater than 3 is an upper bound for A; 1 or any rational number less than 1 is a lower bound for A.

The last example suggests the following definition.

Definition 2.2. Let F be an ordered field and let $A \subset F$. A is said to be *bounded* iff A has an upper bound and a lower bound. If F is an ordered field and $x \in F$, we can define the *absolute value* $|x|$ of x by

$$|x| = \begin{cases} x, & \text{if } x > 0 \\ 0, & \text{if } x = 0 \\ -x, & \text{if } x < 0. \end{cases}$$

An immediate consequence of this definition is the following.

■ **Theorem 2.1.** Let $A \subset F$ where F is an ordered field. A is bounded iff there exists $M > 0$ such that

$$|x| \leq M \quad \text{for all} \quad x \in A.$$

Proof: If A is bounded and $x \in A$, then $x \leq m$ where m is an upper bound for A and $x \geq m'$ where m' is a lower bound for A. Define $M = \max(|m|, |m'|)$. It follows that $|x| \leq M$ for all $x \in A$ since $x \leq m \leq |m| \leq M$ and $-x \leq -m' \leq |m'| \leq M$.

Conversely, if $|x| \leq M$ for all $x \in A$, then $-M \leq x \leq M$ so that M and $-M$ will serve as upper and lower bounds, respectively, for A. ■

The next stage in our definition of a complete ordered field involves the notion of a least upper bound.

Definition 2.3. An element $\bar{u}$ of an ordered field is said to be a *least upper bound* or *supremum* (written sup A) for the subset A of F iff
(1) $\bar{u}$ is an upper bound for A, and
(2) if u is an upper bound for A, then $\bar{u} \leq u$.

(NOTE: (2) says u is the "least" of the upper bounds for A.)

The definition of *greatest lower bound* or *infimum* of A (written inf A) is left to the reader.

In Example 2.1 above neither sup A nor inf A exists since A has neither an upper bound nor a lower bound. In Example 2.2 sup A does not exist since A has no upper bound; on the other hand, inf $A = 1$. In Example 2.3, sup $A = 3$; inf $A = 1$.

The next example is very important; it illustrates a distinction between the rational and real numbers which we want to emphasize. We assume that the reader is familiar with the fact that any repeating decimal (we consider terminating decimals—like $3.7100 \cdots$—to be included in the set of repeating decimals) is a rational number, and conversely.

Example 2.4. (A subset of the rationals with an upper bound but no least upper bound.) Let F denote the set of all rational numbers. This is our universe; only rational numbers exist. Define $A = \{1, 1.01, 1.01001, 1.010010001, \cdots\}$. Then 2 and 1 are upper and lower bounds, respectively, for A. Note that $|x| \leq 2$ for all $x \in A$ so that A is bounded. Observe that inf $A = 1$ but sup A does not exist. The reason for nonexistence of sup A is that the real number $1.010010001 \cdots$ is not rational; it is irrational since it is a nonrepeating decimal. Thus, since we are recognizing only rational numbers, the symbol $1.010010001 \cdots$ is meaningless. Herein lies an essential distinction between the rational numbers and the real numbers. That is, if we consider

$$A = \{1, 1.01, 1.01001, \cdots\}$$

to be a subset of the rationals, then A has an upper bound but no least upper bound (in the rationals); on the other hand, if we look upon A as a subset of the reals, A does indeed have a supremum (namely, the irrational but real number $1.010010001 \cdots$). It is because of this situation that we say (suggestively but imprecisely) that if we plot the rational numbers on a straight line, we find many "holes"; that is, the rationals are "incomplete." Following is the precise mathematical formulation.

Definition 2.4. The ordered field F is called *complete* iff every subset $A \subset F$ **with an upper bound** has a least upper bound.

Finally, then, we have the following.

Definition 2.5. The real numbers are a *complete ordered field*.

It is important to later work to understand the difference between the *maximum* of a set and the *supremum* or least upper bound of a set. The distinction, though simple, is crucial in many instances. The maximum of a set must actually *belong* to the set. Of course, the supremum of a set need not belong to the set. For emphasis, we lay down the following formal definition.

Definition 2.6.   Let A be a set of real numbers. The real number a is called the *maximum* of A iff (1) $a \in A$ and (2) $a = \sup A$.

Similarly, the *minimum of A is m* iff (1) $m \in A$ and (2) $m = \inf A$.

Example 2.5.   Let $A = \{x \mid 0 \leq x < 1\}$. Then $\sup A = 1$. However, A has no maximum. On the other hand, $\min A = \inf A = 0$.

An important fact which we shall frequently employ is that every nonempty finite set of positive numbers has a minimum. We now prove the more general statement that *every nonempty finite set of real numbers has a minimum.* The proof is by induction on the number of elements of the finite set in question. Let A be a set with one element, call it a_1. Then $\inf A = a_1$ and $a_1 \in A$. Hence $\min A = a_1$. The statement is valid, therefore, for sets with *one* element.

Next suppose every set of real numbers with n elements has a minimum and suppose that $A = \{a_1, a_2, \cdots, a_{n+1}\}$ has $n + 1$ elements. If we remove an element a_k from A there remains a set B with n elements and hence B has a minimum by the induction hypothesis; call it b. We now focus on showing that the set $\{a_k, b\}$ with two elements has a minimum. However, this is an immediate consequence of the trichotomy axiom which says that exactly one of $a_k = b$ or $a_k < b$ or $b < a_k$ holds.

[A formula for obtaining the minimum of the two numbers a_k, b can be arrived at on intuitive grounds (see Fig. 2.1)].

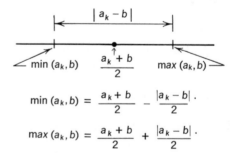

$$\min(a_k, b) = \frac{a_k + b}{2} - \frac{|a_k - b|}{2}.$$

$$\max(a_k, b) = \frac{a_k + b}{2} + \frac{|a_k - b|}{2}.$$

Fig. 2.1   Maximum and minimum of a set of two numbers.

In addition, it is easy to check that $\min\{a_k, b\}$ is also the minimum of our set A (see Section 2.3, Exercise 8). This completes the proof.

Finally, if we have a nonempty finite set A of positive numbers, then by the result above A has a minimum. Clearly, min A must be a positive number since min $A \in A$. Hence we derive the following.

■ **Theorem 2.2.** Every nonempty finite set of positive numbers has a minimum which is a positive number.

It is important to note, however, that an infinite set of positive numbers may not even have a minimum, much less a positive minimum. For example, this is the case with the set $A = \{1, \frac{1}{2}, \frac{1}{3}, \cdots, 1/n, \cdots\}$.

2.2 DECIMAL REPRESENTATION OF THE REAL NUMBERS

Our purpose here is to show that every real number (that is, every element of a complete ordered field) can be represented as a decimal. To guide our thinking, we refer to Fig. 2.2, thinking of the given real number a as being

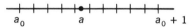

$$a_0 \qquad a \qquad a_0 + 1$$

Fig. 2.2 Decimal representation of a real number.

represented by a point on a line ("the real-number line"). For ease of exposition, we assume a to be nonnegative. Although we use the figure as an aid to our intuition, we base our entire argument on the axioms for a complete ordered field or consequences thereof. Let a_0 denote the largest integer $\leq a$. To see that such an integer exists, let $S = \{k \mid k \text{ an integer}, k \leq a\}$. Then $S \neq \emptyset$ since $0 \in S$. Since S is bounded above by a, sup S exists. On intuitive grounds, we expect that sup $S = a_0$ is an integer. A formal proof of this is called for in Section 2.7, Exercise 7. We assume that result here. Let a_1 denote the largest integer such that

$$a_0 + \frac{a_1}{10} \leq a$$

[a_1 exists for the same reason that a_0 does; that is, a_1 is the largest integer $\leq$ the nonnegative number $10(a - a_0)$]. Note that a_0 will be the integral part of the decimal representing a, and a_1 will be the "tenths digit" in the representation. (In Fig. 2.2, we would have $a_1 = 4$.) In general, assuming that $a_0, a_1, a_2, \cdots, a_{n-1}$ have been determined, let a_n denote the largest integer such that

$$a_0 + \frac{a_1}{10} + \frac{a_2}{10^2} + \cdots + \frac{a_{n-1}}{10^{n-1}} + \frac{a_n}{10^n} \leq a. \qquad (2.1)$$

When we say that $a_0.a_1a_2a_3 \cdots$ is the decimal representation of a, we mean that:

$$(1) \quad 0 \le a_k \le 9, \; a_k \text{ an integer}, \; k = 1, 2, \cdots$$

and

$$(2) \quad \text{The series } \sum_{k=0}^{\infty} \frac{a_k}{10^k} \text{ converges to } a.$$

These we now prove. To simplify the notation, let $[x]$ denote the greatest integer $\le x$. Note that $[a] = a_0 \ge 0$ (since $a > 0$).

Proof of (1): The proof is by induction. We first show that $0 \le a_1 \le 9$. By definition of a_1, a_1 is the largest integer such that $[a] + a_1/10 \le a$. Now $[a] + 0/10 \le a$ and therefore $a_1 \ge 0$. Furthermore,

$$\frac{a_1}{10} \le a - [a] < 1$$

and consequently $a_1 < 10$ which, in turn, implies $a_1 \le 9$. Thus $0 \le a_1 \le 9$ is proved.

Suppose then that $0 \le a_{n-1} \le 9$. We must prove $0 \le a_n \le 9$. If we had

$$\frac{a_n}{10^n} \ge \frac{1}{10^{n-1}} \tag{2.2}$$

then

$$[a] + \frac{a_1}{10} + \cdots + \frac{a_{n-1}}{10^{n-1}} + \frac{1}{10^{n-1}} \le [a] + \frac{a_1}{10} + \cdots + \frac{a_{n-1}}{10^{n-1}} + \frac{a_n}{10^n} \le a,$$

or

$$[a] + \frac{a_1}{10} + \cdots + \frac{a_{n-1}+1}{10^{n-1}} \le a,$$

which is a contradiction to the definition of a_{n-1}. It follows that (2.2) must be denied, that is,

$$\frac{a_n}{10^n} < \frac{1}{10^{n-1}}$$

and so $a_n < 10$ from which we conclude that $a_n \le 9$. To show that $a_n \ge 0$, we simply note that

$$[a] + \frac{a_1}{10} + \cdots + \frac{a_{n-1}}{10^{n-1}} + \frac{0}{10^n} \le a \tag{2.3}$$

(by definition of a_{n-1}) and conclude that from the definition of a_n, it follows from (2.3) that $a_n \ge 0$. This completes the proof of (1). ∎

Proof of (2): We will use the well-known theorem: Every series of non-negative real numbers whose partial sums are bounded above is convergent. The proof of this theorem depends in an essential way on the *completeness* of the ordered field with which we are concerned. Later on we shall give a formal proof of this (Theorem 3.6). We begin by utilizing the fact that since $a_k \leq 9$, for all positive integers k, we have

$$a_0 + \frac{a_1}{10} + \frac{a_2}{10^2} + \cdots + \frac{a_n}{10^n} \leq a_0 + 9\left[\frac{1}{10} + \frac{1}{10^2} + \cdots\right]$$

$$= a_0 + 9\left[\frac{\frac{1}{10}}{1 - \frac{1}{10}}\right]$$

$$= a_0 + 1.$$

This shows that the sequence of partial sums of our series in (2) is bounded above. But the terms of the series are nonnegative and therefore the monotonic nondecreasing sequence of partial sums has a limit; that is, the series converges. Now

$$a - \left(a_0 + \frac{a_1}{10} + \cdots + \frac{a_n}{10^n}\right) < \frac{1}{10^n} \tag{2.4}$$

for if this difference were $\geq 1/10^n$, then we would have

$$a_0 + \frac{a_1}{10} + \cdots + \frac{a_n + 1}{10^n} \leq a,$$

a contradiction to the defining property of a_n. But (2.4) may be written

$$\left|a - \left(a_0 + \frac{a_1}{10} + \cdots + \frac{a_n}{10^n}\right)\right| < \frac{1}{10^n}.$$

(Why?) Since $1/10^n$ can be made arbitrarily small by choosing n sufficiently large, this says that the series converges to a. In the above proof we assumed $a > 0$. The proof for $a < 0$ is similar. As a matter of fact, $a < 0 \Rightarrow -a > 0$, and so we can apply the above procedure to $-a$. ∎

Let us summarize our results in

■ **Theorem 2.3.**   If a is an arbitrary element of a complete ordered field, then a can be represented as an infinite decimal.

Conversely, it can be shown that the collection of all decimals with the appropriate definitions of addition and multiplication forms a complete ordered field. We shall not go into details here. (See, however, Section 2.3, Exercise 5.) The proof is tedious and, at times, difficult.*

2.3 EXERCISES

1. The decimal (base 10) representation of a real number was carried out above. Develop the analogous representation for the binary (base 2) system; for the base b (b an integer > 1).

---

* See J. F. Ritt's *Theory of Functions*, New York: King's Crown Press, 1947.

2. The field of complex numbers can be defined as the set of all ordered pairs (a, b) of real numbers satisfying the following:

$$(a, b) = (c, d) \quad \text{iff } a = c \text{ and } b = d.$$
$$(a, b) + (c, d) = (a + c, b + d).$$
$$(a, b)(c, d) = (ac - bd, ad + bc).$$

[If you are accustomed to writing a complex number in the form $a + bi$, this corresponds to (a, b) in the above notation; thus, for example, $0 + i$ or simply i corresponds to $(0, 1)$ in the present notation.]

Prove that the complex numbers do indeed form a field by verifying the field axioms listed in the Appendix and show, moreover, that no definition of $<$ will lead to an ordered field.

[HINT: Consider two cases: $i = (0, 1) < (0, 0) = 0$ and $i > 0$.]

3. Show that if the supremum of a set of real numbers exists, then it is unique. To do this, let A be a set of real numbers and suppose that sup $A = a$. Also suppose sup $A = b$. Now show that $a = b$.

[HINT: $a \leq b$ since a is the *least* upper bound of A and b is an *upper* bound for A.]

4. Show that for the subset A of real numbers defined by

$$A = \{1, 1.01, 1.01001, \cdots\},$$

we have sup $A = 1.010010001 \cdots$.

5. (a) Given the (infinite) decimal representations of two real numbers a and b. Suggest definitions for $a + b$ and ab.

[HINT: Work first with the decimals aborted to n places; that is, if $a = a_0.a_1a_2 \cdots$, and $b = b_0.b_1b_2 \cdots$, consider $a_0.a_1a_2 \cdots a_n$ and $b_0.b_1b_2 \cdots b_n$.]

(b) Consider the function f which associates with the real number a its decimal representation:

$$f(a) = a_0.a_1a_2a_3 \cdots.$$

Likewise, let

$$f(b) = b_0.b_1b_2b_3 \cdots.$$

Show that if $c = a + b$ and if

$$f(c) = c_0.c_1c_2c_3 \cdots,$$

then $c_0.c_1c_2c_3 \cdots = a_0.a_1a_2a_3 \cdots + b_0.b_1b_2b_3 \cdots$; that is, $f(a + b) = f(a) + f(b)$. We say: f preserves addition. Show that the function f also preserves multiplication; that is,

$$f(ab) = f(a)f(b).$$

6. Prove that min $(a, b) = [(a + b) - |a - b|]/2$.

[HINT: There are two cases according as min $(a, b) = a$ or min $(a, b) = b$.]

7. Show that every finite set of real numbers has a maximum.

8. Show that if min $A = a$ and if min $B = b$, then

$$\min (A \cup B) = \min \{a, b\} = \min \{\min A, \min B\}.$$

9. Consider the set S of those rational points of the open interval $(0, 1)$ obtained by dividing the interval into two equal parts, then dividing each of these two intervals into two equal parts, and so on. More precisely, let $S = \bigcup_{n=1}^{\infty} S_n$ where

$$S_n = \left\{ \frac{k}{2^n} \,\middle|\, k = 1, 2, \cdots, 2^n - 1 \right\}.$$

Similarly, put $T = \bigcup_{n=1}^{\infty} T_n$ where

$$T_n = \left\{ \frac{k}{3^n} \,\middle|\, k = 1, 2, \cdots, 3^n - 1 \right\}.$$

Prove that $S \cap T = \varnothing$.

10. Generalize Exercise 9 as follows: Let p be an arbitrary prime number and define

$$\mathcal{S}_p = \bigcup_{n=1}^{\infty} S_n \quad \text{where } S_n = \left\{ \frac{k}{p^n} \,\middle|\, k = 1, 2, \cdots, p^n - 1 \right\}.$$

(a) Show that if p, q are distinct primes, then $\mathcal{S}_p \cap \mathcal{S}_q = \varnothing$.

(b) Show that $\bigcup_{p \in P} \mathcal{S}_p$, where P denotes the set of all prime numbers, does not exhaust the rational numbers belonging to the open interval $(0, 1)$.

[HINT: Does $\frac{1}{6}$ belong to some set $\mathcal{S}_p$?]

2.4   CARDINAL NUMBERS

In distinguishing between the set of all real numbers and the set of all rational numbers, it was pointed out that although both sets form ordered fields, only the real numbers form a *complete* ordered field.

There is yet another distinction that we want to make clear. It has to do with the "number of elements" in the two sets. A naïve reaction to this statement would run as follows: Since the rational numbers form a proper subset of the reals, there must be more elements in the latter (whatever this might mean). We shall prove shortly that in a precise sense "there are more real numbers than there are rational numbers"; however, this is *not* a consequence of the fact that the rationals form a proper subset of the reals. As a matter of fact, in the order of ideas which we develop it will be shown that even though the integers form a proper subset of the rationals, it is not the case that there are more rationals than integers. The apparent dilemma here stems from the fact that we are dealing with infinite sets and we are tempted to carry over to these sets statements which are valid for finite sets. Unfortunately, this is not always possible. We begin our discussion with finite sets.

Let us make the definition that the set V of vowels in the English alphabet is defined by

$$V = \{a, e, i, o, u\}.$$

Another definition: The set O of oceans is given by

$$O = \{\text{Atlantic, Pacific, Indian, Arctic, Antarctic}\}.$$

We say: There are 5 vowels; there are 5 oceans. These sets apparently have the common property of having the "same *number* of elements." The precise meaning of this statement is that we can set up a one-to-one correspondence between the elements of V and O. This idea can be carried over to infinite sets. In general, we lay down

Definition 2.7.   Two sets A and B are said to be *equivalent* (written $A \sim B$) or to have *the same cardinal number* iff there exists a one-to-one correspondence between the elements of A and B.

It is easy to show that the relation of equivalence of sets is an equivalence relation. Let S be a fixed set and consider all subsets of S. If $A \subset S$, we have $A \sim A$, since the identity function on A (that is, the function f defined by $f(x) = x$ for all $x \in A$) establishes that $A \sim A$.

Next, suppose $A \sim B$ and let f be a one-to-one function on A onto B. Then f^{-1} is one-to-one on B onto A, and therefore $B \sim A$. Hence $A \sim B \Rightarrow B \sim A$.

Finally, if we have $A \sim B$ and $B \sim C$, then there exist one-to-one functions f, g where f is on A onto B and g is on B onto C. The reader should check that the composite function gf defined by

$$gf(x) = g(f(x)) \quad \text{for all } x \in A$$

is a one-to-one function on A onto C and, consequently, we have $A \sim C$.

It follows from Theorem 1.1 that the equivalence relation $\sim$ on subsets of S partitions the collection of all subsets of S into equivalence classes. In a given equivalence class we find all subsets $A, B, \cdots, C, \cdots$ of S for which $A \sim B \sim \cdots C \sim \cdots$, that is, all subsets of S having "the same cardinal number." A cardinal number may therefore be regarded as a symbol for such an equivalence class. For example, the cardinal number "5" may be considered as a symbol for a certain class of sets among which we find the sets V and O mentioned above. This paves the way to

Definition 2.8. The set A is said to have *cardinal number n* (n a positive integer) iff A is equivalent to the particular subset $\{1, 2, \cdots, n\}$ of natural numbers. If the set A is empty or has cardinal number n, then A is said to be *finite*. Any set which is not finite is called *infinite*. A set which is equivalent to the set of all positive integers is called *denumerable*. A set which is finite or denumerable is called *countable*.

Example 2.6. The set of roots of the equation $x(x - 2)(x - 5) = 0$ is the set $\{0, 2, 5\}$. It is finite and has cardinal number 3. It is, consequently, countable, but not denumerable. The set of roots of $\sin x = 0$ is denumerable.

Example 2.7. The set E of all even natural numbers is equivalent to the set N of all natural numbers.

To prove this, associate with each natural number n, the natural number $2n$:

$$f(n) = 2n.$$

Since $f(n) = f(m) \Rightarrow n = m$, f is a one-to-one function on N onto E. Hence $E \sim N$. Note that E is a proper subset of N.

Definition 2.9. The symbol $\aleph_0$ (read aleph-null; $\aleph$, aleph, is the first letter of the Hebrew alphabet) denotes the cardinal number of the set N of all natural numbers or any set equivalent to N, that is, any denumerable set. We write:

$$\overline{N} = \aleph_0,$$

reading $\overline{N}$ as "the cardinal number of N." In general, $\overline{A}$ denotes the cardinal number of the set A.

Example 2.8. The set of all integers is denumerable. To see this, we "count" the integers by the scheme suggested in Fig. 2.3.

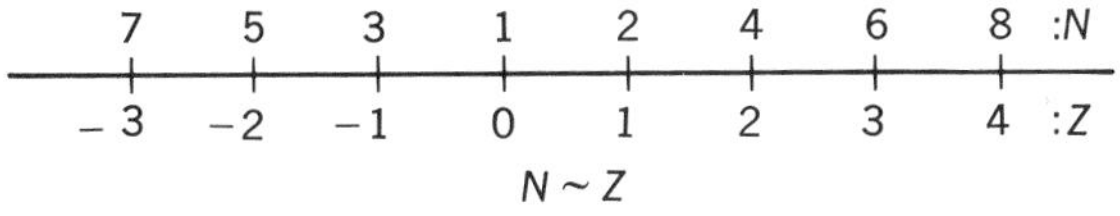

7	5	3	1	2	4	6	8	:N
-3	-2	-1	0	1	2	3	4	:Z

$$N \sim Z$$

Fig. 2.3   Equivalence of integers and positive integers.

To be precise, we consider the function f whose domain is the integers and defined by

$$f(j) = \begin{cases} 2j, & \text{if } j > 0 \\ -2j + 1, & \text{if } j \leq 0. \end{cases}$$

We leave it to the reader to show that f is one-to-one on the integers onto the positive integers. Thus, if Z denotes the set of all integers, then we have

$$\overline{Z} = \aleph_0.$$

Examples above show that it is possible for a set to be equivalent to a proper subset of itself. To be sure, our examples of sets exhibiting this property were infinite sets. As a matter of fact, the property of a set of admitting a one-to-one correspondence with a proper subset of itself is characteristic of infinite sets; that is, infinite sets and only these, have this property. This is the content of the next two theorems.

■ **Theorem 2.4.**   If the set A is infinite, then there exists a proper subset B of A such that A is equivalent to B.

The idea of the proof runs as follows: In succession, we will show: (1) Every infinite set contains a denumerable subset. (2) The theorem is valid for every denumerable set. (3) Finally, using (1) and (2) we will show that the theorem is valid for an arbitrary infinite set.

(1) If A is infinite, then A is not empty and hence contains an element; call it a_1. The set A with a_1 removed is not empty (for if it were, A would be finite with cardinal number 1), hence $A - \{a_1\}$ contains an element; call it a_2. Next, let $a_3 \in A - \{a_1, a_2\}$ and, in general, let $a_n \in A - \{a_1, a_2, a_3, \cdots, a_{n-1}\}$. This process of choosing elements $a_1, a_2, a_3, \cdots$ cannot terminate, for if it did, A would not be infinite. Thus we see that A contains a denumerable set $\{a_1, a_2, \cdots\}$.

(2) Let $\{a_1, a_2, \cdots\}$ be a denumerable set. Associate a_{n+1} with a_n. This function, that is, $f(a_n) = a_{n+1}$, establishes a one-to-one correspondence between $\{a_1, a_2, a_3, \cdots\}$ and the proper subset $\{a_2, a_3, \cdots\}$. Thus every denumerable set contains an equivalent proper subset.

(3) In view of (1) and (2), if A is any infinite set, we may assume that $a_n \in A, n = 1, 2, \cdots$, and the function defined by

$$f(x) = \begin{cases} a_{n+1} \text{ if } x = a_n \\ x \text{ if } x \neq a_n \text{ for all } n \end{cases}$$

sets up a one-to-one correspondence between A and the proper subset $A - \{a_1\}$. ■

We now consider the converse: if a set A is equivalent to a proper subset $B \subsetneq A$, then A is infinite. We choose to prove the equivalent statement: If A is finite and B is a proper subset of A, then A is not equivalent to B. To accomplish our goal, we first prove:

Lemma.   If the domain of a function has n elements, then its range will contain at most n elements.

Proof: By induction on n. Let f be a function with a one-element domain. The range of f must contain exactly one element, by the very definition of function, so the lemma is true for $n = 1$.

The second phase of the induction proof utilizes the concept of *restriction* of a function. If f is the function $f = \{(a, a'), (b, b'), (c, c')\}$, then by the *restriction* of f obtained by removing the element a from the domain of f, we mean the function $\{(b, b'), (c, c')\}$. In general, if f is a function with domain D and $A \subset D$, then by the *restriction* of f to A is meant the function g with domain A such that $g(x) = f(x)$ for all $x \in A$.

Suppose then that the statement holds for any function with a domain having k elements and let f be a function with $k + 1$ elements in its domain. If we remove one element, say a_j, from the domain of f, the resulting restriction of f is a function g whose domain consists of k elements and hence by the induction hypothesis the range of g has at most k elements. But to arrive at f from g, we simply adjoin to g the pair $(a_j, f(a_j))$, where at most one element, namely, $f(a_j)$, is adjoined to the range of g. But the range of g had at most k elements and consequently the range of f has at most $k + 1$ elements. This proves the lemma. ∎

Now let f be a one-to-one function on A onto $B \subset A$. Suppose the domain A of f contains n elements. By the lemma, it follows that B has at most n elements. If B had k elements with $k < n$, then the range A of f^{-1} would have (again by the lemma) at most k elements, a contradiction, since A has n elements with $n > k$. Thus B has precisely n elements. This proves the following theorem.

■ **Theorem 2.5.**   A nonempty finite set cannot be equivalent to a proper subset of itself.

Let us now proceed to the main result of this section. We have hinted that the sets of rational and real numbers can be distinguished as to cardinality. Both sets, of course, are infinite. We will now show, however, that the set of rational numbers is denumerable whereas the set of real numbers is not denumerable.

The plan of our proof that the set of rational numbers is denumerable is to show first that the set $\mathcal{P}$ of positive rational numbers is denumerable. We will show that a one-to-one correspondence between $\mathcal{P}$ (the positive rationals) and $I_\mathcal{P}$ (the positive integers) exists. The proof of the theorem is then completed by noting that $\mathfrak{N}$ (the negative rationals), and $I_\mathfrak{N}$ (the negative integers) can therefore be put in one-to-one correspondence and hence $\mathcal{P} \cup \{0\} \cup \mathfrak{N}$ (that is, the set of all rational numbers) is equivalent to $I_\mathcal{P} \cup \{0\} \cup I_\mathfrak{N}$ (the set of all integers). But the set of all integers is denumerable (see Example 2.8) and consequently the theorem will be proved.

First we need the following.

Lemma. Every infinite subset of a denumerable set is denumerable.

Proof: Let $A = \{a_1, a_2, a_3, \cdots\}$ be the distinct elements of the denumerable set A and let $B \subset A$, where B is infinite. Define a function on the positive integers as follows:

$f(1) =$ the smallest positive integer k such that $a_k \in B$.
$f(2) =$ the smallest positive integer $k > f(1)$ such that $a_k \in B$.
.
.
.

$f(n) =$ the smallest positive integer $k > f(n - 1)$ such that $a_k \in B$.

(NOTE: For every positive integer n, $f(n)$ exists for if this were not the case B would be finite.)

Bearing in mind that the sequence $\{a_n\}$ is the function a with $a(n) = a_n$ (domain of a is the positive integers), we form the composite function af (for example, $af(1) = a(f(1)) = a_{f(1)}$). Clearly, the domain of af is the set of all positive integers since this is the domain of f. The range of af is the set

$$B = \{a_{f(1)}, a_{f(2)}, \cdots\}.$$

But $af(n) = af(m) \Rightarrow a(f(n)) = a(f(m)) \Rightarrow a_{f(n)} = a_{f(m)} \Rightarrow f(n) = f(m) \Rightarrow n = m$; that is, af establishes a one-to-one correspondence between the set of all positive integers and the set B. ∎

Our problem, then, is to show that the set $\mathcal{P}$ of positive rationals is denumerable. Let m/n be a rational number with $m > 0$ and $n > 0$. Consider the function defined by

$$f\left(\frac{m}{n}\right) = 2^m 3^n.$$

f is clearly a function on the positive rationals onto a proper subset of the positive integers. To show that f has an inverse function we need the "fundamental theorem of arithmetic" or "unique factorization theorem": *Every positive integer can be factored into primes in precisely one way if we ignore the order of the prime factors.* For example, the prime factorization of the positive integer 72 (that is, $72 = 2^3 \cdot 3^2$) contains precisely three 2's and two 3's.

The unique factorization theorem enables us to prove the existence of f^{-1} as a function; for suppose that $f(m/n) = f(r/s)$. This means that $2^m 3^n = 2^r 3^s$; that is, the positive integers $2^m 3^n$ and $2^r 3^s$ are equal, and therefore by the unique factorization theorem $m = r$ and $n = s$. Consequently $m/n = r/s$, meaning that we have shown

$$f\left(\frac{m}{n}\right) = f\left(\frac{r}{s}\right) \Rightarrow \frac{m}{n} = \frac{r}{s}.$$

Thus f establishes a one-to-one correspondence between the set of all positive rationals and an infinite subset of the positive integers. Invoking the lemma, we conclude that the positive rationals are denumerable. Recalling the plan outlined above, we have the following.

■ **Theorem 2.6.**   The set of all rational numbers is denumerable.

Let us summarize our findings with respect to cardinal numbers before moving on. We denote the finite cardinal numbers by the symbols

$$0, 1, 2, 3, \cdots.$$

We have introduced the symbol $\aleph_0$ for the cardinal number of the set of all natural numbers, and we have shown that even the set of all rational numbers has cardinal number $\aleph_0$. In other words, all of the infinite sets which we have analyzed as to cardinal number have turned out to belong to the class denoted by $\aleph_0$. Are there infinite sets which do not have cardinal number $\aleph_0$? Indeed there are. As a matter of fact, we now show that the set of all rational numbers and the set of all real numbers can be distinguished in this respect.

■ **Theorem 2.7.**   The set of all real numbers is not denumerable.

The proof is by contradiction. Suppose that the set of all real numbers could be arranged in a sequence, that is, could be put in one-to-one correspondence with the natural numbers. Using the decimal representation of real numbers and ignoring the integral part of the decimal representation, let the one-to-one correspondence be as in Fig. 2.4 where each of a_{ij} is one

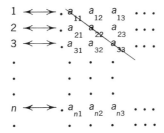

Fig. 2.4   Nondenumerability of the real numbers.

of the digits $0, 1, 2, \cdots, 9$. We now construct a real number (to be denoted by $0.b_1 b_2 b_3 \cdots$) which is different from all of those enumerated. To do this, we inspect the diagonal digits in the above list, that is, the digits a_{11}, a_{22}, a_{33}, $\cdots$, a_{nn}, $\cdots$. If $a_{11} = 1$, we put $b_1 = 2$; if $a_{11} \neq 1$, we put $b_1 = 1$. In general, we define

$$b_n = \begin{cases} 2, & \text{if } a_{nn} = 1 \\ 1, & \text{if } a_{nn} \neq 1. \end{cases}$$

The resulting decimal

$$0.b_1b_2b_3 \cdots$$

is different from all of the numbers listed since it differs from the nth number of the list in the nth decimal place. This is a contradiction, since we supposed *all* real numbers to be enumerated. [It should be noted that the decimal representation of a real number is not unique since, for example, $0.4999 \cdots = 0.5000 \cdots$ (these two decimals differ in every decimal place, yet they are equal). We have avoided the difficulty of not being able to claim that two numbers are distinct even if they differ in every decimal place by constructing a number free from 0's and 9's.]

What we have shown is that not even those real numbers between 0 and 1 form a denumerable set. If, however, the set of real numbers was denumerable, then the infinite subset of reals between 0 and 1 would be denumerable according to the lemma preceding Theorem 2.6. This contradiction yields the theorem (see also Section 2.5, Exercise 10).

Thus the cardinal number of the set of all real numbers is not $\aleph_0$. It is customary to denote this new cardinal number by c (the symbol c is suggested by the fact that we speak of the *continuum* of real numbers).

Definition 2.10. A set A is said to *have cardinal number c* iff A is equivalent to the set of all real numbers. We then write $\overline{\overline{A}} = c$.

2.5 EXERCISES

1. Show that any two closed intervals $[a, b]$ and $[c, d]$ are equivalent.

    [HINT: See Fig. 2.5, and construct a function to prove the equivalence.]

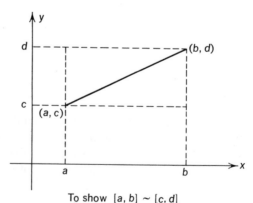

To show $[a, b] \sim [c, d]$

Fig. 2.5 Equivalence of two closed intervals.

2. Show that the set R of all real numbers is equivalent to the set of all positive reals.

[HINT: Consider the function f defined by $f(x) = e^x$].

3. Show that the set R of all real numbers is equivalent to the open interval $(-\pi/2, \pi/2)$.

[HINT: Consider $f(x) = \text{Arctan } x$.]

4. (a) Show that the set of all rational points in the xy plane, that is, the set of all ordered pairs (r, s) where r and s are rational numbers, is denumerable.

[HINT: Prove the general result that if $\overline{\overline{A}} = \aleph_0$ and $\overline{\overline{B}} = \aleph_0$, then $\overline{\overline{A \times B}} = \aleph_0$.]

(b) Show that the set of all ordered triples (r, s, t) where r, s, and t are rational numbers, is denumerable. (This set is the set of all rational points in "3-space".)

(c) Generalize (a) and (b) to the rational points in "n-space" where n is a positive integer.

5. (a) Show that the union of a denumerable number of denumerable sets, disjoint in pairs, is denumerable.

[HINT: Use Fig. 2.6, "count" $a_{11}, a_{12}, a_{21}, a_{13}, a_{22}, a_{31}, \cdots.$]

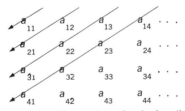

Fig. 2.6   The union of a denumerable number of pairwise disjoint sets is denumerable.

(b) Show that the hypothesis "disjoint in pairs" in part (a) is not necessary.

6. (a) Let $A = \{a_1, a_2, \cdots, a_n\}$ be a set with cardinal number n. Consider the class of all subsets of A, known as the power set of A, and denoted by 2^A. Show that the number of elements of 2^A is 2^n.

[HINT: An element of 2^A is a subset S of A and is determined by its characteristic function χ_S defined by

$$\chi_S(x) = \begin{cases} 1, & \text{if } x \in S \\ 0, & \text{if } x \notin S. \end{cases}$$

If we think of the elements of A as being ordered and write the "n-tuple" $(a_1, a_2, \cdots, a_n)$, then we can represent χ_S by writing a "1" or a "0" in the kth place according as a_k does or does not belong, respectively, to S. For example, $(1, 0, 0, \cdots, 0, 1)$ with 0's except in the 1st and nth positions corresponds to the set $\{a_1, a_n\}$.]

(b) Prove, by induction, that $2^n > n$ for all positive integers n.

7. Note that in Exercise 6 if A has n elements (where n is a positive integer), then the power set 2^A of A has 2^n elements and we have $2^n > n$. The purpose of this exercise is to generalize this. Let S be any nonempty set and let 2^S be the class of all subsets of S. Show:

(a) S is equivalent to a proper subset of 2^S.

(b) There is no one-to-one function on S onto 2^S.

[HINT: Do this by contradiction. Suppose S_x is the subset of S corresponding to the element x of S. Now consider the subset T of S defined by

$$x \in T \text{ iff } x \notin S_x,$$

and investigate the question: Of what element of S is T the image? Consider two cases: Either $x \in S_x$ or $x \notin S_x$. (This ingenious idea is due to Georg Cantor.).]

(c) Give an example of an infinite set whose cardinality is neither $\aleph_0$ nor c.

8. Prove: If $A_1 \sim B_1$ and $A_2 \sim B_2$ and if $A_1 \cap A_2 = \varnothing$ and $B_1 \cap B_2 = \varnothing$, then $A_1 \cup A_2 \sim B_1 \cup B_2$.

9. Show that the function f defined in Example 2.8 is one-to-one on the integers onto the positive integers.

10. Show that the set R of all real numbers is equivalent to the interval $(0, 1)$.

[HINT: Show that any two open intervals are equivalent, then use Exercise 3.]

11. Show that $[0, 1] \sim [0, 1)$.

[HINT: For $\frac{1}{2^n} \in [0, 1]$, put $f(\frac{1}{2^n}) = \frac{1}{2^{n+1}}$, $n = 0, 1, 2, \cdots$. For $x \in [0, 1]$, $x \neq \frac{1}{2^n}$, put $f(x) = x$.]

2.6 SOME PROPERTIES OF THE REAL NUMBERS

In this section we prove several facts about the real number system which will serve as tools in arriving at more important results.

A. ABSOLUTE VALUE AND THE TRIANGLE INEQUALITY

Of great value in analysis is the notion of the *absolute value* $|x|$ of the real number x. Recall that

$$|x| = \begin{cases} x & \text{if } x > 0 \\ 0 & \text{if } x = 0 \\ -x & \text{if } x < 0. \end{cases}$$

Using this idea of absolute value, the *distance* between two real numbers x and y is defined by $|x - y|$. This notion of distance then has the following properties:

(1) $|x - y| \geq 0$ and $|x - y| = 0$ iff $x = y$.
(2) $|x - y| = |y - x|$.
(3) $|x - y| + |y - z| \geq |x - z|$.

(NOTE: The distance between x and y is simply a function defined by $d(x, y) = |x - y|$ whose domain is $R \times R$ (R = real numbers) and whose range is a subset of the nonnegative reals. In this context, we may rewrite (1) $d(x, y) \geq 0$ and $d(x, y) = 0$ iff $x = y$, (2) $d(x, y) = d(y, x)$, and (3) $d(x, y) + d(y, z) \geq d(x, z)$.)

The first two statements (1) and (2) are immediate consequences of the definition of absolute value. The third property is a basic tool in analysis and is referred to as the *triangle inequality*. The reason for calling (3) the *triangle inequality* stems from the fact that if each of x, y, z is interpreted as a complex number in the plane, then (3) can be interpreted as asserting that the sum of two sides of a triangle is not less than the third side. (See Supplement to Chapter 3.) To prove (3), we first prove the following theorem.

■ **Theorem 2.8.** If a and b are real numbers, then

$$|a + b| \leq |a| + |b|. \tag{2.5}$$

Proof: From the definition of $|a|$, we have that

$$\pm a \leq |a|. \tag{2.6}$$

Similarly,

$$\pm b \leq |b|. \tag{2.7}$$

Adding (2.6) and (2.7), it follows that

$$\pm(a + b) \leq |a| + |b|. \tag{2.8}$$

Noting that one of the numbers $+(a + b)$ and $-(a + b)$ must be equal to $|a + b|$, we conclude that (2.8) implies

$$|a + b| \leq |a| + |b|. \quad ■$$

To prove (3) above, we simply replace a and b in (2.5) by $x - y$ and $y - z$, respectively.

B. AN IMPORTANT PROPERTY OF SUPREMUM

Let A be a set of real numbers and suppose sup A exists. Put $a = \sup A$. The real number a then has the property that if we select any number whatever to the left of it, there will be a member of A to the right of such a number. Here is the formal statement.

■ **Theorem 2.9.** Let $a = \sup A$. For every $\epsilon > 0$, there exists $x \in A$ (x depending on ϵ) such that $a - \epsilon < x \leq a$.

Proof: That $x \leq a$ for all $x \in A$ is obvious since a is an upper bound for A. Suppose the remaining inequality $a - \epsilon < x$ is false. Then there exists a positive number ϵ_0 such that $a - \epsilon_0 \geq x$ for all $x \in A$. This says that $a - \epsilon_0$ is an upper bound for A and since a is the least upper bound of A, we have $a \leq a - \epsilon_0$. Since ϵ_0 is positive, this is a contradiction. ■

This property of the supremum of a set will be used over and over again, so the reader should understand it thoroughly before reading on.

There is, of course, an analogous property of the infimum of a set. If the reader cannot state and prove it, he is referred to Section 2.7, Exercise 8.

C. A TECHNIQUE FOR SHOWING $a \leq b$ and $a = b$

Suppose we have two numbers a and b and we want to show that $a \leq b$. It is then sufficient to prove that $a < b + \epsilon$ for all $\epsilon > 0$. Formally we have the following.

■ **Theorem 2.10.** If a and b are two fixed numbers such that $a < b + \epsilon$ for all $\epsilon > 0$, then $a \leq b$.

Proof: The only alternative to the conclusion is that $a > b$. If this were the case, then $a - b$ would be a positive number. Choose $\epsilon = a - b$ and get, from the hypothesis of the theorem, that $a < b + \epsilon = b + (a - b) = a$, a contradiction. ■

Corollary. $|a - b| < \epsilon$ for all $\epsilon > 0 \Rightarrow a = b$.

Proof: We have $a - b < \epsilon$ and $a - b > -\epsilon$; that is, $a < b + \epsilon$ and $b < a + \epsilon$. Hence $a \leq b$ and $b \leq a$ which imply $a = b$. ■

This corollary is a very useful tool. It tells us that if we want to conclude that two real numbers a, b are equal, it is sufficient to show that the distance $|a - b|$ between them is less than an arbitrary positive number. Obviously, the condition is also necessary; that is, $a = b \Rightarrow |a - b| < \epsilon$ for all $\epsilon > 0$.

D. DENSENESS OF RATIONALS AND IRRATIONALS IN REALS

Often problems in analysis require invoking the fact that between any two real numbers one can always find a rational and an irrational number. These properties are described by saying that *the rationals are dense in the reals* and *the irrationals are dense in the reals*.

We first approach the problem from a geometric standpoint in order to motivate an analytic proof which is given subsequently. Let $a < b$ be the two given real numbers and suppose, for the time being, that $a \geq 0$ (see Fig. 2.7). Now $b - a > 0$; therefore, $1/(b - a) > 0$. We can find a natural

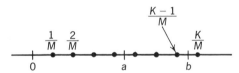

Fig. 2.7   Denseness of rationals in reals.

number M such that $M > 1/(b - a)$ (that is, there are arbitrarily large natural numbers). It follows that $1/M < b - a$. This means that *we have found a rational number* (namely, $1/M$) *less than the distance between a and b.* Next we plot the points

$$\frac{1}{M}, \frac{2}{M}, \frac{3}{M}, \ldots.$$

Let K/M be the first of these points falling to the right of b. Then $(K - 1)/M$ will serve as the required rational number between a and b.

Let us now be precise. We are given that $0 < a < b$. Clearly, $b - a > 0$. The reader will prove (Section 2.7, Exercise 1) that the reciprocal $1/(b - a)$ of a positive number is positive; that is, $1/(b - a) > 0$. We now need the result that for any positive number, we can find a larger natural number. Since this fact is used frequently, we call it Theorem 2.11.

■ **Theorem 2.11.** If ϵ is an arbitrary positive number, there exists a positive integer M such that $M > \epsilon$.

Proof: Suppose the statement false. Then there is a positive number p such that $p \geq n$ for all positive integers n. This says that the set N of all positive integers has p as an upper bound. By the completeness axiom for the real numbers, it follows that N has a least upper bound, say $p^* = \sup N$. Thus $p^* \geq n + 1$ for all positive integers n. But $p^* - 1 \geq n$ says that the number $p^* - 1$ is an upper bound for N. Since p^* is the least upper bound of N, this implies $p^* \leq p^* - 1$. This contradiction yields the theorem. ∎

We now resume our argument. Choosing $\epsilon = 1/(b - a)$, we conclude from Theorem 2.11 that there is a positive integer M such that $M > 1/(b - a)$ and, therefore, we have

$$\frac{1}{M} < b - a \tag{2.9}$$

(proof is left to the reader; see Section 2.7, Exercise 2). Since $b > 0$ and $M > 0$, we know that $bM > 0$ and hence again by Theorem 2.11 there exists a positive integer k such that $k > bM$. Consider the set S of all such k; that is, put

$$S = \{k \mid k > bM, k \text{ a positive integer}\}.$$

Being a set of positive integers, S has a minimum (see Section 2.7, Exercise 3); call it K. Thus

$$K > bM \quad \text{and} \quad K - 1 \leq bM, \tag{2.10}$$

since $K \in S$ and $K = \inf S$, respectively. Rewriting (2.10), we obtain

$$\frac{K - 1}{M} \leq b < \frac{K}{M}. \tag{2.11}$$

From (2.9) and (2.11)

$$a = b - (b - a) < \frac{K}{M} - \frac{1}{M} = \frac{K - 1}{M}.$$

In other words, from the above and (2.11) we have

$$a < \frac{K - 1}{M} \leq b. \tag{2.12}$$

We are essentially through since $(K - 1)/M$ is a rational number. However, the inequalities (2.12) tell us that the rational number $(K - 1)/M$ may coincide with the larger (b) of the two given numbers. If this happens (that is, if $(K - 1)/M = b$), then we invoke (2.9) to get

$$a < b - \frac{1}{M} = \frac{K - 1}{M} - \frac{1}{M} = \frac{K - 2}{M} < b.$$

In any event, then, we can always succeed in finding a rational number r such that $a < r < b$ for any two given real numbers a, b with $0 \leq a < b$.

Finally, if $a < b$ but also $a < 0$, there is an integer N such that $N > -a$ by Theorem 2.11 so that $N + a > 0$ and we now apply the above argument to the pair of numbers $N + a$, $N + b$. We obtain a rational number r with

$$N + a < r < N + b,$$

that is,

$$a < r - N < b,$$

which says that $r - N$ will serve as the required number. Here, then, is our result stated formally.

■ **Theorem 2.12.** If a and b are two real numbers and if $a < b$, then there exists a rational number r such that $a < r < b$.

We should like also to show that an irrational number can always be found between two distinct real numbers. To accomplish this, we first prove that the irrationals are dense in the rationals.

■ **Theorem 2.13.** If r, s are rational and $r < s$, then there is an irrational number x such that $r < x < s$.

Proof: Define $x = r + (\sqrt{2} - 1)(s - r)$. Since $s - r$ is positive, it follows that the product $(\sqrt{2} - 1)(s - r) > 0$, and consequently $r < x$. Also,

$$x = r + (\sqrt{2} - 1)(s - r)$$
$$= (2 - \sqrt{2})r + (\sqrt{2} - 1)s$$
$$< (2 - \sqrt{2})s + (\sqrt{2} - 1)s = s$$

and therefore $x < s$. Details are completed by showing that x is irrational. This we leave to the reader (see Section 2.7, Exercise 4).

Finally, we prove the following.

■ **Theorem 2.14.** If a and b are two real numbers and if $a < b$, then there exists an irrational number t such that $a < t < b$.

Proof: Apply Theorem 2.12 to get a rational number r such that $a < r < b$. Apply Theorem 2.12 again, using r and b as the given numbers to get a rational number s such that $a < r < s < b$. Now apply Theorem 2.13, obtaining an irrational t with $a < r < t < s < b$. ∎

2.7 EXERCISES

1. Show that if $a > 0$, then $1/a > 0$.
2. Show that if $0 < a < b$, then $1/a > 1/b$.
3. Show that if A is an arbitrary set of positive integers, then A has a minimum. (We say: The positive integers are *well-ordered*.)

4. Show that if r, s are rational, $r \neq s$, then $x = r + (\sqrt{2} - 1)(s - r)$ is irrational.

5. Prove that if p is a prime number, then $\sqrt{p}$ is irrational.

6. Prove the extension of the triangle inequality: If

$$A = \{a_1, a_2, \cdots, a_n\}$$

is a finite set of real numbers, then

$$\left| \sum_{k=1}^{n} a_k \right| \leq \sum_{k=1}^{n} |a_k|.$$

7. Show that if S is a set of integers and sup S exists, then sup S is an integer.

[HINT: Let sup $S = a_0$. Let $\epsilon > 0$. By Theorem 2.9 $\exists\, x \in S \ni$ $a_0 - \epsilon < x \leq a_0$. Now show that $|a_0 - x| < \epsilon$.]

8. Prove that if $a = \inf A$ and if $\epsilon > 0$, then there exists $x \in A$ such that $a \leq x < a + \epsilon$.

9. Prove that if r is rational and if t is irrational, then $r + t$ is irrational. What can you say about $r - t$? rt? r/t?

[HINT: Give an indirect proof, taking into account that the rationals form a field.]

10. Explain the "corollary" to Theorem 2.12: The rationals are dense in the irrationals.

3

The Limit Concept

INTRODUCTION

Basic to all analysis is the concept of *limit*. We begin our study by reviewing the notion of *limit of a sequence* of real numbers. Now a sequence is a special function (its domain being the set of all positive integers), and we want to have the concept of limit apply to more general functions f where the domain of f contains some interval I of real numbers and the range of f is some set of real numbers. Specifically, we want to attach a meaning to "the limit of $f(x)$ as x approaches a" [$\lim_{x \to a} f(x)$] where a belongs to the open interval I (or is an endpoint of I) and we would like this definition to be based on our notion of limit of a sequence. One difficulty that must be overcome stems from the fact that there are many different sequences of real numbers which converge to a given number a and we want to exclude especially the constant sequence $a, a, a, \cdots$. The decision to exclude the constant sequence is justified on the grounds that $\lim_{x \to a} f(x)$ is expected to indicate the behavior of the function f for points "near a" and is to have nothing at all to do with the value $f(a)$ of f at a; indeed, f need not even be defined at a for $\lim_{x \to a} f(x)$ to be meaningful. We resolve the problem by considering two approaches to the notion of limit, labeling them "the sequential approach" and "the neighborhood approach." We then show that in the case of real functions of a real variable (which is our main concern), the two definitions are equivalent and may therefore be used interchangeably. We shall see that this freedom to choose either orientation to the concept of limit will simplify much of our subsequent investigation.

Finally, we introduce the notion of a subsequence and show that all subsequences of a convergent sequence converge to the same limit as the sequence. We also establish two equivalent sufficient conditions for convergence of special kinds of sequences known as monotonic.

3.1   LIMIT OF A SEQUENCE

Definition 3.1. Let $\{a_n\}$ be a sequence of real numbers. We say that $\{a_n\}$ *converges* to the real number a (written $a_n \to a$) or that *the limit of* $\{a_n\}$ *as n tends to infinity is* a (written $\lim_{n \to \infty} a_n = a$ or simply $\lim a_n = a$) iff for every $\epsilon > 0$, there exists a natural number N (which usually depends on ϵ although this is by no means necessary) such that

$$n > N \Rightarrow |a_n - a| < \epsilon.$$

Remark

We frequently paraphrase this definition by saying "to show that a given sequence $a_1, a_2, a_3, \cdots$ converges to a, one must show that the distance $|a_n - a|$ can be made arbitrarily small for all sufficiently large n."

Example 3.1.   (Limit of a constant sequence.) The sequence $c, c, c, \cdots$ has limit c.

Proof: $|c - c| = 0 < \epsilon.$ ∎

Example 3.2.   (A sequence with no limit.) The sequence $-1, 1, -1, 1, \cdots$ has no limit.

To say that a sequence $\{x_n\}$ has no limit is to say that for every real number x, there is an $\epsilon > 0$ (usually depending on x) such that no matter what natural number N is selected, there is a corresponding $n > N$ such that $|x_n - x| \geq \epsilon$.

Thus, let x be any real number. Take $\epsilon = 1/2$. Then for any natural number N, we know that we can find $n > N$ such that $x_n = 1$ and $x_{n+1} = -1$. Consequently it is impossible to have

$$|x_{n+1} - x| < \tfrac{1}{2} \quad \text{and} \quad |x_n - x| < \tfrac{1}{2}$$

for this would imply that

$$|x_{n+1} - x_n| \leq |x_{n+1} - x| + |x - x_n| < 1$$

and this is false since $|x_{n+1} - x_n| = |-1 - 1| = 2$. Therefore, the sequence $(-1)^n$, $n = 1, 2, 3, \cdots$ has no limit.

Example 3.3. The sequence $\{n/(n + 1)\}$, n a natural number, converges to 1 since the distance $|n/(n + 1) - 1|$ between the nth term $n/(n + 1)$ of the sequence and the fixed number 1 is equal to $1/(n + 1)$ and therefore can be made arbitrarily small by choosing n sufficiently large. More precisely, let $\epsilon > 0$ be given. We know (Theorem 2.11) that there is a natural number N such that $N + 1 > 1/\epsilon$ and therefore $n > N$ implies $n > N > 1/\epsilon - 1$ so that $n + 1 > 1/\epsilon$ and hence

$$n > N \Rightarrow \left| \frac{n}{n + 1} - 1 \right| = \frac{1}{n + 1} < \epsilon.$$

As we have seen, some sequences have no limits. However, it is an important fact that if a sequence has a limit, it has only one. This we now prove. The reader will note the important role played by the triangle inequality in this and many of the succeeding proofs.

■ Theorem 3.1. If the limit of a sequence $\{a_n\}$ exists, then it is unique, that is,

$$\text{if } a_n \to a \text{ and if } a_n \to b, \text{ then } a = b.$$

Proof: (The idea of the proof is to show that the distance $|a - b|$ is less than an arbitrary positive number, thus forcing $a = b$ by the corollary to Theorem 2.10.) We estimate

$$|a - b| = |a - a_n + a_n - b| \leq |a - a_n| + |a_n - b|$$

and leave it to the reader to complete the details. ■

Besides having a unique limit, a convergent sequence is always bounded, as we now prove.

■ Theorem 3.2. If the sequence $\{a_n\}$ is convergent, then it is bounded.

Proof: Suppose $a_n \to a$ and let $\epsilon = 1$. Then, according to the definition of limit, there is a positive integer N such that

$$n > N \Rightarrow |a_n - a| < 1.$$

But $|a_n| - |a| \leq |a_n - a|$ (triangle inequality), hence

$$n > N \Rightarrow |a_n| < |a| + 1,$$

which asserts that all the terms of our sequence except possibly $a_1, a_2, \cdots,$ a_N lie in the open interval $(-|a| - 1, |a| + 1)$. It follows that if

$$M = \max \{|a_1|, |a_2|, \cdots, |a_N|, |a| + 1\},$$

then we shall have $|a_k| \le M$ for all positive integers k; that is, the convergent sequence $\{a_n\}$ is bounded. ∎

There are some further consequences of the definition of limit of a sequence that the reader should have well in hand; they appear as exercises below. (Note especially Exercises 1, 2, 3.) The main tool in most of the proofs is the triangle inequality:

$$|x + y| \le |x| + |y|.$$

3.2 EXERCISES

1. Prove that if $x_n \to x$ and $y_n \to y$, then

   (a) $x_n + y_n \to x + y$
   (b) $x_n - y_n \to x - y$
   (c) $x_n y_n \to xy$

   [HINT: $|x_n y_n - xy| = |x_n y_n - x_n y + x_n y - xy| \le |x_n| \, |y_n - y| + |y| \, |x_n - x|$. Now invoke Theorem 3.2.]

   (d) $\dfrac{x_n}{y_n} \to \dfrac{x}{y}$ (provided $y_n \ne 0, y \ne 0$).

   [HINT: First show that under the hypotheses, y_n is bounded away from 0, that is, $\exists N$ and $\exists h > 0 \ni n > N \Rightarrow |y_n| > h$. You will see why you need this when you write: $|x_n/y_n - x/y| = |(x_n y - xy_n)/y_n y|$.]

2. Prove that if $x_n \ge y_n$ and if $x_n \to x$ and if $y_n \to y$, then $x \ge y$.

   [HINT: If $x < y$, then $(y - x)/2 > 0$. Make use of this positive number in the definition of limit to arrive at a contradiction.]

3. Show that if one sequence tends to 0 and a second sequence is bounded, then the product sequence has limit 0; that is, if $x_n \to 0$ and $|y_n| \le M$ (M a fixed positive number), then $x_n y_n \to 0$. Apply this result to the sequence $\{\sin n/n\}$.

4. Show that the sequence

$$1 + \frac{1}{2}, -1 + \frac{1}{2}, 1 + \frac{1}{3}, -1 + \frac{1}{3}, \cdots, 1 + \frac{1}{n}, -1 + \frac{1}{n}, \cdots$$

has no limit.

5. (a) Find two sequences $\{a_n\}$, $\{b_n\}$ neither of which has a limit yet the limit of the product $\{a_n b_n\}$ exists.

   (b) Do the same thing for the sum $\{a_n + b_n\}$.

6. Let p be a fixed positive number. Show that the sequence with $a_n = \sqrt[n]{p}$ has 1 as its limit.

   [HINT: First prove the lemma: If $h > 0$, then $(1 + h)^n \geq 1 + nh$ (use induction on n). Now consider three cases: $p = 1$, $p > 1$, $p < 1$. The case $p = 1$ is trivial. If $p > 1$, put $\sqrt[n]{p} = 1 + h_n$ and invoke the lemma to obtain $p \geq 1 + nh_n$ or $0 < h_n \leq (p - 1)/n$. Now pass to the limit. Finally, if $p < 1$, use the fact that $1/p > 1$, reducing the problem to the previous case. The reader will appreciate this result more if he sketches the graphs of $y = \sqrt{x}$, $y = \sqrt[3]{x}$, $\cdots$, $y = \sqrt[n]{x}$, chooses $p > 0$ and draws segments of lengths $\sqrt{p}$, $\sqrt[3]{p}$, $\cdots$, $\sqrt[n]{p}$ on the various graphs.]

7. Show that $\lim_{n \to \infty} (\sqrt{n + k} - \sqrt{n}) = 0$, where k is an arbitrary positive number.

   [HINT: Write

   $$\sqrt{n + k} - \sqrt{n} = (\sqrt{n + k} - \sqrt{n})(\sqrt{n + k} + \sqrt{n})/(\sqrt{n + k} + \sqrt{n}).]$$

8. Prove that $\lim_{n \to \infty} n!/n^n = 0$.

9. Evaluate $\lim_{n \to \infty} \sum_{k=1}^{n} 1/n(n + 1)(n + 2)$.   (Ans. ¼)

   [HINT: Use partial fraction decomposition on $1/n(n + 1)(n + 2)$ to determine the finite sum, then pass to the limit.]

10. Find $\lim_{n \to \infty} n^{100}/(1 + h)^n$, $h > 0$.

11. Show that $\lim_{n \to \infty} \sqrt[n]{n} = 1$.

    [HINT: Set $\sqrt[n]{n} = 1 + h_n$, $h_n > 0$ where $n > 1$ (justification?). Then $n = (1 + h_n)^n \geq 1 + nh_n + n(n - 1) h_n^2/2$. (Why?) It follows that $n - 1 \geq n(n - 1) h_n^2/2$. (Why?) Hence $1 \geq nh_n^2/2$ (divide by $n - 1$). Thus far we have $n > 1 \Rightarrow h_n^2 \leq 2/n$. Therefore $0 < h_n \leq \sqrt{2}/\sqrt{n}$. Now pass to the limit as $n \to \infty$.]

12. (a) Study the definition: $\lim_{n \to \infty} a_n = \infty$ iff for every $K > 0$, there exists a positive integer N (depending on K) such that $n > N \Rightarrow a_n > K$. Show that $\lim_{n \to \infty} a_n = \infty$ if $a_n = 1 + 1/2 + \cdots + 1/n$.

    (b) Define $\lim_{n \to \infty} a_n = -\infty$.

13. Write out a complete proof of Theorem 3.1.

14. Prove that an infinite sequence of integers converges iff its terms are all equal from some point on.

15. Using Definition 3.1, prove:

    (a) $a_n \to a$ iff $\forall \epsilon > 0$, $\exists N \ni n > N \Rightarrow |a_n - a| < \epsilon/2$

    (b) $a_n \to a$ iff $\forall \epsilon > 0$, $\exists N \ni n > N \Rightarrow |a_n - a| < M\epsilon$

    where M is an arbitrary but fixed positive number

3.3 THE SEQUENTIAL APPROACH

Now that the notion of limit has been defined for the special function called a sequence, the "sequential" approach to limit for an arbitrary real-valued function is at hand.

Definition 3.2. Let f be a real-valued function whose domain contains an open interval I of real numbers and let $a \in I$ or let a be an endpoint of I. Let b be a real number. We say that *the limit of $f(x)$ as x approaches a is b* [written $\lim_{x \to a} f(x) = b$] iff for every sequence $x_n \to a$, $x_n \neq a$, it follows that $f(x_n) \to b$ (assuming, of course, that $f(x_n)$ makes sense, that is, that x_n belongs to the domain of f).

More concisely, let x_n belong to the domain of f. Then

$$\lim_{x \to a} f(x) = b \text{ iff } x_n \to a, x_n \neq a \Rightarrow f(x_n) \to b.$$

Example 3.4. If $f(x) = \dfrac{x^2 - 4}{x - 2}$, $x \neq 2$, we have $\lim_{x \to 2} f(x) = 4$, for let $x_n \to 2$, $x_n \neq 2$. Then

$$\lim_{n \to \infty} \frac{x_n^2 - 4}{x_n - 2} = \lim_{n \to \infty} \frac{(x_n + 2)(x_n - 2)}{(x_n - 2)} = \lim_{n \to \infty} (x_n + 2) = 4.$$

[Justify the cancellation of the $(x_n - 2)$'s in the above calculation. Also note that $f(2)$ is undefined.]

Example 3.5. If $f(x) = x \sin(1/x)$, $x \neq 0$, we have $\lim_{x \to 0} f(x) = 0$, for let $x_n \to 0$, $x_n \neq 0$. Then

$$\lim_{n \to \infty} x_n \sin(1/x_n) = 0.$$

(The reader should see Sec. 3.2, Exercise 3 if he is not convinced.)

Example 3.6. Consider the function, defined for $0 \leq x \leq 1$, by

$$f(x) = \begin{cases} 0, & \text{if } x \text{ is irrational} \\ 1, & \text{if } x \text{ is rational.} \end{cases}$$

Let r be a real number with $0 \leq r \leq 1$. Then $\lim_{x \to r} f(x)$ does not exist, for we can find a sequence $\{x_n\}$ of real numbers with x_{2k-1} rational and x_{2k} irrational $(k = 1, 2, 3, \cdots)$ such that $x_n \neq r$, $x_n \to r$ but $\{f(x_n)\}$ is the sequence $1, 0, 1, 0, \cdots$.

3.4 EXERCISES

1. Prove that if $\lim_{x\to a} f(x)$ exists, then it is unique.

[HINT: If $\lim_{x\to a} f(x) = b$ and if $\lim_{x\to a} f(x) = c$, show that $b = c$ by proving that $|b - c| < \epsilon$ for arbitrary $\epsilon > 0$.]

2. Prove that if $\lim_{x\to a} f(x) = b$ and if $\lim_{x\to a} g(x) = c$, then

(a) $\lim_{x\to a} [f(x) \pm g(x)] = b \pm c$,

(b) $\lim_{x\to a} [f(x)g(x)] = bc$,

(c) $\lim_{x\to a} \dfrac{f(x)}{g(x)} = \dfrac{b}{c}$, provided $g(x) \neq 0$ and $c \neq 0$.

3. Prove that if $f(x) \geq g(x)$ for all x, and if $\lim_{x\to a} f(x) = b$ and $\lim_{x\to a} g(x) = c$, then $b \geq c$.

4. Prove that if $\lim_{x\to a} f(x) = 0$ and if $g(x)$ is *bounded* (that is, there is a constant M such that $|g(x)| \leq M$), then $\lim_{x\to a} f(x)g(x) = 0$.

5. Find the limits, if they exist (give formal proofs):

(a) $f(x) = \begin{cases} x, & \text{if } x \text{ is irrational} \\ 1 - x, & \text{if } x \text{ is rational.} \end{cases}$

   $\lim_{x\to a} f(x) = ?$ (Consider three cases: $a = \frac{1}{2}$; a is rational $\neq \frac{1}{2}$; a is irrational.)

(b) $\lim_{x\to 0} x \cos \dfrac{1}{x}$.

(c) $\lim_{x\to 0} \dfrac{1}{x} \tan x$.

(d) $\lim_{x\to 0} x \tan \dfrac{1}{x}$.

(e) $\lim_{x\to 0} \dfrac{1}{x}$.

6. Show that

$$\lim_{n\to\infty} (\cos \pi x)^{2n} = \begin{cases} 1, & \text{if } x \text{ is an integer} \\ 0, & \text{otherwise.} \end{cases}$$

7. Define precisely: $\lim_{x\to a} f(x) = \infty$; $\lim_{x\to a} f(x) = -\infty$; $\lim_{x\to\infty} f(x) = b$; $\lim_{x\to\infty} f(x) = \infty$. (Sec. 3.2, Exercise 12(a) may help.)

3.5 THE NEIGHBORHOOD APPROACH

Now we give our second approach to the concept of limit. We offer yet another definition of "$\lim_{x\to a} f(x) = b$," fully aware that we have already attached a meaning to this notation; our justification for a second definition lies in the fact that we subsequently (Section 3.6) prove the two concepts equivalent.

Definition 3.3.   Let f be a real-valued function whose domain contains an open interval I of real numbers and let $a \in I$ or let a be an endpoint of I. We say that the *limit of f as x approaches a is the real number b* [written $\lim_{x \to a} f(x) = b$] iff for every $\epsilon > 0$ there is a $\delta > 0$ such that

$$0 < |x - a| < \delta \Rightarrow |f(x) - b| < \epsilon, \tag{3.1}$$

assuming, of course, that x belongs to the domain of f.

(NOTE: $0 < |x - a|$ requires that $x \neq a$. Thus when we speak of the limit of f as x tends to a we explicitly exclude the possibility that $x = a$; we are concerned only with values of x "near a.")

Before showing the equivalence of the present definition and our previous one, we want to indicate why we call Definition 3.3 the "neighborhood approach." A *neighborhood $N(c)$* of the real number c is simply any open interval of real numbers with c as midpoint, that is,

$$N(c) = \{u \mid |u - c| < r, r > 0\}$$
$$= \{u \mid c - r < u < c + r, r > 0\}.$$

Sometimes it is convenient to emphasize the "size" of a neighborhood of a point, and so we introduce the following definition.

Definition 3.4.   By an *r neighborhood of c* [written $N(c; r)$] we mean the set

$$N(c; r) = \{u \mid |u - c| < r, r > 0\}.$$

We call r the *radius* of the neighborhood $N(c; r)$. By a *deleted neighborhood $N'(c)$* of the real number c is meant any neighborhood of c with c *removed*; that is,

$$N'(c) = \{u \mid 0 < |u - c| < r, r > 0\}$$
$$= N(c) - \{c\}.$$

Returning to the above definition of $\lim_{x \to a} f(x) = b$, we note that the given positive number $\epsilon > 0$ is used in connection with restricting $f(x)$ to the ϵ neighborhood $N(b; \epsilon)$ of b. [See (3.1) above.] Therefore, instead of being given the positive number $\epsilon > 0$, we could just as well suppose that we are given $N(b; \epsilon)$. Similarly, the positive number $\delta > 0$, which must be found once $\epsilon > 0$ is specified, serves only to determine the *deleted neighborhood $N'(a)$* of a; that is,

$$N'(a) = \{x \mid 0 < |x - a| < \delta\}.$$

Consequently, our definition can be phrased in the language of neighborhoods.

Definition 3.5. $\lim_{x \to a} f(x) = b$ iff for every neighborhood $N(b)$ of b, there exists a corresponding neighborhood $N(a)$ of a such that

$$x \in N'(a) \Rightarrow f(x) \in N(b). \tag{3.2}$$

We can carry out a further refinement of the definition by borrowing some set-theoretic ideas. First, we have no right to speak of $f(x)$ unless we are assured that x belongs to the domain of the function f. This assurance can be obtained by letting S denote the domain of f and then replacing (3.2) by the statement $x \in N'(a) \cap S \Rightarrow f(x) \in N(b)$. Finally, introduce the following.

Definition 3.6. If A is a subset of the domain S of f, the *image $f(A)$ of A under f* means the set

$$f(A) = \{f(x) \mid x \in A\}.$$

Keeping in mind that $X \subset Y$ means $x \in X \Rightarrow x \in Y$, we have the following elegant definition.

Definition 3.7. $\lim_{x \to a} f(x) = b$ iff for every $N(b) \Rightarrow \exists N(a) \ni$

$$f((N'(a) \cap S) \subset N(b).$$

Example 3.7.   The $\tfrac{1}{3}$ neighborhood of 1 is the set

$$N(1; \tfrac{1}{3}) = \{x \mid |x - 1| < \tfrac{1}{3}\} = \{x \mid \tfrac{2}{3} < x < \tfrac{4}{3}\}.$$

The corresponding *deleted* neighborhood is

$$N'(1; \tfrac{1}{3}) = \{x \mid 1 < x < \tfrac{4}{3} \quad \text{or} \quad \tfrac{2}{3} < x < 1\}.$$

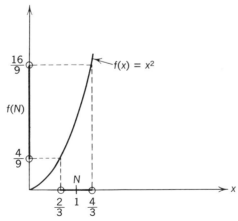

Fig. 3.1 $N(1; \tfrac{1}{3})$ and $f(N(1; \tfrac{1}{3}))$ are shown for $f(x) = x^2$.

If $f(x) = x^2$ for all real x, and if we write N instead of the bulky $N(\tfrac{1}{3}; 1)$, then the image $f(N)$ (see Fig. 3.1) is

$$f(N) = \{f(x) \mid x \in N\}$$
$$= \{f(x) \mid \tfrac{2}{3} < x < \tfrac{4}{3}\}.$$

That is, $f(N)$ is the open interval $(\tfrac{4}{9}, \tfrac{16}{9})$.

Example 3.8. The 0.5 neighborhood of 0.1 is

$$N(0.1; 0.5) = \{x \mid -0.4 < x < 0.6\}.$$

Moreover,

$$N'(0.1; 0.5) = \{x \mid 0.1 < x < 0.6 \quad \text{or} \quad -0.4 < x < 0.1\}.$$

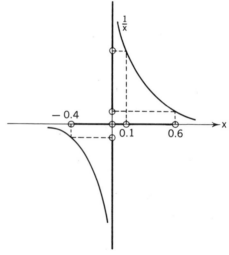

Fig. 3.2 $S \cap N'(0.1; 0.5)$ and $f(S \cap N'(0.1; 0.5))$ are shown for $f(x) = 1/x$, $x \neq 0$.

If $f(x) = 1/x$ for all $x \neq 0$, and if S denotes the domain of f, then (see Fig. 3.2)

$$S \cap N'(0.1; 0.5) = N'(0.1; 0.5) - \{0\}.$$

Furthermore,

$$f(S \cap N'(0.1; 0.5)) = \{y \mid y < -\tfrac{5}{2}\} \cup \{y \mid \tfrac{5}{3} < y < 10\} \cup \{y \mid y > 10\}.$$

Example 3.9. Let $f(x) = x^2$. We will prove formally that $\lim_{x \to a} x^2 = a^2$. Let $\epsilon > 0$. We want to determine $\delta > 0$ such that $0 < |x - a| < \delta$ will imply $|x^2 - a^2| < \epsilon$. We assume such a δ exists, writing

$$|x^2 - a^2| = |x - a| \cdot |x + a| = |x - a| \cdot |x - a + 2a|$$
$$\leq |x - a| [|x - a| + 2|a|] < \delta(\delta + 2|a|).$$

The problem therefore reduces to choosing δ so that

$$\delta(\delta + 2|a|) \leq \epsilon.$$

Working with the inequality, and adding $|a|^2$, we get

$$\delta^2 + 2|a|\delta + |a|^2 = \epsilon + |a|^2$$

or

$$(\delta + |a|)^2 = \epsilon + |a|^2$$

or

$$\delta = -|a| + \sqrt{\epsilon + |a|^2}.$$

It is easy to verify that with this choice of δ the required condition will prevail. We leave this to the reader. For sake of comparison, let us now take the sequential approach to the same problem. To show $\lim_{x \to a} x^2 = a^2$, we assume that $x_n \to a$, $x_n \neq a$, and use Section 3.2, Exercise 1(c), to conclude that $x_n^2 \to a^2$. This completes the proof.

3.6 EQUIVALENCE OF SEQUENTIAL AND NEIGHBORHOOD APPROACHES TO THE LIMIT CONCEPT

Our main purpose now is to prove the following theorem.

■ **Theorem 3.3.** If $\lim_{x \to a} f(x) = b$ in the sequential sense, then $\lim_{x \to a} f(x) = b$ in the neighborhood sense, and conversely.

Proof: For ease of exposition, we consider two conditions:

(1) If $\epsilon > 0$, $\exists \delta > 0 \ni 0 < |x - a| < \delta \Rightarrow |f(x) - b| < \epsilon$,

(2) $x_n \to a$, $x_n \neq a \Rightarrow f(x_n) \to b$.

We first show that $(1) \Rightarrow (2)$. The hypotheses are that (1) holds and that $x_n \to a$, $x_n \neq a$. We are to conclude that $f(x_n) \to b$.

Let $\epsilon > 0$. We know by (1) that $\exists \delta > 0 \ni 0 < |x - a| < \delta \Rightarrow |f(x) - b| < \epsilon$. Now, since $x_n \to a$ and δ is a positive number, we conclude (from the definition of $x_n \to a$, $x_n \neq a$) that

$$\exists N \ni n > N \Rightarrow 0 < |x_n - a| < \delta.$$

Hence, replacing x by x_n in (1), we have that $|f(x_n) - b| < \epsilon$, showing that $f(x_n) \to b$. Thus $(1) \Rightarrow (2)$ is proved.

It remains to prove that $(2) \Rightarrow (1)$. We find it easier to show the contrapositive; that is, negation of (1) implies negation of (2).

Now the negation of (1) is

(1′) $\exists \epsilon > 0 \ni$ for every $\delta > 0$, $\exists x \ni 0 < |x - a| < \delta$ and $|f(x) - b| \geq \epsilon$.

We are to conclude that (2) is false; that is,

(2') $\exists x_n \rightarrow a, \; x_n \neq a \ni f(x_n) \nrightarrow b.$

In (1') we have an $\epsilon > 0$ (over which we have no control) but we may take any $\delta > 0$. We successively choose [in (1')] $\delta = 1, \frac{1}{2}, \frac{1}{3}, \cdots, 1/n, \cdots$ and obtain the corresponding sequence $x_1, x_2, x_3, \cdots, x_n, \cdots$ such that $0 < |x_n - a| < 1/n$ and $|f(x_n) - b| \geq \epsilon.$ Overall, this means that we have found a sequence $x_1, x_2, \cdots$ such that $x_n \rightarrow a, \; x_n \neq a,$ yet $f(x_n) \nrightarrow b.$ ∎

One virtue of the equivalence of the two concepts of limit given above is that we are able to take whichever approach seems more tractable in a given situation. To illustrate, suppose we want to show that $\lim_{x \rightarrow 0} \sin (1/x)$ does not exist. According to the sequential approach, all we need do is find a sequence $x_n \rightarrow 0, \; x_n \neq 0$ such that $\{\sin (1/x_n)\}$ does not converge. This is

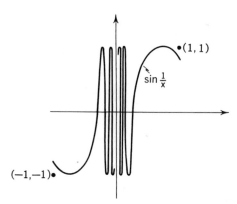

Fig. 3.3   Graph of $f(x) = \sin (1/x), \; x \neq 0.$

easy to do since $\sin (1/x)$ oscillates between 1 and -1 as x tends to 0 (see Fig. 3.3). In particular,

$$\sin \frac{1}{x} = 1 \text{ if } \frac{1}{x} = \frac{\pi}{2} + 2k\pi, \; k = 0, 1, 2, \cdots,$$

that is, if

$$x = \frac{2}{(4k + 1)\pi} \qquad (3.3)$$

and

$$\sin \frac{1}{x} = -1 \text{ if } \frac{1}{x} = \frac{3\pi}{2} + 2k\pi, \; k = 0, 1, 2, \cdots,$$

that is, if

$$x = \frac{2}{(4k + 3)\pi}. \qquad (3.4)$$

Thus if we choose x alternately from (3.3) and (3.4), we arrive at the sequence $x_1 = 2/\pi$, $x_2 = 2/3\pi$, $x_3 = 2/5\pi$, $x_4 = 2/7\pi$, $\cdots$. Hence sin $(1/x_1) = 1$, sin $(1/x_2) = -1$, sin $(1/x_3) = 1$, sin $(1/x_4) = -1$, $\cdots$ and, consequently, we conclude that $\lim_{x \to 0}$ sin $(1/x)$ does not exist. Compare this with the neighborhood approach in which we would have to show that no matter what real number b we take, there is a corresponding $\epsilon > 0$ such that for every $\delta > 0$, we can find an x with $0 < |x - 0| = |x| < \delta$ yet $|\sin (1/x) - b| \geq \epsilon$. This is apparently a more formidable task which would lead, however, to the same conclusion. As a matter of fact, we would ultimately be led to constructing a sequence similar to the one above.

The main difference, then, in attacking this problem through the sequential approach as opposed to the neighborhood approach is that in the latter case what has to be done is more immediately clear.

On the other hand, we emphasize that the neighborhood approach is often more convenient in theoretical investigations. As a matter of fact, in the abstract setting of a topological space, the "sequential limit" and the "neighborhood limit" are not equivalent concepts and, moreover, the concept of "sequential limit" proves to be inadequate.

3.7   EXERCISES

1–4. Prove the same theorems stated in Section 3.4, Exercises 1–4, taking the neighborhood approach to the concept of limit. Compare the proofs with those you gave previously via "sequential limits." Which do you prefer?

5. Let $f(x) = e^x$, $-\infty < x < \infty$. Compute $f(N'(1; 1))$. Does the set $f(N'(1; 1))$ have a maximum? Minimum? Supremum? Infimum?

6. Let x be a fixed real number. Consider the collection of all neighborhoods of x. What is the cardinal number of this collection?

7. Prove: If $\lim_{x \to a} f(x) = b > 0$, then $\exists N(a) \ni x \in N'(a) \Rightarrow f(x) > 0$.

3.8   SUBSEQUENCES AND MONOTONIC SEQUENCES

It is clear that the sequence $\{1, 2, 1, 3, 1, 4, 1, 5, \cdots, 1, n, \cdots\}$ has no limit. However, if we consider the sequence $\{1, 1, 1, \cdots\}$ obtained by taking every other term of the original sequence, it does have a limit. This kind of situation occurs frequently, and we should like to exploit it. First, it is necessary to be more precise in describing how we want the second sequence to be related to the first one. For this purpose, we lay down the following definition.

Definition 3.8. Let $\{a_1, a_2, a_3, \cdots\}$ be any sequence of real numbers and let $\{n_1, n_2, n_3, \cdots\}$ be any sequence of increasing positive integers; that is,

$$n_1 < n_2 < n_3 < \cdots.$$

The sequence

$$\{a_{n_1}, a_{n_2}, a_{n_3}, \cdots\}$$

is then called a *subsequence* of $\{a_1, a_2, a_3, \cdots\}$.

Remark

From the definition of n_k, it follows that $n_k \geq k$ for all positive integers k. Proof by induction on k is left to the reader (see Section 3.9, Exercise 1).

Example 3.10. Let $a_1 = 1$, $a_2 = 2$, $a_3 = 1$, $a_4 = 3$, $\cdots$, $a_{2n-1} = 1$, $a_{2n} = n + 1$, $\cdots$. Since $1 < 3 < 5 < 7 < \cdots$, the sequence $\{a_1, a_3, a_5, \cdots\}$ is a subsequence of the original sequence. This is, of course, the sequence $\{1, 1, 1, \cdots\}$. Many other subsequences of $\{a_1, a_2, \cdots\}$ may be obtained. For example, since

$$n_1 = 2 < n_2 = 2^2 < n_3 = 2^3 < \cdots < n_k = 2^k,$$

$a_{n_1} = a_2 = 2$, $a_{n_2} = a_4 = 3$, $\cdots$, $a_{n_k} = a_{2^k} = a_{2(2^{k-1})} = 2^{k-1} + 1$, $\cdots$ is another subsequence of $\{a_1, a_2, \cdots\}$.

The above example illustrates that it is possible for a sequence to be non-convergent, yet have a convergent subsequence. On the other hand, if a sequence converges, then its replacement by a subsequence will not affect the limit, as we now prove.

■ **Theorem 3.4.** If $\lim_{n\to\infty} a_n = a$ and if $\{a_{n_1}, a_{n_2}, \cdots, a_{n_k}, \cdots\}$ is a subsequence of $\{a_1, a_2, \cdots\}$, then $\lim_{k\to\infty} a_{n_k} = a$.

Proof: By hypothesis, for every $\epsilon > 0$, there is a positive integer N such that

$$n > N \Rightarrow |a_n - a| < \epsilon. \tag{3.5}$$

Now

$$k > N \Rightarrow n_k \geq k > N$$

(see remark following Definition 3.8) which, in turn, according to (3.5) implies

$$|a_{n_k} - a| < \epsilon.$$

Thus, we have that for every $\epsilon > 0$, there exists N such that

$$k > N \Rightarrow |a_{n_k} - a| < \epsilon.$$

Hence $\lim_{k\to\infty} a_{n_k} = a$. ∎

Obviously, the single assumption that a sequence has a convergent subsequence will not guarantee that the sequence converges. However, for certain kinds of sequences called *monotonic* this condition does suffice.

Definition 3.9.   A sequence $\{a_n\}$ is called *monotonic increasing* (and we write $a_n \uparrow$) iff

$$a_{n+1} \geq a_n$$

for all positive integers n. We call $\{a_n\}$ *strictly increasing* iff $a_{n+1} > a_n$ for all n. $\{a_n\}$ is called *monotonic decreasing* (written $a_n \downarrow$) iff

$$a_{n+1} \leq a_n$$

for all positive integers n. We call $\{a_n\}$ *strictly decreasing* iff $a_{n+1} < a_n$ for all n. A sequence is called *monotonic* iff it is either monotonic increasing or monotonic decreasing.

■ **Theorem 3.5.**   If a monotonic increasing sequence $\{a_n\}$ has a convergent subsequence $\{a_{n_k}\}$, then $\{a_n\}$ converges. Moreover, $\lim_{n \to \infty} a_n = \sup \{a_1, a_2, \cdots\}$.

Proof: Suppose $\{a_{n_k}\}$, $k = 1, 2, \cdots$ converges to a. Then, for every $\epsilon > 0$, there exists a positive integer K such that

$$k > K \Rightarrow |a_{n_k} - a| < \epsilon. \tag{3.6}$$

We claim that the integer n_{K+1} will serve in showing that $a_n \to a$, for let n be any fixed integer with

$$n > n_{K+1}. \tag{3.7}$$

We want to show that $|a_n - a| < \epsilon$. To do this, we observe that there is a positive integer $K + m$ such that

$$n < n_{K+m} \tag{3.8}$$

since Definition 3.8 requires that n_k tend to infinity as k tends to infinity. Because $\{a_p\}$ is a monotonic increasing sequence, (3.7) and (3.8) imply

$$a_{n_{K+1}} \leq a_n \leq a_{n_{K+m}}. \tag{3.9}$$

From (3.6) we have (taking $k = K + 1$)

$$|a_{n_{K+1}} - a| < \epsilon,$$

in particular

$$a - \epsilon < a_{n_{K+1}}. \tag{3.10}$$

Again from (3.6) we have (since $K + m > K$ for all m)

$$a_{n_{K+m}} < a + \epsilon. \tag{3.11}$$

It follows from (3.9) and (3.10) that

$$a - \epsilon < a_n$$

and from (3.9) and (3.11) that

$$a_n < a + \epsilon.$$

The last two inequalities yield

$$|a_n - a| < \epsilon$$

and the first part of the theorem is proved.

To show that $\lim a_n = \sup \{a_1, a_2, \cdots\}$, we again set $a = \lim a_n$, for convenience. We must show (by definition of supremum) that:

(1) $a \geq a_n$ for all positive integers n

and

(2) $b \geq a_n, n = 1, 2, \cdots \Rightarrow a \leq b.$

To prove (1), note that if n is fixed, we have $a_{n+k} \geq a_n$ for all $k = 1, 2, \cdots$. Noting that this is a special case of Section 3.2, Exercise 2, and passing to the limit as $k \to \infty$, we get $\lim_{k \to \infty} a_{n+k} = a \geq a_n$, proving (1). To prove (2), we assume $b \geq a_n$ for all n. Passing to the limit, we have immediately $b \geq a$ (see Section 3.2, Exercise 2). ∎

Theorem 3.5 gave a sufficient condition for a monotonic increasing sequence to converge, the condition being that it have a convergent subsequence. As a variant of this theorem, another sufficient condition for convergence is that the monotonic increasing sequence be bounded above. This constitutes Theorem 3.6.

■ **Theorem 3.6.**   If the sequence $a_n \uparrow$ is bounded above (that is, $\exists M$ such that $|a_n| \leq M$ for all n), then $\{a_n\}$ converges.

Proof: We shall use Theorem 3.5 in the proof. Thus all we need do is show that $\{a_n\}$ has a convergent subsequence. To do this, note that since a_n is bounded, the *set*

$$\{a_1, a_2, \cdots\}$$

of real numbers has a supremum; call it a. Invoking Theorem 2.9 repeatedly, taking $\epsilon = 1, \frac{1}{2}, \cdots, 1/n, \cdots$, we obtain the required subsequence. (Details are left to the reader.) ∎

Finally, we point out that the last two theorems are equivalent in the sense that either may be obtained as a consequence of the other. Proof is left to the reader, but we state the result in the following form.

■ **Theorem 3.7.**   Let $\{a_n\}$ be a monotonic increasing sequence. $\{a_n\}$ has a convergent subsequence iff $\{a_n\}$ is bounded.

It should be noted that Theorems 3.5, 3.6, and 3.7 have analogs for monotonic decreasing sequences. (Formulations of these and their proofs are left to the reader.)

Example 3.11. The sequence $a_1 = 1 + 1/1!$, $a_2 = 1 + 1/1! + 1/2!$, $\cdots$, $a_n = 1 + 1/1! + 1/2! + \cdots + 1/n!$, $\cdots$ is clearly monotonic increasing. It is bounded by the number 3, for

$$a_n = 1 + 1 + 1/1\cdot2 + 1/1\cdot2\cdot3 + \cdots + 1/1\cdot2\cdot3 \cdots n$$
$$< 1 + 1 + 1/2 + 1/2^2 + \cdots + 1/2^n < 3.$$

Hence by Theorem 3.6, $\lim a_n$ exists. This limit is, by definition, the number e. We express this by writing

$$e = 1 + 1 + \frac{1}{2!} + \frac{1}{3!} + \cdots.$$

3.9 EXERCISES

1. Prove (for notation see Definition 3.8) that $n_k \geq k$ for all positive integers k. (Use induction on k.)
2. Supply the details in proving Theorem 3.6.
3. Prove Theorem 3.7.
4. Prove that the limit of the sequence

$$\sqrt{2},\ \sqrt{2 + \sqrt{2}},\ \sqrt{2 + \sqrt{2 + \sqrt{2}}},\ \cdots$$

   exists and is equal to 2.
5. Let $0 < a_1 < b_1$. Define

$$a_2 = \sqrt{a_1 b_1} \qquad b_2 = \frac{a_1 + b_1}{2},$$

$$a_3 = \sqrt{a_2 b_2} \qquad b_3 = \frac{a_2 + b_2}{2},$$

   and, in general,

$$a_n = \sqrt{a_{n-1} b_{n-1}} \qquad b_n = \frac{a_{n-1} + b_{n-1}}{2}.$$

   Show that (1) $\{a_n\}$ converges, (2) $\{b_n\}$ converges, and (3) the limits of these sequences coincide.

   [HINT: From $0 \leq (u - v)^2 = u^2 - 2uv + v^2$, it follows that $(u^2 + v^2)/2 \geq uv$.]

6. Let a, b be positive numbers.
   (a) Show that the sequence

   $$a_1 = \frac{1}{2}\left(a + \frac{b}{a}\right),\ a_2 = \frac{1}{2}\left(a_1 + \frac{b}{a_1}\right),\ \cdots,\ a_n = \frac{1}{2}\left(a_{n-1} + \frac{b}{a_{n-1}}\right),\ \cdots$$

   decreases monotonically.

   [HINT: Show that $a_1^2 \geq b$ by using the fact that for positive numbers u, v we have $(u + v)/2 \geq \sqrt{uv}$. (See Hint in Exercise 5.) Hence, in general, $a_n^2 \geq b$. Use this to prove $a_n - a_{n+1} \geq 0$.]
   (b) The sequence $\{a_n\}$ is bounded below and therefore because of (a), above, it converges.
   (c) Use (a) and (b) to show that the equation $x^2 = b$, $b > 0$ has a unique positive solution.

   [HINT: Let $\lim a_n = A$. Show that $2a_n a_{n+1} = a_n^2 + b$ and hence, passing to the limit, $A^2 = b$.]
   (d) Estimate $\sqrt{3}$.
7. We say that the function f is *strictly monotonic increasing* $(f\uparrow)$ iff $u < v \Rightarrow f(u) < f(v)$. Show that

   $$f\uparrow\ \Rightarrow \exists f^{-1} \quad \text{and} \quad f^{-1}\uparrow.$$

8. Show that if an arbitrary sequence $\{x_n\}$ of real numbers does not have a strictly decreasing subsequence, then it must have an increasing subsequence.

   [HINT: Consider the set $S = \{x_M \mid x_M > x_k, \forall k > M\}$. There are two cases: (1) $\bar{S}$ is finite; (2) $\bar{\bar{S}} = \aleph_0$.]

Supplement to Chapter 3

The concept of limit and most of the theorems of this chapter can be carried over to the case of a complex-valued function of a complex variable. In this supplement we indicate how this can be accomplished, leaving most of the details to the reader. No difficulty will be experienced by the student who has a firm grasp of the ideas already discussed.

The *complex number system* can be defined to be the set

$$C = \{(x, y) \mid x, y \text{ real}\}$$

(instead of writing (x, y), one often finds $x + iy$ in its place in the literature), together with equality defined by $(x, y) = (u, v)$ iff $x = u$ and $y = v$ and the operations of addition and multiplication for pairs of elements (x, y), $(u, v) \in C$ defined by

$$(x, y) + (u, v) = (x + u, y + v)$$

$$(x, y)(u, v) = (xu - yv, xv + yu).$$

(See Section 2.3, Exercise 2.) We leave it to the reader to verify that the complex numbers form a field but not an ordered field. We assume the reader is familiar with the fact that the complex numbers can be interpreted geometrically as the set of all points in a plane (that is, $R \times R$) or the set of all vectors in a plane with initial point at the origin $(0, 0)$.

If $(x, y) \in C$ and $(u, v) \in C$, we define the *distance* between these two points (denoted by $|(x, y) - (u, v)|$) by the well-known formula from plane analytic geometry:

$$|(x, y) - (u, v)| = \sqrt{(x - u)^2 + (y - v)^2}.$$

(NOTE: This definition is justified on the grounds that $|x + iy| = |(x, y)| = |(x, y) - (0, 0)| = \sqrt{x^2 + y^2}$. In particular, $|x| = |x + i0| = |(x, 0)| = \sqrt{x^2}$.)

To simplify the notation, let us agree to put $z = (x, y)$, $w = (u, v)$ in the rest of our discussion. Then $|z - w|$ denotes the distance between z and w, and the analogy with the real-number case (see Section 2.6) is carried further by the following theorem.

■ **Theorem 3.8.** The notion of distance between complex numbers introduced above satisfies the following:

(1) $|z - w| \geq 0$ and $|z - w| = 0$ iff $z = w$,
(2) $|z - w| = |w - z|$,
(3) $|z - w| + |w - q| \geq |z - q|$ (q is a complex number).

Properties (1) and (2) are easy to verify. To prove (3), we need the *triangle inequality* for complex numbers.

■ **Theorem 3.9.** For all complex numbers z, w, $|z + w| \leq |z| + |w|$.

This theorem, in turn, depends on the important *Cauchy-Schwarz inequality*, which follows.

■ **Theorem 3.10.** If x, y, u, v are arbitrary real numbers, then

$$|xu + yv| \leq \sqrt{x^2 + y^2} \sqrt{u^2 + v^2}.$$

(NOTE: The quantity $xu + yv$ is the (vector) dot product of $z = x + iy$ and $w = u + iv$.)

Proof: Now $(xt + u)^2 + (yt + v)^2 \geq 0$ where t is an arbitrary real number, since a sum of squares of real numbers is always nonnegative. But the left member is quadratic in t; that is, we may write

$$(x^2 + y^2)t^2 + 2(xu + yv)t + (u^2 + v^2) \geq 0. \qquad (3.12)$$

But either $x^2 + y^2 = 0$ or $x^2 + y^2 > 0$. If the first condition prevails, the inequality of our theorem holds trivially (check it directly, putting $x = y = 0$). If $x^2 + y^2 > 0$, we choose $t = -(xu + yv)/(x^2 + y^2)$ and substitute into (3.12) to get

$$(u^2 + v^2)(x^2 + y^2) \geq (xu + yv)^2.$$

Taking principal square roots and noting that

$$\sqrt{(xu + yv)^2} = |xu + yv|,$$

the inequality is proved. ∎

Thus (3) of Theorem 3.8 is proved by the sequence of implications:

$$\text{Theorem } 3.10 \Rightarrow \text{Theorem } 3.9 \Rightarrow (3).$$

Final details are left to the exercises immediately following this supplement.

The concept of limit of a sequence $\{a_n\}$ of real numbers (Definition 3.1) carries over verbatim to a sequence of complex numbers.

Definition 3.10. We write $\lim a_n = a$ iff for every $\epsilon > 0$, $\exists N \ni n > N \Rightarrow |a_n - a| < \epsilon$. Here a and a_n are, of course, complex numbers.

Convergent sequences of complex numbers have the following properties:

■ **Theorem 3.11.** If the sequence $\{a_n\}$ of complex numbers has a limit, then the limit is unique (see Theorem 3.1).

■ **Theorem 3.12.** If the sequence $\{a_n\}$ of complex numbers is convergent, then it is bounded (see Theorem 3.2).

Proof of Theorem 3.11 follows verbatim the proof of Theorem 3.1, given earlier, for the statement

$$|z - w| < \epsilon \text{ for all } \epsilon > 0 \Rightarrow z = w$$

is valid when z and w are complex numbers. To see this, we observe that $|z - w| = \sqrt{(x - u)^2 + (y - v)^2} < \epsilon$ for all $\epsilon > 0 \Rightarrow \sqrt{(x - u)^2} = |x - u| \leq \sqrt{(x - u)^2 + (y - v)^2} < \epsilon$ and $\sqrt{(y - v)^2} = |y - v| < \epsilon$ for all $\epsilon > 0$. Since x, y, u, v are real numbers, it follows (from the corollary to Theorem 2.10) that $x = u$ and $y = v$.

Proof of Theorem 3.12 is, word for word, repetition of the proof of Theorem 3.2.

The formal definition of an *r neighborhood* $N(c; r)$ of the complex number c is precisely the same as Definition 3.4:

$$N(c; r) = \{z \mid |z - c| < r, r > 0\}.$$

As a matter of fact, we see for the first time why we call r the *radius* of the neighborhood: Indeed, $N(c; r)$ is simply the *interior* of the circle with center at c and radius r. (Note carefully that the "circumference" of the circle which determines a neighborhood of the center of the circle is *excluded* from the neighborhood, just as the endpoints of an interval (which determine a neighborhood of their midpoint) are excluded from the neighborhood.) The *deleted neighborhood* $N'(c; r)$ of c is defined as the r neighborhood of c with c removed; that is,

$$N'(c; r) = \{z \mid 0 < |z - c| < r, r > 0\}.$$

Definition 3.6 carries over intact to the case where the domain and range of f are subsets of the complex numbers:

If A is a subset of the domain S of f, the *image* $f(A)$ *of* A *under* f is the set

$$f(A) = \{f(z) \mid z \in A\}.$$

With these definitions, we are ready for the sequential approach to limits.

Definition 3.11. Let f be a complex-valued function whose domain contains the interior of some circle γ, and let a be a point interior to γ or let $a \in \gamma$. We write $\lim_{z \to a} f(z) = b$ iff for every sequence $z_n \to a$, $z_n \neq a$, it follows that $f(z_n) \to b$.

We also introduce Definition 3.12, paralleling our earlier discussion.

Definition 3.12. (Neighborhood approach to limit.) We write $\lim_{z \to a} f(z) = b$ iff for every $\epsilon > 0$, $\exists \delta > 0 \ni 0 < |z - a| < \delta \Rightarrow |f(z) - b| < \epsilon$. Equivalently, with $S =$ domain of f, we have (see Definition 3.7) $\lim_{z \to a} f(z) = b$ iff for every $N(b) \Rightarrow \exists N(a) \ni f(N'(a) \cap S) \subset N(b)$.

Theorem 3.3, which asserts the equivalence of Definitions 3.11 and 3.12, is again valid and, moreover, precisely the same proof holds for the complex number case.

Although the concept of a subsequence and Theorem 3.4 carry over to complex numbers, the notion of monotonic sequence for complex numbers is meaningless since the complex number field is not an ordered field.

3.10 EXERCISES

1. Prove the triangle inequality for complex numbers z, w:

$$|z + w| \leq |z| + |w|.$$

[HINT: Use Theorem 3.10.]

2. Prove that if z, w, q are arbitrary complex numbers, then

$$|z - w| + |w - q| \geq |z - q|.$$

[HINT: Use the triangle inequality proved in Exercise 1.]

3. Prove Theorem 3.12: If $\{a_n\}$ is a convergent sequence of complex numbers, then $\{a_n\}$ is bounded; that is, $\exists M > 0 \ni |a_n| \leq M$ for all positive integers n.

4. Prove that if $\{a_n\} = \{x_n + iy_n\}$ is a sequence of complex numbers which converges to the complex number $x + iy$, then $x_n \to x$ and $y_n \to y$.

5. We define the *real part* of the complex number $x + iy$ or (x, y) to be the real number x and the *imaginary part* of $x + iy$ to be the real number y. If S is any set of complex numbers, we can form the set of all real parts of members of S (call this set S_r) and the set of all imaginary parts of members of S (call it S_i). Show that if S is bounded, then S_r and S_i are both bounded, and conversely.

6. If $z = x + iy$, then the *conjugate of z* is $\bar{z} = x - iy$. Prove:
    (a) $\overline{z + w} = \bar{z} + \bar{w}$.
    (b) $\overline{zw} = \bar{z}\bar{w}$.
    (c) $\bar{\bar{z}} = z$.
    (d) $z\bar{z} = |z|^2$.

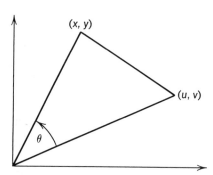

Fig. 3.4   Exercise 7: Geometric proof of Cauchy-Schwarz inequality.

7. Here is another proof of the Cauchy-Schwarz inequality. Apply the law of cosines to the triangle in Fig. 3.4 to get

$$(x - u)^2 + (y - v)^2 = (x^2 + y^2) + (u^2 + v^2) - 2\sqrt{x^2 + y^2}\sqrt{u^2 + v^2}\cos\theta.$$

Now use the fact that $|\cos\theta| \leq 1$.

8. Define $A_n = \{z \mid |z + i| > 1/n\}, n = 1, 2, \cdots$. Find $\bigcup_{n=1}^{\infty} A_n$, $\bigcap_{n=1}^{\infty} A_n$.

4

Three Important
Theorems

INTRODUCTION

The purpose of this chapter is to introduce the ideas essential to the statements of three useful theorems and to prove these theorems. All three results are classical—basic theorems of analysis which find widespread applications and, in this sense, may be classified as "tool theorems." They are known as:

(1) The Bolzano-Weierstrass theorem
(2) The structure theorem for open sets of real numbers
(3) The Heine-Borel covering theorem.

Roughly speaking, the first theorem says that if an infinite set S of real numbers is distributed over an interval of finite length, then there is at least one real number, not necessarily a member of S, about which the points of S "accumulate."

The second theorem is concerned with the nature of a special kind of set of real numbers called an open set. Being a "structure theorem," it is supposed to reveal how to describe an object (in this case an open set of real numbers) in terms of simpler objects (in this case open intervals of real numbers). In particular, it asserts that a nonempty open set of real numbers is the union of a countable number of disjoint open intervals.

The third theorem guarantees that from every infinite collection of open sets whose union contains a closed interval (of finite length) of real numbers, one can select a *finite* number of the open sets whose union will still contain the closed interval.

Very likely these three theorems will appear to the reader to be abstract and perhaps of questionable value. It is only through application of these results, observing how they replace a complicated situation with a tractable one, that we come to understand and appreciate them.

The proofs which we offer make extensive use of the basic property of the supremum of a set of real numbers (Theorem 2.9) and the fundamental theorem connecting the concepts of equivalence relation and partition (Theorem 1.1).

4.1   ACCUMULATION POINTS OF A SET; THE BOLZANO-WEIERSTRASS THEOREM

In studying the concept of a limit, it is important to consider, besides a sequence, an arbitrary set A of real numbers, attach a meaning to "limit points" or "accumulation points" of the set A, and study the properties of these accumulation points of A. Accordingly, this is what we shall do. Let A be an arbitrary set of real numbers. To make matters concrete, let us imagine the elements of A to be plotted on the real number line. Now, intuitively speaking, the accumulation points of A are the points of the real number line, *not necessarily points of A*, about which the points of A "accumulate," that is, a real number ξ (*not necessarily in A*) is called an accumulation point of A iff there are members of A arbitrarily close to ξ. The precise meaning is contained in the following definition.

Definition 4.1.   Let A be a set of real numbers. A real number ξ (not necessarily in A) is called a *limit point of A* or an *accumulation point of A* iff for every $\epsilon > 0$, there exists an $x \in A$ such that

$$0 < |x - \xi| < \epsilon.$$

We can say the same thing in the language of neighborhoods: ξ is an *accumulation point of A* iff every deleted neighborhood $N'(\xi)$ of ξ contains a point of A.

To put it elegantly, ξ is an *accumulation point of A* iff for every neighborhood $N(\xi)$ of ξ we have

$$N'(\xi) \cap A \neq \varnothing.$$

If A is a set, we shall denote the set of all accumulation points of A by A'; A' is called the *derived set* of A.

Remark 1

We emphasize again that accumulation points of a set A need not belong to A. For example, the set $A = \{x \mid 0 < x < 1\}$ of all real numbers in the unit open interval has, besides every point of A, two additional limit points: 0 and 1. The number 1 is a limit point of A since an arbitrary deleted neighborhood $N'(1; \delta)$, $\delta > 0$, will contain points of A. For similar reasons, $0 \in A'$. Thus $A' = \{x \mid 0 \le x \le 1\}$.

Remark 2

It is a useful and immediate consequence of Definition 4.1 that *in every neighborhood of a limit point ξ of a set A there are infinitely many points of A.* To see this, we choose successively smaller neighborhoods of ξ, selecting a

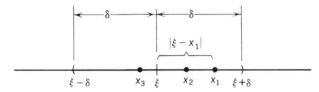

Fig. 4.1   Every neighborhood of a limit point of set A contains infinitely many points of A.

point of A from each neighborhood. Thus, let $N(\xi;\delta)$ be a neighborhood of ξ of radius δ. Applying the definition of limit point, we are guaranteed that

$$N'(\xi;\delta) \cap A \ne \varnothing.$$

Hence let $x_1 \in N(\xi, \delta)$, $x_1 \in A$, $x_1 \ne \xi$ (see Fig. 4.1). Next consider $N(\xi; |x_1 - \xi|)$. We know that

$$N'(\xi; |x_1 - \xi|) \cap A \ne \varnothing.$$

Let $x_2 \in N(\xi; |x_1 - \xi|)$, $x_2 \in A$, $x_2 \ne \xi$. Clearly $x_2 \ne x_1$. Continuing this process by induction, we generate a sequence $\{x_1, x_2, x_3, \cdots\}$ of distinct points of A in the arbitrary neighborhood $N(\xi;\delta)$ of ξ. This proves the assertion.

Obviously, the converse is also true; that is, if every neighborhood of ξ contains infinitely many points of A, then ξ is a limit point of A. Thus, we have the useful result:

■ **Theorem 4.1.** $\xi \in A' \Leftrightarrow$ every neighborhood $N(\xi)$ of ξ contains infinitely many points of A.

Some examples will help us grasp the idea of limit points.

Example 4.1. If A is a finite set, then A has no limit points. (Symbolically, A finite $\Rightarrow A' = \varnothing$.)

To prove this, we simply note that if $\xi \in A'$, then every neighborhood of ξ must contain infinitely many points of A, according to Theorem 4.1. But this is impossible since, to begin with, A has only a finite number of points.

Thus, every finite set is devoid of limit points. Sometimes infinite sets have no limit points as the next example shows.

Example 4.2. The set A of all integers has no limit points.

For, suppose ξ were a limit point of A. Consider the neighborhood $N(\xi;1)$ of radius 1. $N(\xi;1)$ would have to contain infinitely many integers which is clearly impossible. Hence the set of all integers has no limit points.

Some infinite sets have nonempty derived sets containing a finite number of points, as shown by the next example.

Example 4.3. The set A defined by

$$A = \left\{ \frac{1}{n} \,\middle|\, n \text{ is a natural number} \right\}$$

has one limit point, namely, the point 0. (Proof is left to the reader.) Note that $0 \notin A$.

Our next example indicates that a denumerable set can have a denumerable number of limit points.

Example 4.4. The set

$$A = \left\{ n + \frac{1}{k+1} \,\middle|\, n, k \text{ are natural numbers} \right\}$$

has all natural numbers as limit points. (Proof is left to the reader.) It is interesting to note that in this example no member of A is a limit point of A; that is, $A' \cap A = \varnothing$.

Some denumerable sets have uncountably many limit points as the next example shows.

Example 4.5. Consider the set of all rational numbers. *Every* real number is a limit point of this set for, given an open interval with an arbitrary real number x at its center, this interval contains infinitely many rational numbers and therefore x is a limit point of A. Thus a denumerable set can have a continuum of limit points.

Example 4.2 above shows that it is possible to have an infinite set with no limit points. Notice, however, that the set—all natural numbers—of that example cannot be confined to an interval of finite length. As a matter of fact, it is intuitively clear that if an infinite set of real numbers is contained in an interval of finite length, that is, is bounded, then that set must have at least one limit point. To be precise, we have

■ **Theorem 4.2.** (Bolzano-Weierstrass.) Every bounded infinite set A of real numbers has at least one point of accumulation.

To put it another way: If the set A of real numbers contains an infinite number of elements and if $|x| \leq M, \ \forall\, x \in A$, then $A' \neq \varnothing$.

Proof: Let $x, y \in [-M, M]$ and let $\overline{xy}$ denote the closed interval with endpoints x, y (we do not distinguish between $\overline{xy}$ and $\overline{yx}$ and, in case $x = y$, we have that $\overline{xx} = \{x\}$). We define $T = \{x \mid x \in [-M, M]$, and $\overline{xM}$ contains infinitely many points of $A\}$. Now $T \neq \varnothing$ since $-M \in T$. Moreover, T is bounded above by M; that is, $x \in T \Rightarrow x \leq M$. It follows that T has a supremum. There are two cases to consider:

$$(1) \ \sup T = -M; \qquad (2) \ -M < \sup T \leq M.$$

[We leave it to the reader to show that (*a*) $\sup T < -M$ is impossible and (*b*) $\sup T > M$ is impossible.] We shall prove that $\sup T \in A'$, and this will complete the proof of the theorem for this tells us that A' is not empty.

Since $\sup T = -M \geq x$ for all $x \in T$ in case (1), we have the condition

$$x > -M \Rightarrow x \notin T.$$

It follows that for all x such that $-M < x < M$, $\overline{xM}$ contains finitely many points of A. But if the interval $\overline{xM}$ contains finitely many points of A, and we know that the interval $\overline{-MM}$ contains infinitely many points of A, apparently $\overline{-Mx}$ contains infinitely many points of A for all x with $-M < x < M$. From this we conclude that every neighborhood of $-M$ contains infinitely many points of A; that is, $-M \in A'$. This completes case (1).

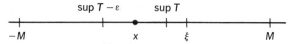

Fig. 4.2   Bolzano-Weierstrass Theorem: A bounded, $\overline{A}$ infinite $\Rightarrow A' \neq \varnothing$.

Turning to case (2) and using Theorem 2.9, we have for every $\epsilon > 0$:

$$\exists x \in T \ni \sup T - \epsilon < x \leq \sup T. \qquad (*)$$

(See Fig. 4.2.) Moreover, for no $\xi > \sup T$ can it be true that $\overline{\xi M}$ contains infinitely many points of A for this would imply $\xi \in T$, contradicting the definition of $\sup T$. Hence the interval $\overline{\xi M}$ contains finitely many points of A, for all ξ with $\xi > \sup T$. So, according to $(*)$ the interval $\overline{xM}$ contains infinitely many points of A, while $\overline{\xi M}$ contains finitely many points of A. Thus $\overline{x\xi}$ contains infinitely many points of A; that is, for every $\epsilon > 0$, $N(\sup T; \epsilon)$ contains infinitely many points of A. This proves that $\sup T \in A'$. ∎

Example 4.6. Let $A = \{1, \frac{1}{2}, \frac{1}{3}, \cdots, 1/n, \cdots\}$. Then $x \in A \Rightarrow |x| \leq 1$, so we may take $M = 1$ in the proof of Theorem 4.2. Moreover, if $T = \{x \mid x \in [-1, 1]$ and $\overline{x1}$ contains infinitely many points of $A\}$, then T is the closed interval $[-1, 0]$. Hence $\sup T = 0$, and indeed the number 0 is a point of accumulation of A since every neighborhood of 0 contains infinitely many points of A.

4.2 EXERCISES

In Exercises 1 to 6, find the set of all accumulation points as indicated.

1. $A = \{p \mid p$ is a prime number$\}$. Find A'.
2. $A = \{x \mid x$ is irrational$\}$. Find A'.
3. $A = \{1, 1.01, 1.01001, 1.010010001, \cdots\}$. Find A'.
4. $A = \{x \mid |x + 2| > 5\}$. Find A'.
5. $A = \{n \pm (1/k) \mid n, k$ integers, $k \neq 0\}$. Find A'.
6. $A = \{x \mid |x - 1| < 3\}, B = \{x \mid |x + 1| < 1\}$. Find $(A \cup B)', (A \cap B)',$ $(A \vartriangle B)'$. (See Sec. 1.2, Exercise 4).

7. Show that the derived set has the following properties:
   (a) $A = \varnothing \Rightarrow A' = \varnothing$.
   (b) $A \subset B \Rightarrow A' \subset B'$.
   (c) $x \in A' \Rightarrow x \in (A - \{x\})'$.
   (d) $(A \cup B)' = A' \cup B'$.
8. Show that if $\{I_n\}$, $n = 1, 2, 3, \cdots$, is a nested sequence of closed intervals with lengths tending to zero (that is, if $I_n = \{x \mid a_n \leq x \leq b_n\}$, $n = 1, 2, 3, \cdots$, and if $I_1 \supset I_2 \supset I_3 \cdots$, and $\lim |a_n - b_n| = 0$), then there exists one and only one real number ξ such that $\xi \in \bigcap_{n=1}^{\infty} I_n$.

   [HINT: Show that the least upper bound of the set $A = \{a_1, a_2, \cdots\}$ coincides with the greatest lower bound of the set $B = \{b_1, b_2, \cdots\}$ and that this common number is the number sought.]
9. Show that in Exercise 8 it is essential that the intervals I_n be *closed*.

   [HINT: Consider the sequence $J_n = (0, 1/n)$ of *open* intervals.]
10. Use the result in Exercise 8 to give another proof of the Bolzano-Weierstrass theorem.

    [HINT: Let $[-M, M]$ contain the infinite set A. Cut the interval $[-M, M]$ into two equal parts $I_1 = [-M, 0]$ and $J_1 = [0, M]$. At least one of I_1, J_1 must contain an infinite number of points of A. Why? Suppose that I_1 is this interval. Now subdivide I_1 into two equal parts and argue that at least one of these (call it I_2) contains infinitely many points of A. In this way, generate a nested sequence $I_1 \supset I_2 \supset \cdots$ of closed intervals with lengths tending to 0. Invoke Exercise 8.]
11. Use the Bolzano-Weierstrass theorem to prove the following theorem. If a monotonic nondecreasing sequence is bounded above, then it has a limit. In symbols, $a_n \leq a_{n+1}$, $n = 1, 2, 3, \cdots$, and $|a_n| < M \Rightarrow \exists \lim a_n$.

    [HINT: Either the sequence has finitely many distinct terms or it has infinitely many distinct terms. In case the first alternative holds, the result is trivial (consider the maximum of the terms); in the remaining case, invoke the Bolzano-Weierstrass theorem to obtain a point of accumulation of the set $\{a_1, a_2, a_3, \cdots\}$ (call it ξ). Show that $a_n > \xi$ for some n leads to a contradiction. Let $\epsilon > 0$. Then there is an a_N such that $|a_N - \xi| < \epsilon$. Why? It follows that $a_N \leq a_{N+1} \leq a_{N+2} \leq \cdots \leq \xi$. Why? Consequently, $n > N \Rightarrow |a_n - \xi| < \epsilon$.]

4.3   THE STRUCTURE THEOREM FOR OPEN SETS OF REAL NUMBERS

A simple but nevertheless useful kind of set is an open interval. Recall that for two real numbers a, b with $a < b$, the *open interval* (a, b) is the set $(a, b) = \{x \mid a < x < b\}$. Related to the idea of an open interval is a neighborhood of a real number. Recall that $N(\xi;r) = \{x \mid |\xi - x| < r, r > 0\}$. Thus $N(\xi;r) = (\xi - r, \xi + r)$ is an open interval with ξ at its midpoint. A more general kind of set which depends on the notion of neighborhood is that of an *open* set.

Definition 4.2.   Let S be a set of real numbers. S is *open* iff

$$\forall x \in S \Rightarrow \exists N(x) \subset S.$$

Thus, S is open if and only if whenever x is in S there is some neighborhood of x which is contained in S.

As a consequence of these definitions, we see immediately that every open interval is an open set for, let $x \in (a, b)$ (See Fig. 4.3.) We can surely produce

Fig. 4.3   Every open interval is an open set.

a neighborhood of x which is contained in (a, b)—all we need do is set $r = \min (x - a, b - x)$. Then $N(x;r)$ will serve as the required neighborhood of x since $N(x;r) \subset (a, b)$ as follows from $y \in N(x;r) \Rightarrow x - r < y < x + r \Rightarrow x - (x - a) \leq x - r < y < x + r \leq x + (b - x)$, that is, $a < y < b$. Hence our statement is proved. On the other hand, the converse is false; that is, if a set S is open, we cannot conclude that it is an open interval. For, let S be the union of two disjoint open intervals. It is easy to verify that S is an open set, but clearly the union of two disjoint open intervals simply is not *an* open interval. Now it is not difficult to see:

(1) If S is the union of any finite number n of disjoint open intervals, then S is open (proof?).

(2) If S is the union of a countable number of disjoint open intervals, then S is open (proof?).

Our successes make it tempting to try taking the union of an uncountable number of disjoint open intervals and ask if such a set is open. However, such a thing as an uncountable number of *disjoint* open intervals does not exist, as we now prove.

■ **Theorem 4.3.**   If T is any collection of disjoint open intervals, then T is at most denumerable.

Proof: Our point of departure is the fact that the rational numbers are denumerable and hence can be enumerated in a sequence

$$\{r_1, r_2, r_3, \cdots, r_n, \cdots\}. \tag{4.1}$$

Now look at an arbitrary open interval I of the given collection T and associate with I the first natural number n such that $r_n \in I$. That is, we suppose $r_1 \notin I, r_2 \notin I, \cdots, r_{n-1} \notin I, r_n \in I$. We then have defined a function by

$$f(I) = n. \tag{4.2}$$

The domain of f is the set of all intervals I of the collection T, and the range of f is a subset of the natural numbers. Moreover, let I and J belong to T. We see that

$$f(I) = f(J) \Rightarrow I = J,$$

for $f(I) = f(J) = m$ means that the rational number r_m belongs to both I and J, and since the intervals of T are disjoint, it follows that $I = J$. This proves that the function (4.2) has an inverse function and, consequently, sets up a one-to-one correspondence between T and a subset of the natural numbers. Clearly, then, T has at most a denumerable number of elements.   ∎

Let us now return to our statement above: If S is the union of a countable number of disjoint open intervals, then S is open. We ask if the converse is also true. The answer is in the affirmative and is an extremely important result which is known as the *structure theorem for open sets of real numbers*. We call this theorem a "structure" theorem for it tells us that the "building blocks" for an open set are open intervals. More precisely, we prove the following theorem.

■ **Theorem 4.4.**   (Structure theorem for open sets of real numbers.) If G is a nonempty open set of real numbers, then G is the union of a countable number of disjoint open intervals.

Proof: We shall define an equivalence relation S on G and obtain the disjoint open intervals of the conclusion of our theorem as the equivalence classes determined by S.

Let $\overline{xy}$ denote the nonempty *closed* interval with endpoints x, y. We do not insist that $x < y$ or $y < x$; as a matter of fact, we agree that $\overline{xx}$ is admissible and it denotes the (degenerate) closed interval whose sole element is the point x. Note that $\overline{xy} = \overline{yx}$. We define the relation

$$S = \{(x, y) \mid x, y \in G, \overline{xy} \subset G\}.$$

The binary relation S is an equivalence relation on G since

(1) $(x, x) \in S$ for all $x \in G$.
(2) $(x, y) \in S \Rightarrow (y, x) \in S$.
(3) $(x, y) \in S$ and $(y, z) \in S \Rightarrow (x, z) \in S$.

It follows from Theorem 1.1 that the equivalence classes $C_x = \{y \mid \overline{xy} \subset G\}$, $x \in G$, form a partition of G; that is:

(1) $\bigcup\limits_{x \in G} C_x = G$

and

(2) $x, y \in G$ and $C_x \neq C_y \Rightarrow C_x \cap C_y = \varnothing$.

We show next that for arbitrary $x \in G$, C_x is an open interval. By definition,

$$C_x = \{y \mid \overline{xy} \subset G\}.$$

Let $a_x = \inf C_x$, $b_x = \sup C_x$. In order to insure that a_x and b_x are always meaningful, we adopt the convention that if a set A does not have a real number as lower bound, we set $\inf A = -\infty$; similarly, $\sup A = \infty$ means that the set A does not have an upper bound. [For example, if $Z = \{0, \pm 1, \pm 2, \cdots\}$, then $\sup Z = \infty$ and $\inf Z = -\infty$. This convention makes it possible to claim that *every* set of real numbers has a supremum and an infimum. It is especially useful in the present theorem since it enables us to handle bounded and unbounded open sets simultaneously.] Moreover, we agree to the usual convention that $-\infty < y < \infty$ for all real numbers y. Then $a_x < b_x$ for, by definition of these, we have $a_x \leq b_x$ and equality is impossible since G is open and consequently $x \in G$ (G is not empty!) implies there exists a neighborhood of x contained in G. Furthermore, $a_x \notin C_x$ for $a_x \in C_x$ would imply that $a_x \in G$ (hence $a_x \neq -\infty$); and since G is open, a neighborhood of a_x would be contained in G and we would therefore be able to produce a real number t less than a_x such that $\overline{xt} \subset G$, a contradiction to the defining property of a_x. Analogously, $b_x \notin C_x$. Moreover, it is clear that if $a_x < y < b_x$, then $y \in C_x$. **Thus for $x \in G$, the equivalence class**

$$C_x = \{y \mid a_x < y < b_x\}$$

is an open interval: that is, C_x is of the form (a, b) or $(-\infty, b)$ or (a, ∞) or $(-\infty, \infty)$ where $a < b$, and a, b are real numbers. These equivalence classes which are disjoint open intervals forming a partition of G are called the *components* of G.

As x varies over G, we obtain at most a denumerable number of distinct open intervals C_x, for these equivalence classes are disjoint and therefore Theorem 4.3 can be invoked. This proves the theorem. ∎

Another important kind of set is a closed set.

Definition 4.3. Let A be a set of real numbers. A is *closed* iff A contains all of its points of accumulation. In symbols

$$A \text{ is closed iff } A' \subset A.$$

Example 4.7. Every closed interval $[a, b]$ $a < b$, is a closed set for if $x \notin [a, b]$, we can find a neighborhood of x which contains no points of $[a, b]$; that is, $x \notin [a, b] \Rightarrow x$ is not an accumulation point of $[a, b]$. But the contrapositive of this is what was to be proved.

Example 4.8. Every finite set of real numbers is closed. To see why this is so, we consider the alternative of claiming that this set, or any set for that matter, is not closed. To make such an assertion about a set A is to state that A has an accumulation point which does not belong to A. According to our definition of accumulation point, however, we cannot entertain the existence of an accumulation point for a set A unless, to begin with, A has infinitely many points. We are consequently led to accept that if A is a finite set, then $A' = \varnothing$. But $\varnothing \subset A$ for an arbitrary set A; hence every finite set is closed. (Recall that we agreed that $\varnothing \subset A$ for all sets A since the denial of this would imply $\exists x \in \varnothing \ni x \notin A$, and we cannot admit "$\exists x \in \varnothing$".)

Example 4.9. The union of a finite number of disjoint closed intervals is a closed set.
Proof is left to the reader (see Section 4.5, Exercise 1).

Example 4.10. The union of a denumerable number of disjoint closed sets is not necessarily closed.
Consider $A = \{1, \frac{1}{2}, \frac{1}{3}, \cdots, 1/n, \cdots\}$. Since the singleton set $\{1/n\}$ for n a fixed positive integer is closed, $A = \{1\} \cup \{\frac{1}{2}\} \cup \cdots \cup \{1/n\} \cup \cdots$ is the union of a denumerable number of disjoint closed sets. However, $A' = \{0\}$, hence $A' \not\subset A$; that is, A is not closed.

Example 4.11. *A set may be neither open nor closed.* The set

$$A = \{x \mid 0 \le x < 1\}$$

is not closed since $1 \notin A$ but $1 \in A'$; it is not open since no neighborhood of 0 is contained in A.

Another example of a nonopen, nonclosed set is afforded by

$$A = \{1, \tfrac{1}{2}, \cdots, 1/n, \cdots\}$$

mentioned in Example 4.10.

In spite of our last example, there is a connection between open and closed sets. It is elaborated in the following theorem.

■ **Theorem 4.5.**   If A is open, then cA is closed; conversely, A closed $\Rightarrow$ cA open.

Proof: To show A open $\Rightarrow cA$ closed, we prove the contrapositive: cA not closed $\Rightarrow A$ not open. Let ξ be an accumulation point of cA with $\xi \notin cA$. Hence $\xi \in A$. It follows that every neighborhood $N(\xi)$ contains points not in A. Hence A is not open.

We leave the similar proof of the converse to the reader (see Section 4.4, Exercise 5).   ∎

Finally, we mention two very important properties of open sets:

(1) The union of an arbitrary collection of open sets is an open set.

(2) The intersection of a finite number of open sets is an open set.

Proofs of these properties will be left to the exercises (Section 4.4, Exercises 6 and 7). Also left to the exercises (Section 4.4, Exercises 8 and 9) are the corresponding properties of closed sets:

(1) The intersection of an arbitrary collection of closed sets is a closed set.

(2) The union of a finite number of closed sets is a closed set.

4.4   EXERCISES

1. Show that the union of a finite number of disjoint closed intervals is a closed set.

2. Define

$$A_{2n+1} = \left\{ x \,\middle|\, \frac{2n}{2n + 1} \leq x \leq \frac{2n + 1}{2n + 2} \right\}, \qquad n = 0, 1, 2, \cdots.$$

   Show that $S = \bigcup_{n=0}^{\infty} A_{2n+1}$ is the union of a denumerable number of disjoint closed intervals; show that S is bounded and that S is not closed.

3. Show that every nonempty open set must contain an uncountable number of points.

4. What can you say about the cardinal number of a closed set?

5. Prove: A closed $\Rightarrow cA$ open.

6. Prove that the union of an arbitrary collection of open sets is an open set.
7. Prove that the intersection of a finite number of open sets is an open set.
8. Prove that the intersection of an arbitrary collection of closed sets is a closed set.

[HINT: If F_α, $\alpha \in \mathcal{Q}$, are closed sets, then cF_α are open sets (by Exercise 5 above). Hence $c(\cap_{\alpha \in \mathcal{Q}} F_\alpha) = \cup_{\alpha \in \mathcal{Q}} cF_\alpha$ is open (by Exercise 6).]

9. Prove that the union of a finite number of closed sets is a closed set.

[HINT: Use Theorem 4.5 and Exercise 7.]
10. Show that the set of all rational numbers is neither open nor closed.
11. Show that the set of all irrational numbers is neither open nor closed.
12. Show that $\varnothing$ is both open and closed; that the set of all real numbers is both open and closed.

[HINT: First show $\varnothing$ is closed. To do this, suppose $\varnothing$ not closed. Then $\exists \xi \in \varnothing' \ni \xi \not\subset \varnothing$. But $\xi \in \varnothing' \Rightarrow$ every $N(\xi)$ contains infinitely many points of $\varnothing$. This is clearly impossible. Hence $\varnothing$ is closed. Now invoke Theorem 4.5: $\varnothing$ closed $\Rightarrow c\varnothing = R$ is open. Theorem 4.5 then implies $\varnothing$ open and R is closed.]

13. Show that the sets $\varnothing$ and R (all real numbers) are the only subsets of R which are both open and closed.

[HINT: Let $S \subset R$, and suppose S is both open and closed. Suppose $S \neq \varnothing$, and let $x \in S$. Since S is open, x belongs to a component open interval of the form (a, b) or $(-\infty, b)$ or (a, ∞) or $(-\infty, \infty)$, according to Theorem 4.4. But S is closed, by hypothesis, hence would have to contain the endpoints a or b, destroying the form of the component in the first three cases; thus $(-\infty, \infty)$, that is, the set of all real numbers, is the only alternative.]

14. Show that the statement, "Every closed set is the union of a countable number of disjoint closed intervals," is false.

4.5 THE HEINE-BOREL COVERING THEOREM

In the study of several concepts of analysis, one is led to consider what is known as an *open cover* of a set. This is simply a collection of open sets whose union covers (that is, contains) the set. Usually we encounter an infinite number of open sets making up the cover. If the covered set S has certain "nice" properties, then a finite number of the open sets can be selected whose union will contain S. One kind of set which qualifies as "nice" in this respect is a closed interval (of finite length), and the precise statement of this fact is called the Heine-Borel covering theorem. Before proving this result, we consider a definition and an example.

Definition 4.4. An *open cover of the set S* is a collection of open sets whose union contains S.

Example 4.12. Associate with each point x of the set $(0, 1]$ the set

$$A_x = \left\{ y \,\middle|\, \frac{x}{2} < y < \frac{3x}{2} \right\}$$

(see Fig. 4.4). The collection of all the A_x's as x varies over $(0, 1]$ is an open cover of the set $(0, 1]$. This open cover contains uncountably many open

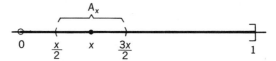

Fig. 4.4   The collection of A_x's, $0 < x \leq 1$, forms an open cover of $(0, 1]$.

sets (in this case open intervals) since there is a one-to-one correspondence between open sets in the cover and real numbers in the set $(0, 1]$. From the cover, suppose we select the following subcollection

$$\{A_1, A_{1/2}, A_{1/3}, \cdots, A_{1/n}, \cdots\}.$$

It is not difficult to see that the union of these open sets contains $(0, 1]$; that is, $\bigcup_{n=1}^{\infty} A_{1/n} \supset (0, 1]$ (we leave it to the reader to check this). In other words, from the continuum of open sets forming the open cover of $(0, 1]$, we can find a *denumerable* subcover, that is, a denumerable subcollection of the original collection which covers $(0, 1]$.

Now we return to our open cover $\{A_x\}$, $x \in (0, 1]$ and ask whether or not a *finite* number of the A_x's can be selected such that their union will contain $(0, 1]$. The answer is negative for let

$$\{A_{x_1}, A_{x_2}, A_{x_3}, \cdots, A_{x_n}\}$$

be any finite number of the open sets of our cover of $(0, 1]$. Put $m = \min \{x_1, x_2, x_3, \cdots, x_n\}$. Then m is a positive number, $0 < m \leq 1$. From the definition of m, it follows that no x satisfying $0 < x \leq m/2$ belongs to the union $\bigcup_{k=1}^{n} A_{x_k}$. Thus no finite subcover of the given cover of $(0, 1]$ exists.

We are now ready to prove the following theorem.

■ **Theorem 4.6.** (Heine-Borel covering theorem.) If $[a, b]$ is a closed interval of real numbers and if $\{G_x\}$, $x \in [a, b]$ is an open cover of $[a, b]$ (that is, G_x is an open set containing x and $\bigcup_{x \in [a, b]} G_x \supset [a, b]$), then there exists a finite number of the G_x's whose union contains $[a, b]$.

To put it another way: Every open cover of a closed interval of real numbers contains a finite subcover.

Proof: As in Theorem 4.4, we let $\overline{xy}$ denote the closed interval with endpoints x, y. For two points x, $y \in [a, b]$, define $x \sim y$ iff a finite subcover of $\overline{xy}$ exists. It is readily checked that the relation $x \sim y$ is an equivalence relation on $[a, b]$; that is,

(1) $x \sim x$ for all $x \in [a, b]$.
(2) $x \sim y \Rightarrow y \sim x$.
(3) $x \sim y$ and $y \sim z \Rightarrow x \sim z$.

Our theorem is proved if we can show that $a \sim b$. Consider any equivalence class of the partition of $[a, b]$ obtained from the relation $\sim$:

$$C_x = \{y \mid y \in [a, b], y \sim x\}.$$

The set $C_x \neq \varnothing$ $(x \in C_x)$ and C_x is bounded above since $C_x \subset [a, b]$. Let sup $C_x = x^*$. Now $x^* \in [a, b]$ since $[a, b]$ is closed (see Section 4.6, Exercise 1). Since $x^* \in [a, b]$, there exists an open set G_{x^*} of our cover with $x^* \in G_{x^*}$. We shall use this to prove that $x^* \in C_x$. To do this, we observe that by the definition of an open set

$$\exists N(x^*; r) \subset G_{x^*}$$

(see Fig. 4.5). Since $x^* = \sup C_x$, there is a point ξ of C_x such that $x^* - r < \xi \leq x^*$, by Theorem 2.9. It follows that a finite subcover of $\overline{x\xi}$ exists since $\xi \in C_x$ implies $\xi \sim x$. Adjoining the open set G_{x^*} to this finite subcover of $\overline{x\xi}$, we obtain a finite subcover of $\overline{xx^*}$; in other words, $x^* \in C_x$.

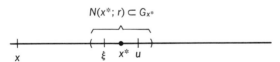

Fig. 4.5   A visual aid to the proof of the Heine-Borel covering theorem for a closed interval of reals.

Clearly, $x^* \leq b$, and if we had $x^* < b$, then by appealing again to G_{x^*} we could find a point u in G_{x^*}, $u > x^*$, such that $u \sim x$, a contradiction to the defining property of x^*. Hence $x^* = b = \sup C_x$. Thus $b \in C_x$. But $x \in [a, b]$ was arbitrary and we concluded $b \in C_x$. In particular, $b \in C_a$; that is, $a \sim b$. ■

4.6 EXERCISES

1. Prove that if $S \neq \varnothing$, $S \subset [a, b] \Rightarrow \sup S \in [a, b]$.

   [HINT: Let $\sup S = \xi$. Either ξ is an accumulation point of S or it is not. Consider both cases. The first one is trivial; use Theorem 2.9 to handle the second case.]

2. Show that the countable subcollection $\{A_{1/n}\}$, $n = 1, 2, 3, \cdots$ mentioned in Example 4.12 is a subcover of $(0, 1]$.

3. Consider the collection of all neighborhoods $N(r;s)$ where r is an arbitrary rational number and s is an arbitrary positive rational number.
   (a) Show that the union of all such sets is an open cover of the set of all real numbers.
   (b) Show that the cover in (a) is denumerable.

4. Consider the collection of all neighborhoods $N(k;1)$ where k is an arbitrary integer.
   (a) Show that this collection is a denumerable open cover of the set of all real numbers.
   (b) Show that no finite subcover exists.

5. (Another proof of the Heine-Borel covering theorem.) We use the notation of Theorem 4.6, letting $\{G_x\}$, $x \in [a, b]$ denote an open cover of $[a, b]$. Cut the interval $[a, b]$ into two equal parts:

$$I_1 = [a, (a + b)/2], \qquad J_1 = [(a + b)/2, b].$$

   If a finite subcover of $[a, b]$ does not exist, then a finite subcover of at least one of I_1, J_1 cannot exist. Why? Without loss of generality, suppose that a finite subcover of I_1 does not exist. Cut I_1 into two equal parts and argue that at least one of the halves of I_1 (call it I_2) has no finite subcover. Why? In this way, generate a sequence $I_1 \supset I_2 \supset I_3 \supset \cdots$ of closed intervals with lengths tending to zero (why?) such that no finite subcover of I_k, $k = 1, 2, 3, \cdots$ exists. Now invoke Section 4.2, Exercise 8, to obtain a point $\xi \in \bigcap_{k=1}^{\infty} I_k$. Show that $\xi \in [a, b]$. Consider G_ξ. G_ξ contains a neighborhood $N(\xi;r)$. Why? But if n is sufficiently large, we have $I_n \subset N(\xi;r)$. Why? However, G_ξ is a finite subcover of I_n and this is a contradiction.

6. Study the proof of Theorem 4.6 given in the text and see if you can modify it to obtain a proof of the stronger theorem: Every open cover of a closed and bounded set of real numbers has a finite subcover.

   [HINT: In defining the relation $x \sim y$ for points of the closed and bounded set S, instead of using the closed interval $\overline{xy}$, work with the part of this closed interval which is contained in S; that is, define, for $x, y \in S$, $x \sim y$ iff a finite subcover of $\overline{xy} \cap S$ exists.]

Supplement to Chapter 4

It is our purpose here to consider the concepts and theorems of this chapter with a view to indicating which can be generalized to the complex numbers. We have proved three important theorems:

(1) The Bolzano-Weierstrass theorem.

(2) The structure theorem for open sets of real numbers.

(3) The Heine-Borel covering theorem.

All three theorems admit of suitable generalizations to the complex number case, although one has to be careful in annunciating a structure theorem for open sets of complex numbers because of the more complicated geometry which is involved.

We begin our discussion with consideration of Section 4.1, which deals with the concept of accumulation point of a set and culminates in the Bolzano-Weierstrass theorem. The concept of point of accumulation of a set carries over verbatim.

Definition 4.5. ξ *is an accumulation point of the set* A of complex numbers iff for every neighborhood $N(\xi)$ of ξ we have $N'(\xi) \cap A \neq \varnothing$.

Moreover, Theorem 4.1 and its proof are valid for the complex number case, that is, an equivalent definition of a point of accumulation of a set is obtained by requiring that in every neighborhood of the point of accumulation of A, one must have infinitely many points of A.

Next we come to the Bolzano-Weierstrass theorem. This theorem can be stated by simply replacing "real numbers" by "complex numbers": Every bounded infinite set A of complex numbers has at least one point of accumulation. The proof offered in the text, however, leaned heavily on the ordering of the real numbers, and since the complex numbers do not form an *ordered* field, we must find a different approach. In Exercises 8 and 10 of Section 4.2 we outlined a second proof of this theorem, and the attack suggested there does admit of generalization as we now explain.

To begin with, a useful and natural generalization of the concept of an interval of real numbers can be defined for the complex numbers.

Definition 4.6. A *closed interval of complex numbers* is the Cartesian product of two closed intervals of real numbers, that is, any set S of the form

$$S = [a, b] \times [c, d]$$

is a closed interval of complex numbers. (An open interval of complex numbers may be defined in the obvious manner.)

Thus a closed interval of complex numbers can be interpreted geometrically as the set of points interior to or on the boundary of a rectangle whose sides are parallel to the coordinate axes.

The following lemma can now be proved.

Lemma. If $I_n = [a_n, b_n] \times [c_n, d_n]$, $n = 1, 2, 3, \cdots$ is a nested sequence of closed intervals of complex numbers with dimensions tending to zero (that is, if $I_1 \supset I_2 \supset I_3 \supset \cdots$ and if $\lim |a_n - b_n| = 0$ and $\lim |c_n - d_n| = 0$), then there exists one and only one complex number ξ such that $\xi \in \cap_{n=1}^{\infty} I_n$.

The proof is easy in view of Exercise 8, Section 4.2, and we therefore omit it. We are now ready for the following theorem.

■ **Theorem 4.7.** (Bolzano-Weierstrass theorem.) If A is a bounded infinite set of complex numbers, then $A' \neq \emptyset$.

Proof: (We give an outline of the proof, leaving details to the exercises.) Since A is bounded, $\exists M > 0 \ni z \in A \Rightarrow |z| < M$. (Geometrically speaking, all the points z of A lie in the interior of a circle of radius M and center at the origin: see Fig. 4.6.)

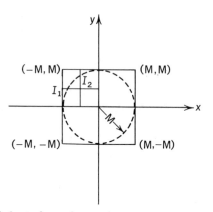

Fig. 4.6   A bounded set of complex numbers.

It is obvious on geometric grounds and easy to prove analytically that $A \subset [-M, M] \times [-M, M]$; that is, all the points of A lie in the interior of a square, side $2M$, center at the origin.

Consider the four *closed* intervals determined by the coordinate axes and the square, that is, the closed intervals

$$[0, M] \times [0, M], \quad [-M, 0] \times [0, M],$$
$$[-M, 0] \times [0, -M], \quad [0, M] \times [0, -M].$$

At least one of these closed intervals contains infinitely many points of A, for if each contained only a finite number of points of A, then A would not be an infinite set. Suppose, for definiteness, that $I_1 = [-M, 0] \times [0, M]$ contains infinitely many points of A. Now subdivide I_1 into four closed intervals (see Fig. 4.6) and argue that at least one of these (call it I_2) contains infinitely many points of A. Continuing in this manner (finite induction), we generate a nested sequence of closed intervals

$$I_1 \supset I_2 \supset I_3 \supset \cdots$$

and since the dimensions of I_n tend to zero as n tends to infinity, we may invoke the lemma above. Thus we get a complex number ξ such that $\xi \in \bigcap_{n=1}^{\infty} I_n$.

It remains to show that ξ is an accumulation point of A. Consider any neighborhood $N(\xi;r)$ (see Fig. 4.7.) Since $\xi \in I_n$ for all $n = 1, 2, 3, \cdots$ and

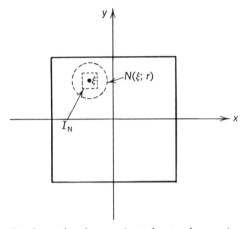

Fig. 4.7   Heine-Borel covering theorem (complex number case).

the dimensions of I_n tend to zero, it follows that for some sufficiently large N we have $I_N \subset N(\xi;r)$. But I_N contains infinitely many points of A; hence $N(\xi;r)$ has this property too. Thus $\xi \in A'$. This completes the proof. ∎

Now we focus on the structure theorem for open sets. As in Definition 4.2, we have the following.

Definition 4.7.   A set S of complex numbers is *open* iff

$$z \in S \Rightarrow \exists N(z) \subset S.$$

We leave it to the reader to show that every open interval of complex numbers is an open set. The set of all rational points in the plane [that is, points of the form (r_1, r_2) with r_1, r_2 rational numbers] is a denumerable set. From this, the statement of Theorem 4.3 and its proof can be carried over with obvious modifications to the complex numbers.

■ **Theorem 4.8.**   Every collection of disjoint open intervals of complex numbers is at most denumerable.

The application of this result to a structure theorem for open sets of complex numbers must be omitted since it would take us too far afield. (The interested reader should consult, for example, M. H. A. Newman's *Elements of the Topology of Plane Sets of Points*, 2nd ed., University Press, Cambridge, 1951.)

The concept of a closed set of complex numbers entails nothing new.

Definition 4.8. A is closed iff $A' \subset A$.

Moreover, the connection between open and closed sets of complex numbers presents no new problems; that is, Theorem 4.5 and its proof carry over without change to the complex number system:

■ **Theorem 4.9.** A is open $\Leftrightarrow cA$ is closed.

Finally, we come to the Heine-Borel covering theorem. The concept of an *open cover* of a set S (Definition 4.4) makes sense just as it stands, when we assume S to be a set of complex numbers.

Definition 4.9.   An *open cover of the set S* is a collection of open sets whose union contains S.

Our proof of the Heine-Borel theorem, however, must be modified since it depended on the order relation for the reals. The idea for the modification is essentially the same as for the Bolzano-Weierstrass theorem and is suggested by Exercise 5, Section 4.6. Details are left to the exercises.

4.7 EXERCISES

1. Show that $\xi = x + iy$ is a point of accumulation of the set S of complex numbers iff every neighborhood $N(\xi)$ contains infinitely many points of S. (Show that the proof of Theorem 4.1 applies here.)
2. (*a*) Prove the lemma preceding Theorem 4.7: Every nested sequence of closed intervals of complex numbers with dimensions tending to zero contains exactly one complex number.
   (*b*) Let A be a bounded set of complex numbers. Define the *diameter* $d(A)$ of A by
   $$d(A) = \sup \{|z - w| \mid z, w \in A\}.$$
   Show that the diameter of an interval of complex numbers is equal to the length of the diagonal of the corresponding rectangle.

(c) Show that if A is closed and bounded, then $d(A) = $ max $\{|z - w| \mid z, w \in A\}$.

(d) Prove the generalization of the lemma stated in (a) as follows: Every nested sequence of *nonempty closed* sets of complex numbers with *diameter* tending to zero contains exactly one complex number.

3. Give a complete proof of the Bolzano-Weierstrass theorem for the complex number case.

4. Show that an open interval of complex numbers is an open set.

5. Prove that every collection of disjoint open intervals of complex numbers is at most denumerable (see Theorem 4.3.)

6. Prove the Heine-Borel theorem for complex numbers: If I is a closed interval of complex numbers and if $\{G_z\}$, $z \in I$, is an open cover of I (that is, G_z is an open set containing z and $\cup_{z \in I} G_z \supset I$), then there exists a finite subcover. (See Exercise 5, Section 4.6, for suggestions.)

7. Prove the generalization of the Heine-Borel theorem: Every open cover of a closed and bounded set of complex numbers contains a finite subcover.

5

Continuity

INTRODUCTION

An important set of functions in analysis is the set of real-valued continuous functions f defined on a closed interval $[a, b]$ of real numbers. We assume the reader to know that:

(1) If $\xi \in (a, b)$, we call f *continuous at* ξ iff

$$\lim_{x \to \xi} f(x) = f(\lim_{x \to \xi} x) = f(\xi).$$

In detail: f is *continuous at* ξ iff for every $\epsilon > 0$, $\exists \delta > 0 \ni$ $|x - \xi| < \delta \Rightarrow |f(x) - f(\xi)| < \epsilon$.

(2) We say f is *continuous on the interval* $[a, b]$ provided that f is continuous at every point of the interval. Continuity at the endpoints a, b is defined in terms of right- and left-hand limits, respectively, that is, by the requirement that $\lim_{x \to a^+} f(x) = f(a)$ and that $\lim_{x \to b^-} f(x) = f(b)$, respectively. To be precise, we define, for example, the *right-hand limit of f at a* ($\lim_{x \to a^+} f(x) = c$) to be a number c with the property that for every $\epsilon > 0$, there is a $\delta > 0$ such that if $x > a$ and $|x - a| < \delta$, then $|f(x) - c| < \epsilon$.

98

In this chapter we prove some of the deeper properties of continuous functions. In particular, we show that:

(1) Every continuous function on a closed interval $[a, b]$ has the property of being *uniformly continuous* on the closed interval $[a, b]$. This means that for a given $\epsilon > 0$, there exists a $\delta > 0$ such that if we choose any two points x, y of $[a, b]$ such that $|x - y| < \delta$, then we will have $|f(x) - f(y)| < \epsilon$. This result, besides being of interest in itself, has some important consequences; in particular, it will be used later (Chapter 7) to show that a continuous function on a closed interval is integrable [that is, a number designated by $\int_a^b f(x)\, dx$ (to be defined later) can be associated with every such function].

(2) Every continuous function on a closed interval *attains a maximum and a minimum*.

(3) Every continuous function on a closed interval has the *intermediate value property* or *Darboux property;* that is, if it assumes two distinct values, then it assumes every value between those two distinct values. During the nineteenth century some mathematicians used the intermediate value property of a function as the *definition* of continuous function. It is therefore interesting and, as a matter of fact, surprising that a large class of discontinuous functions has the intermediate value property (see Theorem 6.7).

5.1 CONTINUITY ON A CLOSED INTERVAL IMPLIES UNIFORM CONTINUITY

Recall that $\lim_{x \to \xi} f(x) = b$ means (see Definition 3.3) that for every $\epsilon > 0$, $\exists \delta > 0 \ni$

$$0 < |x - \xi| < \delta \Rightarrow |f(x) - b| < \epsilon.$$

In particular, $\lim_{x \to \xi} f(x) = f(\xi)$ means: For every $\epsilon > 0$, $\exists \delta > 0 \ni$

$$0 < |x - \xi| < \delta \Rightarrow |f(x) - f(\xi)| < \epsilon.$$

However, since calling f continuous at ξ requires, among other things, that f be defined at ξ, and since the inequality $|f(x) - f(\xi)| < \epsilon$ is automatically satisfied for $x = \xi$, we can dispense with the condition $0 < |x - \xi|$ in discussing continuity of f at ξ.

Suppose that f is continuous on $[a, b]$. This implies that if $\epsilon > 0$, and if $\xi \in [a, b]$, then there exists a $\delta > 0$ (in general δ depends on *both* ϵ and ξ) such that

$$|x - \xi| < \delta \Rightarrow |f(x) - f(\xi)| < \frac{\epsilon}{2}.$$

(We use $\epsilon/2$ instead of ϵ simply to make our final result elegant.) With $\epsilon > 0$ fixed, we emphasize the dependence of δ on ξ by writing δ_ξ. The set

$\{x \mid |x - \xi| < \delta_\xi\}$ is, of course, a neighborhood $N(\xi; \delta_\xi)$ of ξ. Let ξ vary over the entire interval $[a, b]$. Accordingly, we get a collection of neighborhoods, one for each point of $[a, b]$. In other words, we obtain an *open cover of the closed interval* $[a, b]$. We emphasize that *a priori* as ξ varies over $[a, b]$, the radius δ_ξ of the neighborhood $N(\xi; \delta_\xi)$ also varies. As a matter of fact, it is our main purpose here to show that because we are dealing with a closed interval as the domain of f, it is possible to select a single number δ from the collection of δ_ξ's such that

$$|x - y| < \delta \Rightarrow |f(x) - f(y)| < \epsilon$$

whenever $x, y \in [a, b]$. In other words, we want to show that the dependence of δ_ξ on ξ is only superficial. The number δ we seek thus "works uniformly" for all pairs x, y of points of $[a, b]$ whose distance apart is less than δ. This property is important enough to warrant the following definition.

Definition 5.1.   Let S be a subset of the domain of f. f *is uniformly continuous on* S iff for every $\epsilon > 0$, $\exists \delta > 0$ (δ depends on ϵ only) such that if x, y are any two points of S with $|x - y| < \delta$, then $|f(x) - f(y)| < \epsilon$.

Returning to the discussion above, we modify the open cover of $[a, b]$ by replacing each neighborhood $N(\xi; \delta_\xi)$ by $N(\xi; \delta_\xi/2)$ (for technical reasons that will be clear to the reader soon) and then invoke the Heine-Borel covering theorem, concluding that the modified open cover of the closed interval $[a, b]$ contains a finite subcover; that is, a finite number of the neighborhoods $N(\xi; \delta_\xi/2)$ of our collection will cover $[a, b]$. Let the centers of these neighborhoods be $x_1, x_2, \cdots, x_n$. Then

$$\bigcup_{k=1}^{n} N\left(x_k; \frac{\delta_{x_k}}{2}\right) \supset [a, b] \tag{5.1}$$

and, of course, we have

$$|x - x_k| < \delta_{x_k} \Rightarrow |f(x) - f(x_k)| < \frac{\epsilon}{2}. \tag{5.2}$$

The δ we seek is simply one-half the minimum of the *finite* collection of positive numbers δ_{x_k}, $k = 1, 2, \cdots, n$; that is, we define

$$\delta = \tfrac{1}{2} \min \{\delta_{x_1}, \delta_{x_2}, \cdots, \delta_{x_n}\}.$$

What we must now prove is that for $x, y \in [a, b]$, we have

$$|x - y| < \delta \Rightarrow |f(x) - f(y)| < \epsilon.$$

Since $x \in [a, b]$ and $[a, b]$ is covered according to (5.1), it follows that x belongs to one of the neighborhoods of the collection in (5.1), say $N(x_i; \delta_{x_i}/2)$. This means that

$$|x - x_i| < \frac{\delta_{x_i}}{2}$$

for some $i = 1, 2, \cdots, n$. With this i fixed,

$$|y - x_i| \leq |y - x| + |x - x_i| < \delta + \frac{\delta_{x_i}}{2} \leq \delta_{x_i}$$

(since $\delta \leq \delta_{x_i}/2$). Hence both x and y belong to $N(x_i; \delta_{x_i})$. According to (5.2), therefore,

$$|f(x) - f(y)| \leq |f(x) - f(x_i)| + |f(x_i) - f(y)| < \frac{\epsilon}{2} + \frac{\epsilon}{2} = \epsilon.$$

This proves the following theorem.

■**Theorem 5.1.** If f is continuous on the closed interval $[a, b]$, then f is uniformly continuous on $[a, b]$.

Example 5.1. The function defined by $f(x) = x^2$ is uniformly continuous on $[0, 1]$.

Proof: Let $\epsilon > 0$. We are to find $\delta > 0$ such that

$$|x - u| < \delta \Rightarrow |x^2 - u^2| < \epsilon.$$

Now

$$|x^2 - u^2| = |x - u|\,|x + u| \leq 2|x - u|$$

since $|x + u| \leq |x| + |u| \leq 2$ (remember $x, u \in [0, 1]$). We therefore choose $\delta = \epsilon/3$ and get that $|x - u| < \delta$ implies

$$|x^2 - u^2| < 2\delta = 2(\epsilon/3) < \epsilon, \text{ Q.E.D.}$$

(NOTE: The above idea can be utilized to show that $f(x) = x^n$, n a fixed positive integer, is uniformly continuous on $[0, 1]$, for

$$|x^n - u^n| = |x - u|\,|x^{n-1} + \cdots + u^{n-1}|$$
$$\leq |x - u|[|x^{n-1}| + \cdots + |u^{n-1}|] \leq n|x - u|.$$

We now choose $\delta = \epsilon/(n + 1)$ to complete the proof.)

Example 5.2. The function defined by $f(x) = x^2$ is *not* uniformly continuous on the entire real number line.

Proof: Let $\epsilon = 1$. We are to show that for every $\delta > 0$, we can find a pair of numbers x, u such that $|x - u| < \delta$ yet $|x^2 - u^2| \geq 1$.

To insure that x and u are close enough (that is, that $|x - u| < \delta$), let us set $u = x + \delta/2$. Now

$$|x^2 - u^2| = \left|x^2 - \left(x + \frac{\delta}{2}\right)^2\right| = \left|-x\delta - \frac{\delta^2}{4}\right| = \delta\left|x + \frac{\delta}{4}\right|.$$

Let $x > 0$. If we further restrict x to satisfy the condition

$$\delta \left| x + \frac{\delta}{4} \right| = \delta \left(x + \frac{\delta}{4} \right) > 1,$$

so that

$$x + \frac{\delta}{4} > \frac{1}{\delta}$$

or

$$x > \frac{1}{\delta} - \frac{\delta}{4},$$

then the pair x, u $(u = x + \delta/2)$ will have the required properties. We leave it to the reader to verify this.

Example 5.3. If $f(x) = mx + b$ where m, b are constants, then f is uniformly continuous on $(-\infty, \infty)$. We compute

$$|f(x) - f(y)| = |mx + b - (my + b)| = |m| \, |x - y|.$$

Let $\epsilon > 0$. Define $\delta = \epsilon/|m|$. Then if $|x - y| < \delta$, we have

$$|f(x) - f(y)| = |m| \, |x - y| < |m|\delta = \epsilon, \text{ Q.E.D.}$$

Example 5.4. If f, g are uniformly continuous on $(-\infty, \infty)$, the product need not be uniformly continuous. For example, take $f(x) = g(x) = x$ and use Example 5.3 to conclude that f, g are uniformly continuous on $(-\infty, \infty)$ whereas the product, according to Example 5.2, is not.

Example 5.5. If $f(x) = c$, c constant, then f is uniformly continuous on $(-\infty, \infty)$. This is an immediate consequence of the definition of uniform continuity (it is also a special case of Example 5.3). Now consider $f(x) = 1$, $g(x) = x$ and note that the product $f(x)g(x) = x$ is uniformly continuous on $(-\infty, \infty)$. Thus the product of two functions, each of which is uniformly continuous on $(-\infty, \infty)$, *may be* uniformly continuous on $(-\infty, \infty)$. (See also Section 5.2, Exercise 6.)

5.2   EXERCISES

1. Prove that $f(x) = |x|$ is continuous by appealing directly to the ϵ, δ definition of continuity.
2. Show from the definition of uniform continuity that $f(x) = e^x$, $0 \le x \le 1$, is uniformly continuous on $[0, 1]$. Generalize to any closed interval $[a, b]$. (Use the mean value theorem.)
3. Show that $f(x) = e^x$ is not uniformly continuous on $(-\infty, \infty)$.

4. When we say that *f satisfies a Lipschitz condition* on S we mean $x, y \in S$ implies that the secant slope $[f(x) - f(y)]/(x - y)$ is bounded; more precisely, $\exists M > 0$ such that $|f(x) - f(y)| \leq M|x - y|$ for all $x, y \in S$.
   (a) Interpret the condition geometrically.
   (b) Show that $f(x) = \sin x$, $0 \leq x \leq \pi$, satisfies a Lipschitz condition. Deduce from this that $\sin x$ is uniformly continuous on $[0, \pi]$.
   (c) Show that if $f(x)$, $a \leq x \leq b$, satisfies a Lipschitz condition on $[a, b]$, then f is uniformly continuous on $[a, b]$.
5. Show that if f satisfies a Lipschitz condition on the entire real number line, then f is uniformly continuous on the entire real number line (see Exercise 4).
6. (On the algebra of uniformly continuous functions.) Show that if f and g are uniformly continuous on S, then so are the sum $f + g$ and the difference $f - g$. If, in addition, f and g are bounded on S, then the product $f(x)g(x)$ is uniformly continuous on S. In addition, if g is bounded away from 0, that is, if there exists an $M > 0$ such that $0 < M \leq |g(x)|$ for all $x \in S$, then the quotient $f(x)/g(x)$ is uniformly continuous on S.

   [HINT (on the last part):

   $$\left| \frac{f(x)}{g(x)} - \frac{f(y)}{g(y)} \right| = \frac{|f(x)g(y) - g(x)f(y)|}{|g(x)|\,|g(y)|}$$
   $$\leq M^{-2}|f(x)g(y) - f(y)g(y) + f(y)g(y) - g(x)f(y)|$$
   $$\leq M^{-2}[|g(y)|\,|f(x) - f(y)| + |f(y)|\,|g(y) - g(x)|].]$$

7. (a) By appealing to the definition of uniform continuity, prove that $f(x) = x^n$, n a positive integer, is uniformly continuous on a fixed closed interval $[a, b]$ (see Example 5.1).
   (b) Generalize (a) to any polynomial $\sum_{k=0}^{n} a_k x^k$ on a fixed closed interval $[a, b]$.
8. Prove that if f is a continuous function on the set of all reals and if G is an open set, then the inverse image $f^{-1}(G)$ of G is also open.

   [REMEMBER: $f^{-1}(G) = \{x \mid f(x) \in G\}$. Use the neighborhood definition of limit in attacking this problem; that is, f is continuous at a iff for every neighborhood $N(f(a))$ of $f(a)$ there exists a neighborhood $N(a)$ of a such that $f(N(a)) \subset N(f(a))$. Study Definition 3.7 (neighborhood approach to limit) if these suggestions are not clear.]

9. Prove that if a function f, domain all real numbers, has the property that the inverse image $f^{-1}(G)$ of an open set G is always an open set, then f is continuous (see Exercise 8).
10. Show that if f is continuous, it does not follow that f carries open sets into open sets; that is, f continuous and G open do not imply that

$f(G)$ is open. Does a continuous function necessarily carry a closed set into a closed set? Prove or give a counterexample.

11. Show that if f is uniformly continuous on $[a, b]$, then f is continuous on $[a, b]$.

12. (a) Prove: If $f(x) = \ln x$, then f is continuous at $x = 1$.

   [HINT: Let $\epsilon > 0$. Define δ by $\ln (1 - \delta) = -\epsilon$. Now show that $|x - 1| < \delta \Rightarrow |\ln x| < \epsilon$. (Draw the graph of $\ln x$ to see the reason for the choice of δ.)]

   (b) Prove that $f(x) = \ln x$ is continuous at $\xi > 0$.

   [HINT: Write $\lim_{x \to \xi} (x/\xi) = 1$. Invoke (a) to get $\lim_{x \to \xi} \ln (x/\xi) = \ln \lim_{x \to \xi} (x/\xi) = 0$. Now use $\ln (x/\xi) + \ln \xi = \ln x$.]

5.3   THE CONTINUOUS IMAGE OF A CLOSED INTERVAL HAS A MAXIMUM

We first recall the following definition.

Definition 5.2.   Let f be defined on S. We say that f *has a maximum at* $\xi \in S$ iff

$$x \in S \Rightarrow f(\xi) \geq f(x).$$

Using set-theoretic terminology, this is equivalent to saying that the image

$$f(S) = \{f(x) \mid x \in S\}$$

of S under f has a maximum.

Example 5.6.   Let $S = (0, \pi/2)$ and let $f(x) = \sin x$. Then $f(S) = (0, 1)$ and since $\sup f(S) = 1$ but $1 \notin f(S)$, $f(S)$ has no maximum (remember: if T is a set of real numbers, we say that T has a maximum iff $\sup T$ exists and $\sup T \in T$).

Example 5.7.   Let $S = [0, \pi/2]$ and let $f(x) = \sin x$. Then $f(S) = [0, 1]$ and $\max f(S) = 1$.

Our purpose here is to show that the last example is a special case of a general theorem which guarantees that if f is defined on a *closed interval* (of finite length) and if f is *continuous* on that closed interval, then f has a maximum (or, to put it another way, the continuous image of a closed interval has a maximum).

■ **Theorem 5.2.** If f is continuous on the closed interval $[a, b]$, then f has a maximum at some point ξ belonging to $[a, b]$. In symbols: f continuous on $[a, b] \Rightarrow \exists \xi \in [a, b] \ni f(\xi) \geq f(x)$ for all $x \in [a, b]$.

Proof: The set $f([a, b])$ of all values $f(x)$ as x varies over $[a, b]$ is a bounded set of real numbers for, supposing it were not, we could find a sequence $x_1, x_2, \cdots, x_n, \cdots$ of points of $[a, b]$ such that $|f(x_n)|$ tends to infinity with n. To put this another way, we could assume a sequence of points of $[a, b]$ such that

$$|f(x_n)| > n \text{ for all positive integers } n. \tag{5.3}$$

It is easy to find such a sequence. If $f([a, b])$ is unbounded, then clearly there is a point $x_1 \in [a, b]$ such that $|f(x_1)| > 1$. Moreover, there is a point $x_2 \in [a, b]$ such that $|f(x_2)| > 2$ and $|f(x_2)| > |f(x_1)|$. By induction, there is a point $x_n \in [a, b]$ such that $|f(x_n)| > n$ and $|f(x_n)| > |f(x_{n-1})|$. Hence the sequence $\{x_n\}$ has the property that its terms belong to $[a, b]$, are distinct in pairs, and $|f(x_n)| > n$.

However, the infinite bounded *set* $\{x_1, x_2, x_3, \cdots\}$ has a limit point x_0 (by the Bolzano-Weierstrass theorem) which belongs to $[a, b]$. The sequence $\{x_n\}$ has a subsequence $\{x_{n_k}\}$ which converges to x_0 for, let x_0 be a limit point of $\{x_1, x_2, \cdots\}$. Then we may choose n_1 such that $|x_{n_1} - x_0| < 1$. Why? We may then choose x_{n_2} so that $n_2 > n_1$ and $|x_{n_2} - x_0| < \frac{1}{2}$. Why? Assuming that $n_1 < n_2 < \cdots < n_k$ and $|x_{n_k} - x_0| < 1/k$, we may choose n_{k+1} such that $n_{k+1} > n_k$ and $|x_{n_{k+1}} - x_0| < 1/(k+1)$. Then, by continuity of f, it follows that $\{f(x_{n_k})\}$ converges to $f(x_0)$. However, (5.3) denies the convergence of $\{f(x_{n_k})\}$ since $|f(x_{n_k})| > n_k \geq k$ for $k = 1, 2, 3, \cdots$. This contradiction forces us to conclude that f is bounded on $[a, b]$; that is, there exists a number $K > 0$ such that $|f(x)| < K$ for all $x \in [a, b]$.

It follows from completeness of the real number system that the set $f([a, b]) = \{f(x) \mid a \leq x \leq b\}$ has a least upper bound. Put

$$M = \sup \{f(x) \mid a \leq x \leq b\}. \tag{5.4}$$

Now since M is the least upper bound of the set $f([a, b])$, there must be points of the set arbitrarily close to M (Theorem 2.9). Moreover, since each point of the range $f([a, b])$ of f is of the form $f(\xi)$ for some $\xi \in [a, b]$, it follows that there is a sequence of numbers of the form

$$\{f(y_1), f(y_2), f(y_3), \cdots\}$$

where the distance $|f(y_n) - M|$ tends to 0 as n tends to infinity. Although the sequence $\{y_n\}$ may not converge, we may select from it (just as we did above with the sequence $\{x_n\}$) a convergent subsequence, say $\{y_{n_k}\}$. Now $\{y_{n_k}\}$ must converge to a point y of $[a, b]$ since $[a, b]$ contains all of its limit points and, by virtue of the continuity of f, we have

$$y_{n_k} \to y \text{ implies } f(y_{n_k}) \to f(y). \tag{5.5}$$

However, $\{f(y_{n_k})\}$ is a subsequence of $\{f(y_n)\}$, and since $f(y_n) \to M$ it follows from Theorem 3.4 that $f(y_{n_k}) \to M$. In view of this and (5.5) above we conclude that $f(y) = M$. Finally, from the definition of M in (5.4) we see that $f(y) \geq f(x)$ for all $x \in [a, b]$; that is, $f(y)$ is the maximum of $f(x)$ on $[a, b]$. ∎

There is an analogous theorem concerning the existence of a minimum of a continuous function on a closed interval. We leave its formulation and proof to the reader.

Example 5.8.   A function need not be continuous in order to have a maximum. The Dirichlet function, defined on $[0, 1]$ by

$$\psi(x) = \begin{cases} 0, & \text{if } x \text{ is irrational} \\ 1, & \text{if } x \text{ is rational} \end{cases}$$

is discontinuous everywhere, yet it assumes its maximum at every rational number. On the other hand, a continuous function on an open interval may not have a maximum. Consider $f(x) = x^2$ on $(0, 1)$; it illustrates the point.

The *maximum* of f described in Definition 5.2 is also referred to as the *absolute maximum* of f. In contrast with this, we also have the following.

Definition 5.3.   Let f be defined on $[a, b]$ and suppose $\xi \in [a, b]$. We say that f has a *relative maximum* at ξ iff

$$\exists N(\xi) \ni x \in N(\xi) \cap [a, b] \Rightarrow f(\xi) \geq f(x).$$

The connection between these concepts is left to the exercises (Exercise 6, Section 5.5).

5.4   THE INTERMEDIATE VALUE PROPERTY

The reader has no doubt used the "intermediate value property" in estimating the real zeros of a polynomial [that is, the real numbers r (when they exist) such that $p(r) = 0$, where $p(x)$ is a polynomial with real coefficients]. The argument runs roughly as follows: If $p(a)$ is positive while $p(b)$ is negative, there must be a number r, $a < r < b$, such that $p(r) = 0$. This argument succeeds because of the *continuity* of polynomials.

Definition 5.4.   A function f is said to have the *intermediate value property* or the *Darboux property* iff $f(a) < \eta < f(b) \Rightarrow \exists \xi$, $a < \xi < b$, such that $f(\xi) = \eta$.

We first prove the intermediate value property for continuous functions in a special case.

Lemma.   If f is continuous on $[a, b]$ and if $f(a) < 0 < f(b)$, then there is a point ξ, $a < \xi < b$ such that $f(\xi) = 0$.

Proof: Consider the set $S = \{x \mid f(x) < 0, a \leq x \leq b\}$. Since S is not empty ($a \in S$) and S has b as an upper bound, S has a least upper bound. Put $\xi = \sup S$. Let $\epsilon = 1/n$. There exists a point $x_n \in S$ such that $\xi - (1/n) < x_n \leq \xi$ (Theorem 2.9). Letting n tend to infinity, we have that $x_n \to \xi$. Because of the continuity of f at ξ, it follows that $f(x_n) \to f(\xi)$. Moreover, $f(x_n) < 0$ implies $f(\xi) \leq 0$. If $f(\xi) < 0$, then we could invoke continuity of f at ξ to obtain a neighborhood $N(\xi)$ throughout which f would be negative (see Section 5.5, Exercise 4). This would permit the selection of a number $\xi' \in S$ such that $\xi' > \xi$, contradicting the definition of ξ. Hence $f(\xi) = 0$. This proves the lemma.   ∎

We now proceed to the following theorem.

■ **Theorem 5.3.**   Every continuous function has the intermediate value property.

Proof: Suppose $f(a) < \eta < f(b)$ where f is the given continuous function. Consider the continuous function defined by $g(x) = f(x) - \eta$. We have $g(a) < 0$ while $g(b) > 0$. Applying the lemma to g, we conclude that there exists a number ξ, $a < \xi < b$ such that $g(\xi) = 0$. But $g(\xi) = f(\xi) - \eta = 0$ implies $f(\xi) = \eta$.   ∎

5.5 EXERCISES

1. (a) Let f be defined on S. Write down the definition of f has a *minimum* at $\xi \in S$.
   (b) Give the precise meaning and prove: The continuous image of a closed interval has a minimum.

2. (a) Show that $\cos x = x$ has a solution ξ with $0 < \xi < \pi/2$.

   [HINT: Consider $f(x) = \cos x - x$; compute $f(0)$ and $f(\pi/2)$.]
   (b) Let f be defined on $[a, b]$. We say that f has a *fixed point* iff $\exists \xi \in [a, b] \ni f(\xi) = \xi$. Show that every continuous function f on $[a, b]$ into $[a, b]$ has a fixed point.

   [HINT: Consider $g(x) = f(x) - x$.]

3. (a) Show that every third degree polynomial $p(x) = ax^3 + bx^2 + cx + d$, $a \neq 0$ (a, b, c, d real numbers) has a real zero.

(b) Generalize (a) to any polynomial of odd degree. Is the theorem true for a polynomial of even degree? Prove or give a counter-example.

4. Prove that if f is defined on some neighborhood of a and is continuous at a and if $f(a) < 0$, then there exists a neighborhood $N(a)$ such that $x \in N(a)$ implies $f(x) < 0$.

[HINT: In the definition of continuity of f at a, use the positive number $|f(a)|/2$.]

5. Assume that f is continuous on $[a, b]$. Define $G = \{x \mid x \in (a, b)$ and there exists $\xi > x \ni f(\xi) > f(x)\}$. Prove that G is an open set and, if G is not empty, and if (a_k, b_k) is one of the component open intervals of G, then $f(a_k) \leq f(b_k)$. Determine G for the following functions:

(a) $f(x) = \cos x$, $x \geq 0$.

(b) $f(x) = e^x$, $-\infty < x < \infty$.

(c) $f(x) = e^{-x}$, $-\infty < x < \infty$.

(d) $f(x) = x \sin x$, $x > 0$.

6. (a) Prove: If f is defined on $[a, b]$ and has a maximum at $\xi \in [a, b]$, then f has a relative maximum at ξ.

(b) Construct a counterexample to the converse.

5.6 GENERALIZATION

If we examine carefully the proof that continuity of a function on a closed interval implies uniform continuity (Theorem 5.1), we notice the following salient features in the argument:

(1) Continuity of the function f serves to generate an open cover of the domain of f.

(2) The open cover may be replaced by a finite subcover since the domain (closed interval) is a set to which the Heine-Borel theorem applies.

(3) The triangle inequality does the rest.

One means of generalizing the result is to assume that the domain of the function is a set for which the conclusion of the Heine-Borel theorem is valid. Such a set is called *compact*. Formally, we introduce the following.

Definition 5.5.   A set S of real numbers is called *compact* iff every open cover of S contains a finite subcover.

With this definition, we can prove the following generalization of Theorem 5.1: If f is continuous on a compact set S, then f is uniformly continuous on S. Proof is left to the exercises (Section 5.7, Exercise 1).

Example 5.9. The open interval (0, 1) is not compact. To prove this, all we need do is exhibit an open cover of (0, 1) for which no finite subcover exists. To this end, we consider for each $x \in (0, 1)$, the neighborhood $N(x) = \{u \mid u \text{ real}, |u - x| < x/2\}$ (see Fig. 5.1). This collection $\{N(x)\}$, $0 < x < 1$,

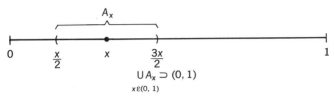

Fig. 5.1   The open interval (0, 1) is not compact.

of neighborhoods is obviously an open cover of (0, 1). Any finite number of these neighborhoods, however, will not cover (0, 1) for, the set of left-hand endpoints of any finite collection has a positive minimum m with $0 < m < 1$ [and therefore $m \in (0, 1)$], but m belongs to none of the neighborhoods making up the finite collection (see also Example 4.12).

Example 5.10. An open set G is not compact. Our point of departure is the fact that every open set G of real numbers is the union of a countable number of disjoint open intervals. Let (a, b) be one of the component open

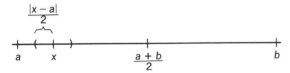

Fig. 5.2   An open set is not compact.

intervals. Associate with each $x \in (a, b)$ a neighborhood $N(x; r)$ of x with radius r where r is the function of x defined by (see Fig. 5.2):

$$r(x) = \begin{cases} \dfrac{|x - a|}{2}, & \text{if } a < x \le \dfrac{a + b}{2} \\[2mm] \dfrac{|x - b|}{2}, & \text{if } \dfrac{a + b}{2} < x < b. \end{cases}$$

In the above, we assumed a and b to be real numbers. If the open set G has a component of the form (a, ∞), put $r(x) = \frac{1}{2}|x - a|$ for $x \in (a, \infty)$. If G has a component of the form $(-\infty, b)$, put $r(x) = \frac{1}{2}|x - b|$ for $x \in (-\infty, b)$. Finally, if $a = -\infty$ and $b = \infty$ (that is, if G is the set of all real numbers), put $r(x) = 1$ for all real numbers x. Carry out this construction in each of the component open intervals of G. The collection of all neighborhoods $N(x; r)$, $x \in G$ obtained in this way is an open cover of G, but no finite subcover exists. (Proof is similar to the idea used in Example 5.9 and is left to the reader: Section 5.7, Exercise 3.)

Example 5.11.   Every clósed interval $[a, b]$ is compact. This is merely a restatement of the Heine-Borel covering theorem.

Thus a sufficient condition for compactness of a set is that it be a closed interval. But we can do better than this. As a matter of fact, we can show that *every closed and bounded set S is compact*. To accomplish this, we re-examine the proof of the Heine-Borel theorem. We need only a slight modification of our definition of the equivalence relation used there in order to obtain a proof of the more general statement at hand. It consists in defining, for two points $x, y \in S$: $x \sim y$ iff a finite subcover of $\overline{xy} \cap S$ exists. In other words, instead of working with the entire closed interval $\overline{xy}$, we simply consider only those points of $\overline{xy}$ which belong to S; that is, $\overline{xy} \cap S$. The proof now proceeds as before (Theorem 4.5) with a, b denoting min S, max S, respectively.

Thus we conclude that a sufficient condition for a set S to be compact is that S be closed and bounded. These same conditions, however, are also necessary. This is the content of the next two results.

■ **Theorem 5.4.**   If S is compact, then S is bounded.

Proof: Consider the collection of neighborhoods of the origin: $N(0; n)$, $n = 1, 2, 3, \cdots$. This is clearly an open cover of S for $\bigcup_{n=1}^{\infty} N(0; n) \supset S$. Since S is compact, a certain finite number of these neighborhoods of the origin covers S. Let M be the maximum of the radii of this finite subcover. Hence

$$x \in S \Rightarrow x \in N(0; M) \Rightarrow |x| < M;$$

that is, S is bounded.   ■

■ **Theorem 5.5.**   If S is compact, then S is closed.

(NOTE: If S is empty, the theorem is trivially true. So assume $S \neq \varnothing$.)

Proof: We prove the contrapositive. Suppose, then, that S is not closed. Then S $(S \neq \varnothing)$ has an accumulation point $\xi \notin S$. We now use this fact to construct an open cover of S (see Fig. 5.3). For arbitrary $x \in S$, we have $|x - \xi| > 0$ since $x \neq \xi$. Therefore, the neighborhood $N(x; |x - \xi|/2)$ does

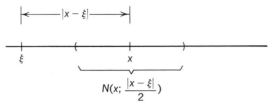

Fig. 5.3   Every compact set is closed.

not contain ξ. The collection of all such neighborhoods as x varies over S constitutes an open cover of S. If S were compact, then a finite subcover would exist:

$$N\left(x_1; \frac{|x_1 - \xi|}{2}\right) \cup N\left(x_2; \frac{|x_2 - \xi|}{2}\right) \cup \cdots \cup N\left(x_n; \frac{|x_n - \xi|}{2}\right) \supset S. \quad (5.6)$$

Let r be the minimum of the radii of these neighborhoods. Then

$$2r \leq |x_i - \xi|, \qquad i = 1, 2, \cdots, n.$$

Now consider the neighborhood $N(\xi; r)$. Let x be an arbitrary element of S. Then x belongs to one of the neighborhoods in (5.6), say, $x \in N(x_k)$. We estimate the distance

$$|\xi - x| \geq |\xi - x_k| - |x_k - x|$$

(by the triangle inequality). But $|\xi - x_k| \geq 2r$, by the definition of r, and $|x_k - x| < r$ since $x \in N(x_k)$. Therefore

$$|\xi - x| \geq 2r - r = r.$$

Since x was an arbitrary element of S, and we have shown that $x \notin N(\xi; r)$, we conclude that $N(\xi; r) \cap S = \varnothing$. A fortiori, then, $N'(\xi; r) \cap S = \varnothing$. But this tells us that ξ is not an accumulation point of S since we have found a deleted neighborhood of ξ which does not intersect S. This is a contradiction. ∎

Summarizing, we have the following theorems.

■ **Theorem 5.6.** S is compact $\Leftrightarrow$ S is closed and bounded.

In addition, if we replace the closed interval $[a, b]$ of Theorem 5.1 by a compact set S, the result becomes Theorem 5.7.

■ **Theorem 5.7.**   If f is a continuous function defined on a compact set S, then f is uniformly continuous on S.

5.7 EXERCISES

1. Prove: If f is continuous on a compact set S, then f is uniformly continuous on S (see Theorem 5.1).

2. Give a direct proof that if $S = \{x \mid x$ is rational and $x \in [0, 1]\}$, then S is not compact; that is, find an open cover of S for which no finite subcover exists.

[HINT: Let t be a fixed irrational number. Consider, for $x \in S$, the collection of neighborhoods $N(x; |x - t|/2)$.]

3. Work out the details in the proof (Example 5.10) that an open set is not compact.
4. Prove the generalization of the Heine-Borel covering theorem: If S is a closed and bounded set and if $\{G_x\}$, $x \in S$ is an open cover of S, then a finite subcover of S exists.
5. Show that if S is an arbitrary set of real numbers and if $\{G_\alpha\}$, $\alpha \in \mathcal{C}$, is an open cover of S, then a countable subcover exists.

[HINT: Let $x \in S$ and suppose $x \in G_\alpha$. Show that there is an open interval I_x with rational endpoints such that $x \in I_x \subset G_\alpha$. Consider the function with domain S defined by $F(x) = I_x$; that is, for each $x \in S$, choose and fix I_x. Next show that the collection of all intervals with rational endpoints is denumerable and therefore the range of F is countable. Replace each I_x in the range of F by the G_α which gave rise to I_x. Show that the collection of such G_α's is a countable subcover of S.]

Supplement to Chapter 5

We raise the question as to what concepts and theorems of this chapter generalize to complex numbers.

Definition 5.6. If $\bar{I}$ is a closed interval of complex numbers, that is, if $\bar{I} = [a, b] \times [c, d]$ where a, b, c, d are real numbers with $a < b$, $c < d$, and if ξ belongs to $\bar{I}$, then we say that the complex-valued function f with domain $\bar{I}$ is *continuous at* ξ iff

$$\lim_{z \to \xi} f(z) = f(\lim_{z \to \xi} z) = f(\xi).$$

Equivalently, f is *continuous at* ξ iff for every $\epsilon > 0$,

$$\exists \delta > 0 \ni |z - \xi| < \delta \Rightarrow |f(z) - f(\xi)| < \epsilon.$$

More generally, let S be a set of complex numbers and let f have domain S. If $\xi \in S$ is a point of accumulation of S ($\xi \in S'$), we say f is *continuous at* ξ iff for every $N(f(\xi))$, $\exists N(\xi) \ni$

$$z \in N(\xi) \cap S \Rightarrow f(z) \in N(f(\xi)).$$

If this condition holds at every point of $S \cap S'$, then we say *f is continuous on S.*

Uniform continuity is defined precisely as for the real case (Definition 5.1), and the important theorem that continuity on a closed interval $\bar{I}$ implies uniform continuity on $\bar{I}$ is valid for complex-valued functions of a complex variable. Indeed, the proof we gave for the real case (Theorem 5.1) need not be altered.

In Section 5.3 we dealt with the concept of a maximum of a real-valued function. Of course, we cannot offer the same definition of maximum for the complex-valued f that we introduced for the real case. However, it does make sense to consider the maximum of the real-valued (actually nonnegative) function $|f|$. This suggests the following definition.

Definition 5.7. Let f be defined on $S \subset$ complex numbers. We say that *f has a maximum at* $\xi \in S$ iff
$$z \in S \Rightarrow |f(z)| \leq |f(\xi)|.$$

With this agreement, Theorem 5.2 is saved. If f is continuous on the closed interval $\bar{I}$, then f has a maximum at some point $\xi \in \bar{I}$. Furthermore, modifications in the proof for the real case are so minor that details may be left to the reader.

The intermediate value property or Darboux property is so inextricably dependent on the concept of order that even the same device just used does not yield an analog of Theorem 5.3. That is to say, if we consider $|f(z)|$ in lieu of $f(z)$, then we are dealing with a nonnegative real-valued function and although the hypothesis $|f(a)| < \eta < |f(b)|$ (where a, b are complex but η is, of course, real) is meaningful, the conclusion (that $\exists \xi$, $a < \xi < b$, $f(\xi) = \eta$) is not. Actually, we can define a notion of "betweenness" for complex numbers which is valuable and assigns a meaning to $a < \xi < b$, but then the resulting statement of the proposed theorem is false. (See Exercise 3 at the end of this supplement.) A fruitful generalization of the intermediate value theorem can be obtained, however. It involves the concept of "connectedness" of a set. (See, for example, T. Apostol's *Mathematical Analysis: A Modern Approach to Advanced Calculus*, Addison-Wesley Publishing Co., Inc., Reading, Mass., 1957.)

Much of the material of Section 5.6 is valid in the complex number case. The notion of a compact set (Definition 5.5) can be introduced *mutatis mutandis*. That a sufficient condition for compactness of a set S of complex numbers is that S be closed and bounded is precisely Exercise 7 in the Supplement to Chapter 4. Furthermore, the facts

$$S \text{ compact} \Rightarrow S \text{ bounded}$$

and

$$S \text{ compact} \Rightarrow S \text{ closed}$$

are proved exactly as for the reals (Theorems 5.4 and 5.5). Hence the following theorem is valid.

■ **Theorem 5.8.** S is compact $\Leftrightarrow$ S is closed and bounded.

In view of the above discussion, we also have the following theorem.

■ **Theorem 5.9.**   If f is a continuous function defined on a compact set S, then f is uniformly continuous on S.

The proof proceeds just like the proof of Theorem 5.1 with obvious minor modifications.

5.8 EXERCISES

1. Prove that $f(z) = z^2$ is uniformly continuous on the closed disk
$$D = \{z \mid |z| \leq 1\},$$
   appealing only to the definition of uniform continuity.
2. Prove that $f(z) = z^2$ is not uniformly continuous on the set of all complex numbers.
3. Let z, w be complex numbers. Define the *line segment joining z, w* (denoted by $L[z, w]$) by
$$L[z, w] = \{\xi \mid \xi = \alpha z + \beta w, \alpha + \beta = 1, \alpha \geq 0, \beta \geq 0\}.$$
   The set $L[z, w]$ is also known as the set of all *convex linear combinations of the vectors z and w.* We say that ξ is *between* z and w iff $\xi \in L[z, w]$.
   (a) Give the geometric interpretation of $L[z, w]$, explaining the need for the restrictions placed on α and β in the analytic definition of $L[z, w]$.
   (b) If z, w, v are complex numbers, interpret geometrically the set $\Delta[z, w, v]$ of all convex linear combinations of z, w, v defined analytically by
   $\Delta[z, w, v]$
   $$= \{\xi \mid \xi = \alpha z + \beta w + \gamma v, \alpha + \beta + \gamma = 1, \alpha \geq 0, \beta \geq 0, \gamma \geq 0\}.$$
4. Prove, for a set S of complex numbers, that S is compact if and only if S is closed and bounded.
5. Prove: If f is a continuous complex-valued function defined on a compact set S of complex numbers, then f is uniformly continuous on S.

6

Differentiability

INTRODUCTION

We assume that the reader knows the following:

(1) Let f be defined on $[a, b]$. If $\xi \in (a, b)$, we call f *differentiable at* ξ iff

$$\lim_{x \to \xi} \frac{f(x) - f(\xi)}{x - \xi}$$

exists. When this limit exists, it is denoted by $f'(\xi)$ (sometimes $df/dx|_{x=\xi}$) and is called the *derivative* of f at ξ.

(2) We say that f is *differentiable on the interval* $[a, b]$ provided that f is differentiable at every point of the interval, differentiability at the endpoints a, b being defined in terms of the right- and left-hand limits, respectively, that is, by the requirement that

$$\lim_{x \to a^+} \frac{f(x) - f(a)}{x - a}$$

and

$$\lim_{x \to b^-} \frac{f(x) - f(b)}{x - b}$$

exist, respectively. These limits are denoted by $f'(a^+)$ and $f'(b^-)$, respectively. $f'(a^+)$ is defined to be a number such that for every $\epsilon > 0$, $\exists \delta > 0 \ni$ $|x - a| < \delta$, $x > a \Rightarrow |[f(x) - f(a)] / (x - a) - f'(a^+)| < \epsilon$. The left-hand derivative $f'(b^-)$ is defined in an analogous manner.

(3) The following rules of calculation with differentiable functions are valid:

(a) $(f \pm g)' = f' \pm g'$.

(b) $(fg)' = fg' + f'g$.

(c) $\left(\dfrac{f}{g}\right)' = \dfrac{gf' - fg'}{g^2}$,   at those points ξ where $g(\xi) \neq 0$.

(d) $[f(g(x))]' = \dfrac{df}{dg} \dfrac{dg}{dx}$ (the chain rule).

(See Section 6.2, Exercise 1.)

(4) If f is differentiable on the open interval (a, b) and continuous on the closed interval $[a, b]$, then there is at least one point ξ, $a < \xi < b$ such that

$$f'(\xi) = \frac{f(b) - f(a)}{b - a}$$

(the mean value theorem of differential calculus). (See Section 6.2, Exercise 5.)

(5) Every differentiable function is continuous.

[*Proof:* $f(x) - f(\xi) = [f(x) - f(\xi)](x - \xi)/(x - \xi)$. We may pass to the limit as $x \to \xi$ since $f'(\xi)$ exists (by hypothesis), and consequently the right member obviously has a limit as $x \to \xi$ and therefore so must the left member. Thus

$$\lim_{x \to \xi} [f(x) - f(\xi)] = f'(\xi) \cdot 0 = 0,$$

which implies $\lim_{x \to \xi} f(x) = f(\xi)$; that is, f is continuous at ξ.] ∎

The set of all functions differentiable on an interval $[a, b]$ is consequently a subset of the continuous functions on $[a, b]$. We may therefore expect a differentiable function to be "better behaved" than a continuous one.

Our purpose in this chapter is to establish some further interesting properties of differentiable functions. In particular, we will show the following to be true.

(1) At every point ξ of differentiability of a function f, f satisfies a Lipschitz condition [this means, roughly speaking, that the straight lines passing through $(\xi, f(\xi))$, and neighboring points $(x, f(x))$ of the graph have bounded slopes].

(2) If f is differentiable at ξ, a linear function (called the differential of f at ξ) can be found which approximates f in a precise sense in a neighborhood of ξ.

(3) Every derivative f' has the intermediate value property.

(4) For a function having successive continuous derivatives $f', f'', \cdots, f^{(n)}$ a formula (Taylor's formula) can be found relating the value of the function and its derivatives at a fixed point a to its value $f(x)$ at a neighboring point x.

(5) Every mapping f of a set S into S satisfying a special Lipschitz condition has a fixed point (that is, a point w such that $f(w) = w$). This so-called "contraction mapping theorem" provides good motivation for introducing the important idea of a Cauchy sequence. We show that Cauchy sequences of real numbers, and only these, are convergent sequences. To put it another way, we characterize convergent sequences (that is, find necessary and sufficient conditions that a sequence of real numbers be convergent).

6.1 THE LIPSCHITZ CONDITION

After having introduced a new concept in mathematics, it is standard practice to seek equivalent versions of that concept. This is done in order to strengthen our grasp of the concept and, at the same time, to admit varied approaches in the exploitation of the concept. We begin with two theorems characterizing differentiability.

Let us suppose that $f'(\xi)$ exists. This means that for every $\epsilon > 0$ there exists $\delta > 0$ such that

$$0 < |x - \xi| < \delta \Rightarrow \left| \frac{f(x) - f(\xi)}{x - \xi} - f'(\xi) \right| < \epsilon. \tag{*}$$

In the language of neighborhoods, for every $N(f'(\xi))$, $\exists N(\xi) \ni$

$$x \in N'(\xi) \Rightarrow \frac{f(x) - f(\xi)}{x - \xi} \in N(f'(\xi)).$$

If we multiply the last inequality in (*) by $|x - \xi|$, we may write

$$x \in N'(\xi) \Rightarrow |f(x) - f(\xi) - f'(\xi)(x - \xi)| < \epsilon|x - \xi|. \tag{6.1}$$

Conversely, if there exists a fixed number, call it $D(\xi)$, and for every $\epsilon > 0$, a neighborhood $N(\xi)$, such that [compare with (6.1) above]

$$x \in N'(\xi) \Rightarrow |f(x) - f(\xi) - D(\xi)(x - \xi)| < \epsilon|x - \xi|,$$

then on dividing the last inequality by $|x - \xi|$, we get

$$x \in N'(\xi) \Rightarrow \left| \frac{f(x) - f(\xi)}{x - \xi} - D(\xi) \right| < \epsilon;$$

that is, $f'(\xi)$ exists and we have $f'(\xi) = D(\xi)$. Hence, the following theorem.

■ **Theorem 6.1.** f is differentiable at ξ iff there exists a fixed number $D(\xi)$ such that for every $\epsilon > 0$, we can find a neighborhood $N(\xi)$ such that

$$x \in N'(\xi) \Rightarrow |f(x) - f(\xi) - D(\xi)(x - \xi)| < \epsilon|x - \xi|.$$

Another statement equivalent to (6.1) can be obtained through this argument: Let f be differentiable at ξ. Consider, for each x, the two numbers $f(x)$ and $f(\xi) + f'(\xi)(x - \xi)$. Suppose we determine the number $\alpha(\xi, x)$ so that

$$f(x) = f(\xi) + f'(\xi)(x - \xi) + \alpha(\xi, x)(x - \xi). \tag{6.2}$$

[We leave it to the reader to provide a geometric interpretation of the quantity $\alpha(\xi, x)(x - \xi)$ appearing in (6.2) (see Fig. 6.1).] Having done this, let $\epsilon > 0$. According to (6.1) $\exists N(\xi) \ni$

$$x \in N'(\xi) \Rightarrow |f(x) - f(\xi) - f'(\xi)(x - \xi)| < \epsilon|x - \xi|.$$

Making use of (6.2),

$$x \in N'(\xi) \Rightarrow |\alpha(\xi, x)(x - \xi)| < \epsilon|x - \xi|,$$

or equivalently,

$$x \in N'(\xi) \Rightarrow |\alpha(\xi, x)| < \epsilon.$$

In other words, $\lim_{x \to \xi} \alpha(\xi, x) = 0$. This proves half of Theorem 6.2 (we leave the other half to the reader).

■ **Theorem 6.2.** $f'(\xi)$ exists iff for each x there is a number $\alpha(\xi, x)$ and a number $D(\xi)$ such that: For every $\epsilon > 0$, $\exists N(\xi) \ni x \in N'(\xi) \Rightarrow f(x) = f(\xi) + D(\xi)(x - \xi) + \alpha(\xi, x)(x - \xi)$ and $\lim_{x \to \xi} \alpha(\xi, x) = 0$.

Example 6.1. The function defined by $f(x) = \sin x$ is differentiable at ξ. Determine $\alpha(\xi, x)$ so that (6.2) holds and $\lim_{x \to \xi} \alpha(\xi, x) = 0$. Putting

$$\sin x = \sin \xi + (x - \xi) \cos \xi + \alpha(\xi, x)(x - \xi),$$

we find

$$\alpha(\xi, x) = \frac{\sin x - \sin \xi}{x - \xi} - \cos \xi.$$

In view of the fact that $\lim_{x \to \xi} (\sin x - \sin \xi)/(x - \xi) = \cos \xi$, it is clear that $\lim_{x \to \xi} \alpha(\xi, x) = 0$. Note that $\alpha(\xi, x)$ is simply the difference between the slope of the "secant" line through $(\xi, f(\xi))$ and $(x, f(x))$ and the slope of the tangent line at $(\xi, f(\xi))$. Thus the condition $\lim_{x \to \xi} \alpha(\xi, x) = 0$ requires that the "secant line slope" approach the "slope of the tangent line."

An interesting application of the characterization of a differentiable function as given in Theorem 6.2 is found in proving the chain rule for differentiation of a composite function [see Section 6.2, Exercise 1, (d)].

The last two theorems may be used as a point of departure in arriving at important consequences of differentiability. One result we have in mind can be motivated as follows: If f has a derivative at ξ, it is not unreasonable to expect that in some neighborhood of ξ the slopes of the secant lines obtained by joining $(x, f(x))$ and $(\xi, f(\xi))$ should be "close" to $f'(\xi)$ and hence should be bounded. To be precise, we introduce the following definition.

Definition 6.1. Let f be defined on an open interval I and let $\xi \in I$. f satisfies a *Lipschitz condition* at ξ iff

$$\exists M > 0 \text{ and } \exists N(\xi) \ni x \in N(\xi) \Rightarrow |f(x) - f(\xi)| \leq M|x - \xi|.$$

Remark

To interpret this condition geometrically, suppose $x \neq \xi$. Then we may write

$$\left| \frac{f(x) - f(\xi)}{x - \xi} \right| \leq M;$$

that is, the "secant slopes" are bounded by M.

■ **Theorem 6.3.** If $f'(\xi)$ exists, then f satisfies a Lipschitz condition at ξ.

Proof: Let $\epsilon > 0$. Invoking Theorem 6.1, we have that

$$\exists N(\xi) \ni x \in N'(\xi) \Rightarrow |f(x) - f(\xi) - f'(\xi)(x - \xi)| < \epsilon|x - \xi|. \quad (6.3)$$

Putting $u = f(x) - f(\xi)$, $v = f'(\xi)(x - \xi)$ and using the triangle inequality $|u| - |v| \leq |u - v|$, (6.3) implies

$$x \in N'(\xi) \Rightarrow |f(x) - f(\xi)| - |f'(\xi)(x - \xi)| < \epsilon|x - \xi|,$$

or

$$|f(x) - f(\xi)| < [|f'(\xi)| + \epsilon]|x - \xi|. \quad (6.4)$$

Fix ϵ (for example, we could take $\epsilon = 1$). Then define $M = |f'(\xi)| + \epsilon$. It follows from (6.4) that $\exists N(\xi)$ such that

$$x \in N'(\xi) \Rightarrow |f(x) - f(\xi)| < M|x - \xi|. \quad (6.5)$$

It is an immediate consequence of (6.5) that

$$x \in N(\xi) \Rightarrow |f(x) - f(\xi)| \leq M|x - \xi|;$$

that is, f satisfies a Lipschitz condition at ξ. ■

Example 6.2. The function f with $f(x) = \ln x$, $x > 0$, is differentiable at $x = 1$. Show that $\ln x$ satisfies a Lipschitz condition at $x = 1$.

Since $f'(1) = 1$, we know that for every $\epsilon > 0$, $\exists \delta > 0 \ni 0 < |x - 1| < \delta$ $\Rightarrow |\ln x/(x - 1) - 1| < \epsilon$. Taking $\epsilon = 1$ and multiplying the last inequality by $|x - 1|$, we get

$$|\ln x - (x - 1)| < |x - 1|.$$

But

$$|\ln x| - |x - 1| \le |\ln x - (x - 1)|$$

and so for $0 < |x - 1| < \delta$, we have

$$|\ln x| < 2|x - 1|.$$

Hence for $|x - 1| < \delta$, we have

$$|\ln x| \le 2|x - 1|,$$

proving that $\ln x$ is Lipschitzian at $x = 1$.

Example 6.3. The converse of Theorem 6.3 is false; that is, a function can be Lipschitzian at a point without being differentiable there.

It suffices to take $f(x) = |x|$, $\xi = 0$ and $M = 1$, for

$$||x| - |0|| = |x| \le 1|x - 0|,$$

proving that $|x|$ satisfies a Lipschitz condition at $x = 0$, but, of course, $|x|$ is not differentiable at the origin.

6.2 EXERCISES

1. Prove the elementary rules of calculation for derivatives (state theorems precisely):

(a) $(f + g)' = f' + g'$

(b) $(fg)' = fg' + f'g$

(c) $\left(\dfrac{f}{g}\right)' = \dfrac{gf' - fg'}{g^2}$, for those $x \ni g(x) \ne 0$.

(d) $[f(g(x))]' = \dfrac{df}{dg}\dfrac{dg}{dx}$ (the chain rule).

[HINT: Since $f'(u_0)$ exists, we can write (Theorem 6.2)

$$f(u) = f(u_0) + f'(u_0)(u - u_0) + \alpha(u_0, u)(u - u_0) \tag{6.6}$$

where $\lim_{u \to u_0} \alpha(u_0, u) = 0$. Since $g'(\xi)$ exists, we have

$$g(x) = g(\xi) + g'(\xi)(x - \xi) + \beta(\xi, x)(x - \xi) \tag{6.7}$$

where $\lim_{x\to\xi}\beta(\xi, x) = 0$. Put $g(x) = u$, $g(\xi) = u_0$ into (6.7), solve for $u - u_0$ and substitute into (6.6) to get

$$f(g(x)) = f(g(\xi)) + f'(g(\xi))[g'(\xi)(x - \xi) + \beta(\xi, x)(x - \xi)]$$
$$+ \alpha(g(\xi), g(x))(g(x) - g(\xi)).$$

So

$$\lim_{x\to\xi}\frac{f(g(x)) - f(g(\xi))}{x - \xi} = \lim_{x\to\xi}f'(g(\xi))[g'(\xi) + \beta(\xi, x)] = f'(g(\xi))g'(\xi)$$

since g is continuous at ξ and $\beta(\xi, x) \to 0$ as $x \to \xi$.]

2. Prove that $f(x) = |x|$ is not differentiable at $x = 0$.
3. Prove that if f is differentiable on (a, b) and has an *extremum* (that is, a maximum or minimum) at an *interior* point ξ of the interval, then $f'(\xi) = 0$.

[HINT: Suppose that f has a maximum at ξ. Then

$$\exists N(\xi) \ni x \in N(\xi) \Rightarrow f(\xi) - f(x) \geq 0. \text{ (Why?)}$$

Consider two cases: $x < \xi$ and $x > \xi$. Show that the first case leads to the inequality $f'(\xi) \geq 0$ while the second implies $f'(\xi) \leq 0$.]

4. Prove Rolle's theorem: If $f(a) = f(b) = 0$ and f is differentiable on (a, b), continuous on $[a, b]$, then $\exists \xi, a < \xi < b \ni$

$$f'(\xi) = \frac{f(b) - f(a)}{b - a} = 0.$$

[HINT: f has a maximum and a minimum since it is continuous on a closed interval; use Exercise 3 to handle the case where the extremum occurs at a point of (a, b).]

5. Prove the mean value theorem of differential calculus: If f is differentiable on the open interval (a, b) and continuous on the closed interval $[a, b]$, then there is at least one point ξ, $a < \xi < b$ such that

$$f'(\xi) = \frac{f(b) - f(a)}{b - a}.$$

[HINT: Consider $F(x) = f(x) - f(a) - [(f(b) - f(a))/(b - a)](x - a)$. (Interpret this geometrically.) Now apply Exercise 4 to $F(x)$.]

6. Show that it is essential in Exercise 3 that we assume that the extremum occurs at an *interior* point by constructing an example to show that the statement omitting this requirement is false.
7. Show that if $f'(\xi) > 0$, then there is a neighborhood of ξ such that $x < \xi < y$, $x, y \in N(\xi)$ *implies* $f(x) < f(\xi) < f(y)$.
8. Prove that if f satisfies a Lipschitz condition at ξ, then f is continuous at ξ.

9. Which is greater, e^π or π^e?

   [HINT: Maximize $f(x) = x^e - e^x$.]

6.3   THE DIFFERENTIAL

One of the most important properties of a differentiable function at a point ξ is the consequent approximability of f in some neighborhood of ξ by a linear function (see Fig. 6.1). Geometrically speaking, if f is differentiable

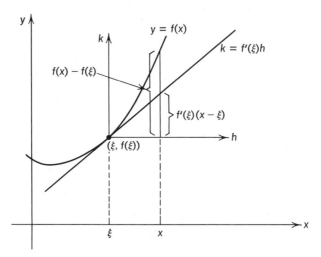

Fig. 6.1   Geometric interpretation of the differential.

at ξ, then a tangent line to the graph of f at ξ can be drawn, and the graph of f can be approximated locally by this tangent line, in a sense to be made precise shortly.

Definition 6.2.   Let f, domain $[a, b]$, be a real-valued function. Let $\xi \in (a, b)$ and assume that the derivative $f'(\xi)$ exists. By the *differential of f at ξ* is meant the function df of two variables ξ, h defined by

$$df(\xi; h) = f'(\xi)h \tag{6.8}$$

where $-\infty < h < \infty$.

We emphasize that df is a function of two variables ξ and h; ξ must be a point at which f is differentiable, and h is an arbitrary real number. Thus the *domain* of the differential $df(\xi; h)$ is the Cartesian product $S \times T$ where S

is the set of all points where f is differentiable and T is the set of all real numbers.

Example 6.4. (*a*) The differential of $f(x) = \sqrt[3]{5 - 2x}$ is the function defined by

$$df(\xi; h) = -\tfrac{2}{3}(5 - 2\xi)^{-2/3}h.$$

The domain of df is the Cartesian product $S \times T$ where S is the set of all real numbers ξ except $\tfrac{5}{2}$ and T is the set of all real numbers h.

(b) The differential of $f(x) = 3^x$ is

$$df(\xi; h) = (3^\xi \ln 3)h$$

where ξ, h are arbitrary real numbers.

From (6.8), we see that

$$df(\xi; x - \xi) = f'(\xi)(x - \xi).$$

Using this definition in Theorem 6.1, we conclude that $\forall \epsilon > 0, \exists N(\xi) \ni$

$$x \in N'(\xi) \Rightarrow |f(x) - f(\xi) - df(\xi; x - \xi)| < \epsilon |x - \xi|.$$

This is the first basic property of the differential. It tells us that if $\epsilon > 0$ is given, then in some corresponding neighborhood of the point of differentiability of f, the increment $\Delta f(x; \xi) = f(x) - f(\xi)$ in the function will be approximated "closely" by the differential $df(\xi; x - \xi)$ in the sense that the numerical value of the ratio of the difference $\Delta f(x; \xi) - df(\xi; x - \xi)$ to the increment $\Delta = x - \xi$ will be less than ϵ. The precise statement follows:

■ **Theorem 6.4.** (Property 1 of the differential: Linear Approximation.)
Let f be differentiable at ξ. For every $\epsilon > 0, \exists N(\xi)$ such that

$$x \in N'(\xi) \Rightarrow |f(x) - f(\xi) - df(\xi; x - \xi)| < \epsilon |x - \xi|. \tag{6.9}$$

To put it in a slightly different way (setting $x - \xi = h$):
For every $\epsilon > 0, \exists \delta > 0$ such that

$$0 < |h| < \delta \Rightarrow |f(\xi + h) - f(\xi) - df(\xi; h)| < \epsilon |h|. \tag{6.10}$$

A second basic property of the differential is the content of the next theorem.

■ **Theorem 6.5.** (Property 2 of $df(\xi; h)$: Linearity in h.)
If a, b, h, k are arbitrary real numbers, then

$$df(\xi; ah + bk) = adf(\xi; h) + bdf(\xi; k).$$

We express this property of the differential by saying that it is *linear in its second variable*.

Proof: By (6.8)

$$df(\xi; ah + bk) = f'(\xi)(ah + bk)$$
$$= af'(\xi)h + bf'(\xi)k$$
$$= adf(\xi; h) + bdf(\xi; k). \quad \blacksquare$$

Example 6.5.   The differential $df(\xi; h)$ is not necessarily linear in ξ. For example, consider $f(x) = x^3$ and $h = 1$. Then

$$df(\xi; 1) = 3\xi^2$$

and

$$df(\eta; 1) = 3\eta^2.$$

On the other hand,

$$df(\xi + \eta; 1) = 3(\xi + \eta)^2 \neq df(\xi; 1) + df(\eta; 1) = 3\xi^2 + 3\eta^2.$$

We have just proved that if f is differentiable at ξ, then it has a differential and its differential has the two properties proved in Theorems 6.4 and 6.5 above. The justification for calling these "basic" properties of the differential lies in the fact that these properties characterize the differential. Theorem 6.6 asserts the sufficiency of these two properties for existence of the differential.

■ **Theorem 6.6.**   Let f be given and let ξ be a fixed real number belonging to the domain of f. If there is a function g with domain all real numbers [we denote the value of g at h by $g(\xi, h)$] with the following two properties:

(1) For every $\epsilon > 0$, $\exists \delta > 0 \ni$

$$0 < |h| < \delta \Rightarrow |f(\xi + h) - f(\xi) - g(\xi, h)| < \epsilon|h|$$

and

(2) $g(\xi, h)$ is linear in h,

then f is differentiable at ξ and $g(\xi, h) = f'(\xi)h = df(\xi; h)$.

Proof: Since $g(\xi, h)$ is linear in h, we note that

$$g(\xi, 1 \cdot h) = hg(\xi, 1)$$

and since $g(\xi, 1)$ is independent of h, we may write

$$g(\xi, h) = hm(\xi) \tag{6.11}$$

where, of course, we have put $m(\xi) = g(\xi, 1)$.

If we now invoke condition (1) and divide the last inequality appearing in (1) by $|h|$, we have

$$\left| \frac{f(\xi + h) - f(\xi)}{h} - \frac{g(\xi, h)}{h} \right| < \epsilon. \tag{6.12}$$

Now substitute (6.11) into (6.12), obtaining the statement:

For every $\epsilon > 0, \exists \delta > 0 \ni$

$$0 < |h| < \delta \Rightarrow \left| \frac{f(\xi + h) - f(\xi)}{h} - m(\xi) \right| < \epsilon.$$

But this statement says that the derivative of f exists at ξ and is equal to $m(\xi)$. Returning to (6.11), we conclude that $g(\xi, h) = f'(\xi)h$. ∎

6.4 EXERCISES

1. Compute the differentials (if they exist) as indicated below:

(a) $f(x) = \begin{cases} x \sin \dfrac{1}{x}, & \text{if } x \neq 0 \\ 0, & \text{if } x = 0. \end{cases}$

   $df(0; h);$ $df(\xi; h)$ for $\xi \neq 0$.

(b) $f(x) = \begin{cases} x^3 \sin \dfrac{1}{x}, & \text{if } x \neq 0 \\ 0, & \text{if } x = 0. \end{cases}$

   $df(0; h);$ $df(\xi; h)$ for $\xi \neq 0$.

(c) $f(x) = \begin{cases} x^{1/2} \sin \dfrac{1}{x}, & \text{if } x \neq 0 \\ 0, & \text{if } x = 0. \end{cases}$

   $df(0; h);$ $df(\xi; h)$ for $\xi > 0$.

(d) Generalization of (a), (b), and (c): Let α be a fixed real number.

   $f(x) = \begin{cases} x^\alpha \sin \dfrac{1}{x}, & \text{if } x \neq 0 \\ 0, & \text{if } x = 0. \end{cases}$

   $df(0; h);$ $df(\xi; h)$ for $\xi > 0$.

   (Consider two cases: $\alpha \leq 1$ and $\alpha > 1$.)

(e) $f(x) = \begin{cases} \dfrac{\sin x}{x}, & \text{if } x \neq 0 \\ 1, & \text{if } x = 0. \end{cases}$

   $df(0; h);$ $df(\xi; h)$ for $\xi \neq 0$.

(f) $f(x) = \ln x, x > 0$.

$df(\xi; h)$ for $\xi > 0$.

2. Let f, g be differentiable at ξ and suppose $df(\xi; h) = f'(\xi)h$ and $dg(\xi; h) = g'(\xi)h$ are the corresponding differentials. Prove the usual rules for operating with differentials:

(a) Show that the differential of the sum $f + g$ exists and that

$$d(f + g)(\xi; h) = df(\xi; h) + dg(\xi; h).$$

(b) Show that

$$d(f - g)(\xi; h) = df(\xi; h) - dg(\xi; h).$$

(c) Show that

$$d(f \cdot g)(\xi; h) = f(\xi)dg(\xi; h) + df(\xi; h)g(\xi).$$

(d) Show that if $g(\xi) \neq 0$,

$$d\left(\frac{f}{g}\right)(\xi; h) = \frac{g(\xi)df(\xi; h) - f(\xi)dg(\xi; h)}{[g(\xi)]^2}.$$

(e) Show that if f is differentiable at $g(\xi)$ and g is differentiable at ξ, then the differential of the composite function $f(g(x)) = m(x)$ is given by

$$dm(\xi; h) = f'(g(\xi))dg(\xi; h).$$

3. The function f is said to be *linear* iff $f(x + y) = f(x) + f(y)$ and $f(cx) = cf(x)$ for all real numbers c, x, and y.

(a) Show that every function of the form $f(x) = mx$, where m is a constant, is linear.

(b) Show that a function of the form $f(x) = mx + b$, with m, b constants and $b \neq 0$, is *not* linear.

(c) Show that $f(x) = \sin x$ is not linear.

(d) Show that if f is linear, then $f(0) = 0$.

(e) Show that if f is linear, then $f(1) = f(c)/c$ for $c \neq 0$. Use this to prove that $f'(0)$ exists and is equal to $f(1)$.

(f) Use the result in (e) to show that if f is linear, then $f(x) = mx$, where $m = f(1)$.

(g) The results in (a) and (f) characterize linear functions. What does this mean?

6.5   EVERY DERIVATIVE HAS THE DARBOUX PROPERTY

We have seen that every continuous function has the Darboux property or intermediate value property (Theorem 5.3). It was remarked that this property, however, is not characteristic of continuous functions; that is, some discontinuous functions exhibit the property. In fulfillment of this statement, we will do the following:

(1) Prove that every function which is the derivative of some function has the Darboux property.

(2) Give an example of a function whose derivative exists but the derivative is discontinuous.

It is a remarkable fact indeed that the sole assumption that a function have the form f' insures that it has the Darboux property.

■ **Theorem 6.7.** If f is differentiable on the closed interval $[a, b]$ with $f'(a) < \eta < f'(b)$, then there exists a real number ξ, $a < \xi < b$, such that $f'(\xi) = \eta$.

Proof: Consider the function g defined on $[a, b]$ as follows:

$$g(x) = \begin{cases} \dfrac{f(x) - f(a)}{x - a}, & \text{if } x \neq a \\ f'(a), & \text{if } x = a. \end{cases}$$

Since f is differentiable on $[a, b]$, and therefore continuous on $[a, b]$, it is clear that g is continuous on $[a, b]$ (note that $\lim_{x \to a} g(x) = f'(a) = g(a)$). By the intermediate value theorem for continuous functions (Theorem 5.3),

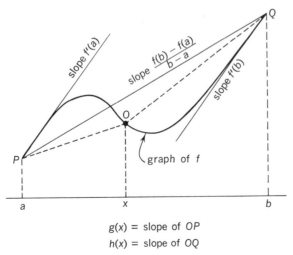

$$g(x) = \text{slope of } OP$$
$$h(x) = \text{slope of } OQ$$

Fig. 6.2 The Darboux property of derivatives.

it follows that g assumes all values (if there are any) between $g(a) = f'(a)$ and $g(b) = [f(b) - f(a)]/[b - a]$. Similarly,

$$h(x) = \begin{cases} \dfrac{f(x) - f(b)}{x - b}, & \text{if } x \neq b \\ f'(b), & \text{if } x = b \end{cases}$$

assumes all values between $f'(b)$ and $[f(b) - f(a)]/(b - a)$. (See Fig. 6.2 for geometric interpretation.)

Now $f'(a) < \eta < f'(b)$, by hypothesis, and hence η belongs to the range of at least one of the functions g, h. We assume for definiteness that η belongs to the range of h, that is,

$$\frac{f(b) - f(a)}{b - a} \leq \eta < f'(b). \tag{6.13}$$

[The remaining case can be disposed of in a similar manner.] If the equality holds in (6.13), we need only invoke the mean value theorem of differential calculus to arrive at the existence of a number ξ, $a < \xi < b$ such that $f'(\xi) = [f(b) - f(a)]/(b - a)$ and the proof is complete. So suppose that $\eta \neq [f(b) - f(a)]/[b - a]$. Now h has the intermediate value property and $h(a) = [f(b) - f(a)]/(b - a)$, while $h(b) = f'(b)$; therefore from (6.13) we conclude

$$\exists \alpha, \ a < \alpha < b, \text{ such that } h(\alpha) = \eta. \tag{6.14}$$

But

$$h(\alpha) = \frac{f(\alpha) - f(b)}{\alpha - b} \tag{6.15}$$

and by the mean value theorem, we know that

$$\exists \xi, \ \alpha < \xi < b, \text{ such that } f'(\xi) = \frac{f(\alpha) - f(b)}{\alpha - b}. \tag{6.16}$$

From (6.14), (6.15), and (6.16) we have

$$\exists \xi, \ a < \xi < b, \text{ such that } f'(\xi) = \eta. \quad \blacksquare$$

Example 6.6. The function f defined by

$$f(x) = \begin{cases} x^2 \sin \dfrac{1}{x}, & \text{if } x \neq 0 \\ 0, & \text{if } x = 0 \end{cases}$$

has a derivative f' which is discontinuous at $x = 0$ (see Fig. 6.3).

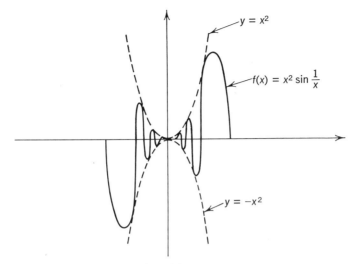

Fig. 6.3 f' is discontinuous at the origin.

First, to show that f is differentiable everywhere, consider two cases: (1) $x \neq 0$, and (2) $x = 0$. If $x \neq 0$, then by the usual rules of elementary calculus, we compute $f'(x) = -\cos(1/x) + 2x \sin(1/x)$. On the other hand, if $x = 0$, we have

$$\lim_{x \to 0} \frac{f(x) - f(0)}{x - 0} = \lim_{x \to 0} \frac{x^2 \sin(1/x)}{x} = \lim_{x \to 0} x \sin \frac{1}{x} = 0;$$

that is, $f'(0) = 0$.

(NOTE: We are careful not to make the error of trying to determine $f'(0)$ by working with the expression $f'(x) = -\cos(1/x) + 2x \sin(1/x)$ and trying to pass to the limit. This is an invalid procedure for it assumes f' is continuous at $x = 0$ (which is precisely what we shall prove to be false). (See, however, Section 6.7, Exercise 1.))

Hence f is differentiable everywhere. But f' is not continuous at $x = 0$, for $\lim_{x \to 0} [-\cos(1/x) + 2x \sin(1/x)]$ does not exist since $\lim_{x \to 0} 2x \sin(1/x) = 0$ and $\lim_{x \to 0} \cos(1/x)$ does not exist. Note that if we solve $\cos(1/x) = -1$, we get $x = 1/(2k + 1)\pi$. It follows that $f'(1/(2k + 1)\pi) = 1$. Since the sequence $x_k = 1/(2k + 1)\pi$ tends to 0 as $k \to \infty$, we see that there exists a sequence $x_k \to 0$ such that $f'(x_k) \equiv 1$. But $f'(0) = 0$, and once again we have proved discontinuity of f' at $x = 0$. It is interesting to interpret this argument geometrically (see the graph in Fig. 6.3). We leave this to the reader.

6.6 THE GENERALIZED MEAN VALUE THEOREM AND TAYLOR'S THEOREM

Let us suppose that the curve shown in Fig. 6.4 is generated by a pair x, y of real-valued functions of the real variable t giving the x, y coordinates, respectively, of a point in the plane as the real variable t runs through the interval $[a, b]$. It may be helpful to interpret t as the "time" and the vector $(x(t), y(t))$ as the position of a particle in the plane at time t. Since the notation $(x(t), y(t))$ is awkward—we have reference to the abundance of parentheses—we shall write simply (xt, yt) and, in general, when there is no confusion likely to result *we shall omit parentheses in function notation, writing xa for x(a), fb for f(b)*, and so forth.

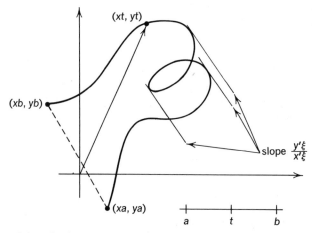

Fig. 6.4 Generalized mean value theorem.

We may think of the position vector (xt, yt) as a *function* of the real variable t. This function is, of course, a collection of ordered pairs

$$S = \{(t, (xt, yt)) \mid a \leq t \leq b\}$$

where the first element t of the ordered pair $(t, (xt, yt))$ is a real number and the second element (xt, yt) is itself an ordered pair or a "two-dimensional vector," as we call it. Note that the condition that S is a function entails the requirement that

$$t_1 = t_2 \Rightarrow (xt_1, yt_1) = (xt_2, yt_2);$$

that is,

$$t_1 = t_2 \Rightarrow xt_1 = xt_2 \quad \text{and} \quad yt_1 = yt_2$$

which is equivalent to requiring that both x and y are functions of t. Examining the curve in Fig. 6.4, it is clear that we could not think of y as a function of x (why?). Thus the "parametric equation" interpretation of the curve is merely a device for bringing the function concept to bear on this situation.

It is not unreasonable to expect that if the functions x, y are "well-behaved," then the slope of the straight line joining the points (xa, ya) and (xb, yb) should equal the slope of the tangent line to the graph at some suitable point. Recalling that the slope of the tangent line to the graph at the point corresponding to t is given by the ratio $y'(t)/x'(t)$, we therefore anticipate a point ξ, $a < \xi < b$, such that

$$\frac{y'(\xi)}{x'(\xi)} = \frac{y(b) - y(a)}{x(b) - x(a)}.$$

In order to allow vanishing of the derivatives, thereby obtaining a more general result, we formulate the following theorem.

■ **Theorem 6.8.** (Generalized Mean Value Theorem.) If x and y are differentiable on the open interval (a, b) and continuous on the closed interval $[a, b]$, then there exists a point ξ, $a < \xi < b$, such that

$$x'(\xi)[y(b) - y(a)] = y'(\xi)[x(b) - x(a)].$$

Proof: For $a \le t \le b$, define

$$f(t) = x(t)[y(b) - y(a)] - y(t)[x(b) - x(a)].$$

Then, by a straightforward calculation, $f(b) - f(a) = 0$ so that $[f(b) - f(a)]/(b - a) = 0$. But f is differentiable on the open interval (a, b) and continuous on the closed interval $[a, b]$, and so we may invoke the mean value theorem to obtain the existence of a point ξ, $a < \xi < b$, such that $f'(\xi) = 0$. But

$$f'(\xi) = x'(\xi)(yb - ya) - y'(\xi)(xb - xa) = 0. \quad ■$$

Example 6.7.   Verify the generalized mean value theorem for the pair x, y of functions where $x(t) = \cos t$, $y(t) = \sin t$, $\pi/2 \le t \le 3\pi/2$.

We seek a point ξ, $\pi/2 < \xi < 3\pi/2$, such that

$$- \sin \xi \, (\sin 3\pi/2 - \sin \pi/2) = \cos \xi \, (\cos 3\pi/2 - \cos \pi/2),$$

that is,

$$(-\sin \xi)(-1 - 1) = (\cos \xi)(0).$$

Obviously, $\xi = \pi$ provides a solution.

We recall that a *polynomial* p in x is a function of the form $p(x) = \sum_{k=0}^{n} a_k x^k$. We speak of a *polynomial over the reals* if the coefficients a_k are real numbers. The class of polynomials is an extremely useful set of functions because of their good behavior; for example, a polynomial in x is integrable, continuous, differentiable, and, as a matter of fact has derivatives of all orders. It is a remarkable fact that if one is given the value of a polynomial together with the values of its derivatives at a single point of its domain, then the value of the polynomial is determined at an arbitrary point of its domain. This is clearly shown by the following formula which is easy to prove (see Section 6.7, Exercise 2):

$$p(x) = p(0) + p'(0)x + \frac{p''(0)}{2!} x^2 + \cdots + \frac{p^n(0)}{n!} x^n. \tag{6.17}$$

(NOTE: This formula relates the values of p and its derivatives at 0 with its value at an arbitrary point x; using the origin 0 is not essential here— an arbitrary point a could be used instead and this would be reflected in the fact that the formula would proceed in powers of $(x - a)$ instead of $(x - 0)$.)

Taylor's formula represents an attempt to obtain a relation analogous to (6.17) for a more general function. Naturally, we shall have to assume derivatives up to and including the nth order if we hope to speak of the nth derivative of the function f. Moreover, since we shall obtain the formula through an application of the generalized mean value theorem, it is not surprising that the hypotheses reflect this fact:

■ **Theorem 6.9.**   (Taylor's Theorem.) If f has continuous derivatives of orders $1, 2, 3, \cdots, n$ on a closed interval $[a, x]$ and if $f^{(n+1)}$ [the superscript denotes the $(n + 1)$th derivative] exists on the open interval (a, x), then there exists a point ξ, $a < \xi < x$, such that

$$f(x) = f(a) + f'(a)(x - a) + \frac{f''(a)}{2!} (x - a)^2 + \cdots + \frac{f^{(n)}(a)}{n!} (x - a)^n$$

$$+ \frac{f^{(n+1)}(\xi)}{(n + 1)!} (x - a)^{n+1}. \tag{6.18}$$

Proof: Consider the function F whose value $F(t)$ at t is defined, for fixed x, by

$$f(x) = f(t) + f'(t)(x - t) + \frac{f''(t)}{2!} (x - t)^2 + \cdots + \frac{f^{(n)}(t)}{n!} (x - t)^n + F(t). \tag{6.19}$$

Applying the generalized mean value theorem to F and G where

$$G(t) = \frac{(x - t)^{n+1}}{(n + 1)!}, \tag{6.20}$$

we conclude that there exists a point ξ, $a < \xi < x$, such that

$$G'(\xi)[F(a) - F(x)] = F'(\xi)[G(a) - G(x)]. \qquad (6.21)$$

We shall prove that (6.21) is nothing more than (6.18) in disguise. To do this, from (6.19) we compute

$$F(x) = 0,$$
$$F(a) = f(x) - f(a) - f'(a)(x - a) - \cdots - f^{(n)}(a)(x - a)^n/n!.$$

By the definition (6.20) of G, we have

$$G(x) = 0,$$
$$G(a) = (x - a)^{n+1}/(n + 1)!.$$

Thus (6.21) may be written

$$G'(\xi)[fx - fa - f'a(x - a) - \cdots - f^{(n)}a(x - a)^n/n!]$$
$$= F'(\xi)(x - a)^{n+1}/(n + 1)!. \quad (6.22)$$

Differentiating (6.19) with respect to t, we have

$$0 = f't - f't + f''t(x - t) - f''t(x - t) + f'''t(x - t)^2/2! - \cdots$$
$$- f^{(n)}t(x - t)^{n-1}/(n - 1)! + f^{(n+1)}t(x - t)^n/n! + F't,$$

and, noting the cancellation of terms in pairs, we conclude that

$$F'(t) = -f^{(n+1)}(t)(x - t)^n/n!. \qquad (6.23)$$

From (6.20) we see that

$$G'(t) = -(x - t)^n/n!. \qquad (6.24)$$

$F'(\xi)$ and $G'(\xi)$ are now obtained from (6.23) and (6.24) and substituted into (6.22). Cancellation of the factor $-(x - \xi)^n/n!$ which appears on both sides of the equality immediately yields the formula (6.18) which we sought. ∎

Example 6.8. Using derivatives of order up to the third, approximate $f(x) = \sin x$ by a polynomial in $x - (\pi/4)$.

We compute $f(\pi/4) = 1/\sqrt{2}$, $f'(\pi/4) = 1/\sqrt{2}$, $f''(\pi/4) = -1/\sqrt{2}$, $f'''(x) = -\cos x$. By Taylor's theorem, $\exists \xi$, $\pi/4 < \xi < x$, such that

$$\sin x = \frac{1}{\sqrt{2}} + \frac{1}{\sqrt{2}}\left(x - \frac{\pi}{4}\right) - \frac{1}{2\sqrt{2}}\left(x - \frac{\pi}{4}\right)^2 - \frac{\cos \xi}{6}\left(x - \frac{\pi}{4}\right)^3.$$

The error committed in using the first three terms in the right member as an approximation to $\sin x$ is estimated from

$$\left|\frac{\cos \xi}{6}\left(x - \frac{\pi}{4}\right)^3\right| \le \frac{1}{6}\left|x - \frac{\pi}{4}\right|^3.$$

Example 6.9. Consider the function f where

$$f(x) = \begin{cases} e^{-1/x^2}, & \text{if } x \ne 0 \\ 0, & \text{if } x = 0. \end{cases}$$

We leave it to the reader to verify that this function has derivatives of all orders at the origin and that they all vanish. Thus if Taylor's theorem is applied to this function, "approximating" $f(x)$ by a polynomial in x, all terms will vanish except the term containing the highest power of x. Hence the "error" in this instance will be the number $f(x)$ being approximated! (See Section 6.7, Exercise 3.)

6.7 EXERCISES

1. Show that if f has a derivative at every point of (a, b) and if $a < \xi < b$ and $\lim_{x \to \xi} f'(x) = m$, then $f'(\xi) = m$.
2. Prove the following formula for polynomials: If $p(x) = \sum_{k=0}^{m} a_k x^k$, then $a_k = p^{(k)}(0)/k!$ where the superscript (k) means kth derivative, $k \neq 0$, and $p^{(0)} = p$.
3. Consider the function defined in Example 6.9. Show that it has derivatives of all orders at the origin and that they all vanish.
4. Show that it is impossible for a function to have a derivative which vanishes at the origin and assumes a constant value $c \neq 0$ elsewhere. (That is, $\nexists f(x) \ni f'(x) = c \neq 0$ for $x \neq 0$ and $f'(0) = 0$).
5. Prove that $(x^n)' = nx^{n-1}$ for all integers n.

   [HINT: (a) If $n = 0$, the function is a constant. Using the definition of derivative, show that the derivative of a constant is 0. (b) For $n \geq 1$, use induction, writing $x^n = xx^{n-1}$. (c) For $n < 0$, write $x^n = 1/x^{-n}$ and use the formula for differentiating a quotient.]

6. Prove that if f is defined on an open interval and if $f' = 0$ everywhere, then f is a constant. [Use the mean value theorem.]
7. Prove that if $f' = g'$ everywhere, then the difference $f - g$ is a constant. [Use the mean value theorem.]
8. In the proof of Theorem 6.7, it was assumed that $[f(b) - f(a)]/(b - a) \leq \eta < f'(b)$. Suppose that $f'(a) < \eta \leq [f(b) - f(a)]/(b - a)$ and complete the proof for this remaining case.
9. Prove one of L'Hospital's rules: If f, g are differentiable on (a, b), continuous on $[a, b]$, $g'(t) \neq 0$ for all $t \in (a, b)$, if $\lim_{t \to a} f'(t)/g'(t)$ exists, and if $f(t) \to 0$, $g(t) \to 0$ as $t \to a$, then $\lim_{t \to a} f'(t)/g'(t) = \lim_{t \to a} f(t)/g(t)$.

   [HINT: $\exists \xi$, $a < \xi < t$, such that
   $$\frac{f(t) - f(a)}{g(t) - g(a)} = \frac{f(t)}{g(t)} = \frac{f'(\xi)}{g'(\xi)}.$$
   (Why?).]

10. Suppose $f'(a) = f''(a) = \cdots = f^{(n)}(a) = 0$, $f^{(n+1)}(a) \neq 0$ and let $f^{(n+1)}$ be continuous at a. Then
    (a) $f(a)$ is a relative maximum if $n + 1$ is even and $f^{(n+1)}(a) < 0$,
    (b) $f(a)$ is a relative minimum if $n + 1$ is even and $f^{(n+1)}(a) > 0$,
    (c) $f(a)$ is neither a relative maximum nor a relative minimum if $n + 1$ is odd.
    (Use Taylor's theorem.)

6.8 CONTRACTION MAPPINGS AND CAUCHY SEQUENCES

Let x be a real number. Then $\cos x$ is a real number and we may therefore talk about $\cos(\cos x)$. Since $\cos(\cos x)$ is a real number, it makes sense to talk about $\cos(\cos(\cos x))$, and so on.

We now raise the following question: For a fixed choice of x, $0 < x < 1$, does the sequence $\cos x$, $\cos(\cos x)$, $\cos(\cos(\cos x))$, $\cdots$ have a limit?

First of all, we shall convince ourselves on geometric grounds that the limit in question does indeed exist. To do this, study Fig. 6.5 where we have

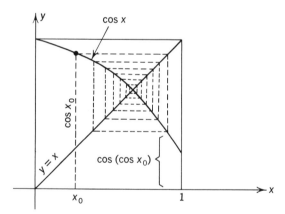

Fig. 6.5   The sequence $\cos x_0$, $\cos(\cos x_0)$, $\cos(\cos(\cos x_0))$, $\cdots$, $0 < x_0 < 1$, converges.

sketched the graphs of $f(x) = \cos x$ and $g(x) = x$. Starting with an arbitrary but fixed x_0 such that $0 < x_0 < 1$, we readily identify the segment of length $\cos x_0$. If we draw the horizontal line $y = \cos x_0$, it intersects $g(x) = x$ in a point whose projection on the x axis has x coordinate $\cos x_0$. (Why?) Now we identify the segment of length $\cos(\cos x_0)$. Continuing this process of invading alternately the graphs of $f(x) = \cos x$ and $g(x) = x$ in the manner described, we obtain a "rectangular spiral" which apparently "settles down" on a point with the property that its x coordinate and its y coordinate are equal [since it lies on the line $g(x) = x$] and, moreover, this limit point obtained has the form $(w, \cos w)$ since it belongs to the graph of $f(x) = \cos x$. We anticipate proving, from these considerations, that the sequence

$$\cos x_0, \cos (\cos x_0), \cos (\cos (\cos x_0)), \cdots \qquad 0 < x_0 < 1$$

has a limit w such that $\cos w = w$.

Our problem now is to show analytically that our geometrically formulated conjecture is correct. To do this, we shall prove a general theorem which can be applied to $f(x) = \cos x$ as a very special case. The key property of a function which enables us to prove the general theorem we have in mind is that of satisfying a *uniform Lipschitz condition*. The definition runs as follows.

Definition 6.3. f satisfies a *uniform Lipschitz condition* on the set S iff $\exists$ a constant M such that

$$u, v \in S \Rightarrow |f(u) - f(v)| \le M|u - v|.$$

(NOTE: This definition should be compared with Definition 6.1 where we spoke of f satisfying a Lipschitz condition *at a point* (also see Section 6.9, Exercise 1).)

It is an easy consequence of this definition that if f satisfies a uniform Lipschitz condition on S, then f is uniformly continuous on S for let $\epsilon > 0$. Put $\delta = \epsilon/M$. Then $|u - v| < \delta$, $u, v \in S \Rightarrow |f(u) - f(v)| \le M|u - v| < M(\epsilon/M) = \epsilon$. Hence f is uniformly continuous on S.

In the statement of the general theorem we are about to prove, we shall use the following notation: Instead of writing $f(x)$, we shall simply write fx; for $f(f(x))$, we write simply f^2x; in general, for the nth *iterate* of $f(x)$, that is, when the "operator" f is applied successively n times, we write f^nx. Observe that in order to guarantee that the iterates $fx, f^2x, f^3x, \cdots$ make sense, we must insist that f *is a function on* $[a, b]$ *whose range is contained in* $[a, b]$. We now introduce the following definition.

Definition 6.4. A function f satisfying the special uniform Lipschitz condition $|fu - fv| \le M|u - v|$ where $0 < M < 1$, is called a *contraction mapping*.

Remark

The reason for calling such a function a contraction mapping is that the distance $|fu - fv|$ between the images fu, fv of u, v is *less* than the distance $|u - v|$; that is, f "contracts distance." As far as we are concerned, *mapping* is another name for *function*.

Definition 6.5. A function f is said to have a *fixed point* w iff $fw = w$.

■ **Theorem 6.10.**   (Contraction mapping theorem.) If f is a contraction mapping of a closed interval $[a, b]$ into $[a, b]$ and if $x_0 \in [a, b]$, then the sequence

$$x_0, fx_0, f^2x_0, f^3x_0, \cdots$$

has a limit w such that $fw = w$. Moreover, the fixed point w is **unique**. In other words: every contraction mapping of $[a, b]$ into $[a, b]$ has a **unique** fixed point.

Proof: Introduce the notation $x_1 = fx_0$, $x_2 = fx_1$, and in general, $x_{n+1} = fx_n$. We shall first prove that under the hypothesis that f is a contraction mapping, the distance $|x_{n+k} - x_n|$ between the $(n + k)$th iterate and the nth iterate of f can be made arbitrarily small by choosing n sufficiently large. Now

$$
\begin{aligned}
|x_{n+k} - x_n| &= |f^{n+k}x_0 - f^nx_0| \quad \text{(by definition of } x_j\text{)}, \\
&\leq M|f^{n+k-1}x_0 - f^{n-1}x_0| \quad \text{(since } f \text{ is a contraction)}, \\
&\leq M^2|f^{n+k-2}x_0 - f^{n-2}x_0| \quad \text{(again } f \text{ is a contraction)}, \\
&\leq M^n|f^kx_0 - x_0| \\
&= M^n|x_k - x_0| \quad \text{(by definition of } x_k\text{)}, \\
&= M^n|x_k - x_{k-1} + x_{k-1} - x_{k-2} + x_{k-2} + \cdots - x_1 + x_1 - x_0| \\
&\leq M^n[|x_k - x_{k-1}| + \cdots + |x_2 - x_1| + |x_1 - x_0|] \\
&\qquad\qquad\qquad\qquad\qquad\qquad\qquad \text{(the triangle inequality)}, \\
&\leq M^n|x_1 - x_0|[1 + M + M^2 + \cdots + M^{k-1}] \\
&\leq M^n|x_1 - x_0| \frac{1}{1 - M}.
\end{aligned}
$$

But $|x_1 - x_0|$ and $1/(1 - M)$ are constants, and since M is a positive number less than 1, the quantity M^n tends to 0 as n tends to infinity. Thus $\lim_{n\to\infty} M^n|x_1 - x_0| \, 1/(1 - M) = 0$ and this implies that for every $\epsilon > 0$, $\exists N$ such that $n > N \Rightarrow |x_{n+k} - x_n| < \epsilon$ for all positive integers k.

This last property of the sequence of iterates is important enough to warrant a definition, so we introduce the following

Definition 6.6.   The sequence $\{x_n\}$ of real numbers is a *Cauchy sequence* (or *fundamental sequence*) iff $\{x_n\}$ satisfies the following condition: for every $\epsilon > 0$, $\exists N \ni n > N \Rightarrow |x_{n+k} - x_n| < \epsilon$ for all positive integers k. This condition is called the *Cauchy condition*.

We shall study Cauchy sequences in detail shortly, but for the present we assume the important result that *every Cauchy sequence has a limit.* This enables us to easily complete the proof of the present theorem for, since the sequence of iterates has been shown to be a Cauchy sequence, it follows that it has a limit (call it w). Now $w \in [a, b]$ since $[a, b]$ is closed; moreover,

$$\begin{aligned} fw &= f(\lim x_n) &&\text{(by definition of } w\text{),}\\ &= \lim fx_n &&\text{(since } f \text{ is continuous),}\\ &= \lim x_{n+1} &&\text{(by definition of } x_{n+1}\text{),}\\ &= w &&\text{(by definition of } w\text{),} \end{aligned}$$

that is, f has a fixed point. We leave the proof of uniqueness of the fixed point to the reader (Section 6.9, Exercise 3). ∎

Now we return to the concept of Cauchy sequence. Roughly speaking, Definition 6.6 says that a Cauchy sequence is a sequence with the property that the distance between pairs of terms can be made arbitrarily small provided the terms are selected beyond a certain place "N" in the sequence. An obviously equivalent version of the definition is to say that the sequence $\{x_n\}$ is *Cauchy* iff

$$\text{for every } \epsilon > 0,\ \exists N \ni n, m > N \Rightarrow |x_n - x_m| < \epsilon. \qquad (6.25)$$

Augustin Cauchy (mid-nineteenth century) called attention to sequences with this property. The reason for the interest in them is that they are precisely the sequences which converge. This is a very remarkable and valuable fact since the criterion for determining whether or not a sequence is Cauchy is intrinsic in the sense that *the test depends only on the terms of the given sequence.* This statement is based solely on the definition of Cauchy sequence for it will be noted that in Definition 6.6 no mention whatever is made of numbers other than the given terms of the sequence; that is, the distance $|x_{n+k} - x_n|$ is uniquely determined when the sequence is given and all one has to do is show that this distance can be made arbitrarily small for n sufficiently large and all positive integers k.

We will now prove that every Cauchy sequence is a convergent sequence (and conversely) so that the test for a Cauchy sequence is also a test for convergence which can be made without the sometimes extremely difficult problem of guessing at what the limit might be (assuming, indeed, that the limit exists).

■ **Theorem 6.11.** (Cauchy condition characterizes convergent sequences.) Let $\{x_n\}$ be a sequence of real numbers.

$$\{x_n\} \text{ is Cauchy} \Leftrightarrow \{x_n\} \text{ converges.}$$

Proof: The implication $\Leftarrow$ is easy to prove. Suppose $\{x_n\}$ converges and let $x = \lim x_n$. Then

$$|x_n - x_m| = |x_n - x + x - x_m| \le |x_n - x| + |x - x_m|. \qquad (6.26)$$

Since $x_n \to x$, if $\epsilon > 0$, there is $N \ni k > N \Rightarrow |x_k - x| < \epsilon/2$. If we choose $n, m > N$, then from (6.26) we see that $|x_n - x_m| < \epsilon$; that is, $\{x_n\}$ is Cauchy.

On the other hand, to show that every Cauchy sequence converges we expect a more difficult problem since we have to show that a limit exists; that is, we shall have to find a candidate for the limit of a given Cauchy sequence. The main tool in accomplishing this is to apply the Bolzano-Weierstrass theorem. To this end, we need the following.

Lemma.   If $\{x_n\}$ is Cauchy, then $\{x_n\}$ is bounded.

Proof: Since $\{x_n\}$ is a Cauchy sequence, if we choose $\epsilon = 1$ we get

$$\exists N \ni n > N \Rightarrow |x_n - x_{n+k}| < 1 \text{ for all } k = 1, 2, 3, \cdots. \qquad (6.27)$$

This says that all the terms of the sequence beginning with x_{N+1} fall within one unit of the point x_{N+1} (see Fig. 6.6). Thus all the terms of the sequence

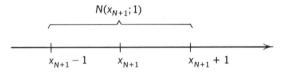

$$N(x_{N+1}; 1)$$

$$x_{N+1} - 1 \qquad x_{N+1} \qquad x_{N+1} + 1$$

Fig. 6.6   Every Cauchy sequence is bounded: $N(x_{N+1}; 1)$ contains all but a finite number of terms of the Cauchy sequence $\{x_n\}$.

except possibly $x_1, x_2, \cdots, x_N$ (a finite number!) are trapped in the interval $[x_{N+1} - 1, x_{N+1} + 1]$. It is clear that if we define

$$M = \max \{|x_1|, |x_2|, \cdots, |x_N|, |x_{N+1} - 1|, |x_{N+1} + 1|\},$$

then we shall have $|x_k| \leq M$ for all $k = 1, 2, 3, \cdots$. This proves the lemma.

We are now ready for the implication in the direction $\Rightarrow$. Our proof proceeds with the consideration of two cases: Either (1) the range of the Cauchy sequence, that is, the *set* $T = \{x_1, x_2, x_3, \cdots\}$, contains only finitely many distinct points, or (2) T has infinitely many distinct points.

In case (1), let the sequence $\{x_n\}$ have the set

$$\{a_1, a_2, \cdots, a_k\} \qquad \text{(all distinct!)}$$

of distinct values. Then compute distances $|a_i - a_j|$ between all distinct pairs $(i \neq j)$ of numbers and define

$$\alpha = \min \{|a_i - a_j|, i \neq j, \quad i, j = 1, 2, \cdots, k\}.$$

Since $\alpha > 0$, we may put $\epsilon = \alpha$ in the definition of Cauchy sequence to get

$$\exists N \ni n > N \Rightarrow |x_n - x_{n+k}| < \alpha, k = 1, 2, \cdots.$$

But from the definition of α, if x_n and x_{n+k} were different numbers, we would have $|x_n - x_{n+k}| \geq \alpha$. It follows that $x_n = x_{n+k}$ for $k = 1, 2, \cdots$. This tells us that the sequence is a constant beginning with x_{N+1} and obviously this constant is the limit of the sequence.

In case (2), the range of the Cauchy sequence is an infinite bounded set (we just invoked the lemma) and by the Bolzano-Weierstrass theorem, this set

$$T = \{x_1, x_2, x_3, \cdots\}$$

has at least one accumulation point (call it x). We now prove that T can have only one point of accumulation. For, suppose y is also an accumulation point of T. If $|x - y| = 0$, we are through; otherwise $|x - y| > 0$. Now set $\epsilon = |x - y|/3$. Then since $\{x_n\}$ is Cauchy,

$$\exists N \ni n, m > N \Rightarrow |x_n - x_m| < \frac{|x - y|}{3}. \tag{6.28}$$

However, in every neighborhood of each of x and y there are infinitely many elements of T since x, y are points of accumulation of T. Hence we can find

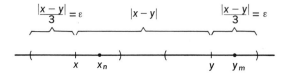

Fig. 6.7   If T is the range of a Cauchy sequence, then either $\overline{T'} = 0$ or $\overline{T'} = 1$.

$n, m > N$ such that $x_n \in N(x; \epsilon)$ and $x_m \in N(y; \epsilon)$ (see Fig. 6.7). But these last conditions:

$$|x_n - x| < \frac{|x - y|}{3} \quad \text{and} \quad |y - x_m| < \frac{|x - y|}{3} \tag{6.29}$$

taken with (6.28) lead to a contradiction since, on the one hand,

$$|x - x_n| + |x_n -- x_m| + |x_m - y| \geq |x - y|$$

(by the triangle inequality), whereas (6.28) and (6.29) imply

$$|x - x_n| + |x_n - x_m| + |x_m - y| < |x - y|.$$

It follows that T has only one point of accumulation x.

Finally, we show that x is the limit of the Cauchy sequence $\{x_n\}$. Let $\epsilon > 0$. Then

$$\exists N \ni n > N \Rightarrow |x_n - x_{n+k}| < \frac{\epsilon}{2}, k = 1, 2, \cdots.$$

But if $n > N$, we have

$$|x_n - x| = |x_n - x_{n+k} + x_{n+k} - x|$$

$$\leq |x_n - x_{n+k}| + |x_{n+k} - x| < \frac{\epsilon}{2} + |x_{n+k} - x| \tag{6.30}$$

for all k. Since x is a point of accumulation of T, every neighborhood of x contains infinitely many terms of T; that is, there is a positive integer k such that $|x_{n+k} - x| < \epsilon/2$. It follows from (6.30) that $|x_n - x| < \epsilon$ for all $n > N$. This completes the proof.   ∎

Now that the proof of the contraction mapping theorem is complete we want to apply it to $f(x) = \cos x$, $0 \leq x \leq 1$. Let $u, v \in [0, 1]$. An application of the mean value theorem yields

$$\cos u - \cos v = (-\sin \xi)(u - v) \qquad u < \xi < v.$$

Now $0 \leq x \leq 1$ implies $|\sin x| \leq \sin 1 < 1$ and therefore

$$|\cos u - \cos v| \leq M|u - v| \qquad \text{where } M = |\sin 1| < 1,$$

proving that f is a contraction mapping. Hence

$$\cos x_0, \cos(\cos x_0), \cos(\cos(\cos x_0)), \cdots, 0 < x_0 < 1,$$

has a limit w with $\cos w = w$.

6.9 EXERCISES

1. Prove the following: If f satisfies a Lipschitz condition at each point of a closed interval $[a, b]$, then f satisfies a uniform Lipschitz condition on $[a, b]$.

   [HINT: Use the same idea that was used to show that a continuous function on a closed interval is uniformly continuous.]
2. Show that every contraction mapping is continuous.
3. Show that the fixed point of a contraction mapping of a closed interval S into S is unique.

   [HINT: Show that $fw = w, fv = v, f$ a contraction mapping $\Rightarrow w = v$.]
4. Prove that $\{x_n\}$ is a Cauchy sequence iff for every $\epsilon > 0$, $\exists N \ni n$, $m > N \Rightarrow |x_n - x_m| < \epsilon$. (See Definition 6.6.)
5. Prove, directly from Definition 6.6, that $x_n = 1/n$ is a Cauchy sequence.
6. Find a necessary and sufficient condition that $f(x) = mx + b$ be a contraction mapping and then find the unique fixed point.
7. The function defined by $f(x) = x^2$, $0 \leq x \leq 1$ has two fixed points on the unit interval. Explain why this is not inconsistent with the contraction mapping theorem.
8. (a) Show that $f(x) = \ln x$, $x \in [e, e^2]$, satisfies a uniform Lipschitz condition with $M < 1$; that is, f is a contraction mapping.
   (b) Does f have a fixed point? Explain.

Supplement to Chapter 6

The formal definition of the derivative of a complex-valued function of a complex variable is the same as for the real case:

$$f'(\xi) = \lim_{z \to \xi} \frac{f(z) - f(\xi)}{z - \xi}$$

where we assume the domain of f contains a neighborhood $N(\xi)$ of ξ. The usual rules of calculus for differentiating sums, differences, products, and quotients are valid. The chain rule for differentiating a composite function is the same. All of these results are proved in the same way as for the real case. The fact that differentiability of f implies continuity of f goes through easily and no change is required in the proof.

In spite of all these similarities, there is a fundamental difference depending on whether the domain of f is complex or real. To see this, suppose $f'(\xi)$ exists where f is a real-valued function of a complex variable. Then, on the one hand, the difference quotient

$$\frac{f(\xi + h) - f(\xi)}{h}$$

will be real if we let h tend to zero through real values and hence $f'(\xi)$ will be real. On the other hand, the difference quotient

$$\frac{f(\xi + ih) - f(\xi)}{ih}$$

will be pure imaginary if we let h tend to zero through real values, and hence $f'(\xi)$ will be a pure imaginary number. Thus $f'(\xi)$ must be zero! In other words, for a real-valued function of a complex variable, either the derivative vanishes or it does not exist.

If we examine the case where f is a complex-valued function of a real variable, then noting that f may be decomposed as follows:

$$f(t) = x(t) + iy(t),$$

where x and y are real-valued functions of the real variable t, we easily see that

$$f'(t) = x'(t) + iy'(t).$$

Thus differentiability of f is equivalent to differentiability of the pair of real functions x, y of the real variable t.

The theory of complex-valued functions of a complex variable is an extensive branch of mathematics devoted to a study of the consequences of differentiability for the structure of a function with this property. We shall not attempt such a program here; our sole purpose is to indicate which concepts and theorems of this chapter can be extended to the complex variable case.

Theorems 6.1 and 6.2 carry over intact to the complex case. The notion of a function satisfying a Lipschitz condition at a point and Theorem 6.3 (stating that differentiability of f at ξ implies this property at ξ) require no modifications. In addition, our definition of the differential and its subsequent characterization given in Section 6.3 carry over intact.

As one would suspect, the Darboux property of a derivative and the generalized mean value theorem of Sections 6.5 and 6.6 cannot be stated for the complex case because of their dependence on the idea of order. However, much stronger consequences of differentiability are proved in complex function theory, so the loss is nil. Moreover, our main application of the generalized mean value theorem was to prove Taylor's theorem and a remarkably more general theorem is available in complex function theory where one assumes simply the existence of f' and arrives at the existence of derivatives of all higher orders!

Finally, all of the concepts and theorems of Section 6.8 are valid without change for the complex case.

7

Integrability

INTRODUCTION

In this chapter we shall be concerned with the class of functions having the property of being "integrable in the Riemann sense." This is a useful and basic class of functions of great importance to more advanced work in analysis. We do not assume that the reader knows something about the theory of such functions; the chapter is essentially self-contained.

The basic definition of integrability which we introduce depends on the notions of *partition* of a closed interval and *refinement of a partition*. It is very likely that the reader who has been exposed to some theory of integrable functions will be familiar with a definition which emphasizes the notions of *partition* and *norm of a partition*. The student is asked to prove the equivalence of our definition and the latter in Exercise 4, Section 7.5. Several other characterizations of the concept of integrability will be found in this chapter. In particular, we find in Section 7.4 that "Riemann's condition" is a necessary and sufficient condition for integrability; in Exercise 3, Section 7.5, we outline a proof that integrable functions are those whose lower and upper "Darboux integrals" exist and are equal; finally, our most elegant characterization of this class of functions will be found in Section 7.6 as "Lebesgue's criterion for Riemann integrability." This last theorem tells us that the Riemann integrable functions are precisely those which are bounded and "continuous almost everywhere." We hasten to add, although we hope that it represents a redundancy, that the phrase "continuous almost everywhere" will be assigned a very precise meaning.

7.1 DEFINITION OF INTEGRABILITY

Since there are several notions of integrability in use today, we begin with a formal definition of the concept which we plan to study. It is the concept of integrability in the sense of B. Riemann (late-nineteenth-century mathematician), and is perhaps the simplest instance of integration of any consequence. Although our definition is not the one used by Riemann, it is equivalent to it. First, we need the preliminary notion of a *partition* of an interval of real numbers.

Definition 7.1. Consider the closed interval $[a, b]$ of real numbers. By a *partition* P of $[a, b]$ (see Fig. 7.1) is meant any finite collection $\{x_0, x_1,$

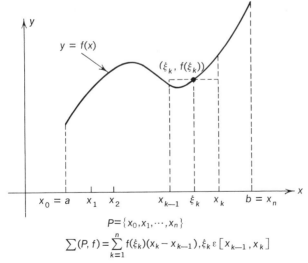

$$P = \{x_0, x_1, \cdots, x_n\}$$

$$\sum(P, f) = \sum_{k=1}^{n} f(\xi_k)(x_k - x_{k-1}), \xi_k \,\varepsilon\, [x_{k-1}, x_k]$$

Fig. 7.1 Partition P and approximate sum $\Sigma(P, f)$.

$\cdots, x_n\}$ of distinct points of $[a, b]$, including the endpoints a, b. For convenience, let us suppose that the points of P have been ordered:

$$a = x_0 < x_1 < x_2 < \cdots < x_{n-1} < x_n = b.$$

Hereafter, in speaking of a partition P, it will be understood that

$$P = \{x_0, x_1, \cdots, x_n\}$$

with the x_k's ordered as indicated above. If P, Q are partitions of $[a, b]$, then we say that P is a *refinement* of Q iff $P \supset Q$ (in the set-theoretic sense).

If f is a real-valued function, $f(x) \geq 0$, $\forall x \in [a, b]$, and if P is a partition of $[a, b]$, we can approximate the "area under the curve f" (see Fig. 7.1) by choosing a point ξ_k in each closed interval $[x_{k-1}, x_k]$ and using the area $f(\xi_k)(x_k - x_{k-1})$ of the rectangle of altitude $f(\xi_k)$ and base $x_k - x_{k-1}$ as the approximate contribution to the "area under the curve" insofar as the subinterval $[x_{k-1}, x_k]$ is concerned. To simplify notation, we put $\Delta x_k = x_k - x_{k-1}$. Thus, having been given f and P, and having selected the points $\xi_k \in [x_{k-1}, x_k]$, $k = 1, 2, \cdots, n$, we use the number

$$\sum (P, f) = \sum_{k=1}^{n} f(\xi_k) \, \Delta x_k$$

to approximate the area under the curve. Strictly speaking, since the number $\sum (P, f)$ is a function of the ξ_k's as well as P and f, we should write $\sum (P, f, \xi_1, \xi_2, \cdots, \xi_n)$ instead of the simpler $\sum (P, f)$. However, the inaccuracy of the latter notation is offset by its simplicity. Occasionally we use $\sum (P, f)$ to denote the *set* of all numbers corresponding to all possible choices of $\xi_1, \xi_2, \cdots, \xi_n$. When this is done, it will be clear from the context. In order to emphasize that the phrase "area under the curve" used above is really meaningless at this point and is only an appeal to intuition, let us formalize our discussion. In what follows we do *not* assume $f(x) \geq 0$, $\forall x \in [a, b]$.

Definition 7.2.   Let f be defined on $[a, b]$ and let $P = \{x_0, x_1, \cdots, x_n\}$ be a partition of $[a, b]$. If $\xi_k \in [x_{k-1}, x_k]$, $k = 1, 2, \cdots, n$, we define

$$\sum (P, f) = \sum_{k=1}^{n} f(\xi_k) \, \Delta x_k$$

where $\Delta x_k = x_k - x_{k-1}$.

Example 7.1.   Let $f(x) = x^2$ on $[0, 1]$. Let $P = \{0, \frac{1}{4}, \frac{1}{2}, 1\}$ and let $\xi_1 = \frac{1}{8}$, $\xi_2 = \frac{3}{8}$, $\xi_3 = \frac{3}{4}$. Then

$$\sum (P, f) = (\tfrac{1}{4})f(\tfrac{1}{8}) + (\tfrac{1}{4})f(\tfrac{3}{8}) + (\tfrac{1}{2})f(\tfrac{3}{4})$$

$$= \tfrac{1}{256} + \tfrac{9}{256} + \tfrac{9}{32} = \tfrac{82}{256} = \tfrac{41}{128}.$$

If we keep P but choose ξ_k to be the left endpoint of the interval $[x_{k-1}, x_k]$, that is,

$$\xi_1 = 0, \xi_2 = \tfrac{1}{4}, \xi_3 = \tfrac{1}{2},$$

then we get

$$\sum (P,f) = f(0)(\tfrac{1}{4}) + f(\tfrac{1}{4})(\tfrac{1}{2} - \tfrac{1}{4}) + f(\tfrac{1}{2})(1 - \tfrac{1}{2})$$
$$= 0 + (\tfrac{1}{16})(\tfrac{1}{4}) + (\tfrac{1}{4})(\tfrac{1}{2}) = \tfrac{9}{64}.$$

Thus in our present example, the set $\{\sum (P, f)\}$ would contain the numbers $\tfrac{41}{128}$, $\tfrac{9}{64}$, among others.

We are now ready for the definition of integrability. Roughly speaking, we want to single out those functions with the property that further refinement of an "already fine" partition P does not "appreciably alter" the set $\sum (P,f)$ of numbers. Here is the precise meaning.

Definition 7.3.   Let f be a real-valued function defined on $[a, b]$. We say that f is *integrable over* $[a, b]$ (in the Riemann sense) iff there exists a number, denoted by $\int_a^b f(x)\, dx$ and called the *integral* of f over $[a, b]$, such that for every $\epsilon > 0$, there is a partition P_ϵ (P_ϵ depends generally on ϵ) such that

$$P \supset P_\epsilon \Rightarrow \left| \sum (P,f) - \int_a^b f(x)\, dx \right| < \epsilon$$

where it is understood that the inequality is to hold when an arbitrary number belonging to the set $\{\sum (P, f)\}$ of numbers is substituted for $\sum (P,f)$.

Remark 1
   This definition is equivalent to the one usually given in elementary calculus texts (see Section 7.5, Exercise 4).

Remark 2
   Note that if $P_\epsilon = P' \cup P''$ and if $P \supset P_\epsilon$, then P is a refinement of both P' and P'': $P \supset P'$ and $P \supset P''$. This simple fact is resorted to frequently in subsequent arguments.

Remark 3
   When the integral $\int_a^b f(x)\, dx$ exists, it is unique for we have a number A such that

$$\left| \sum (P,f) - A \right| < \tfrac{\epsilon}{2} \text{ for all } P \supset P',$$

and suppose there exists B such that

$$\left| \sum (P,f) - B \right| < \frac{\epsilon}{2} \text{ for all } P \supset P''.$$

If we define $P_\epsilon = P' \cup P''$ and take any partition $P \supset P_\epsilon$, we get (for a fixed choice of $\xi_1, \xi_2, \cdots, \xi_n$ associated with partition P)

$$|A - B| = \left| A - \sum (P,f) + \sum (P,f) - B \right|$$
$$\leq \left| A - \sum (P,f) \right| + \left| \sum (P,f) - B \right| < \epsilon.$$

This proves that $A = B$; that is, the integral is unique.

It is easy to show that a necessary condition for (Riemann) integrability of the function f is boundedness of f. In other words, if f is integrable, then f is bounded. We prove the contrapositive:

■ **Theorem 7.1.** If f is not bounded on $[a, b]$, then f is not integrable on $[a, b]$.

Proof: We first make an observation. Let P be any partition of $[a, b]$. If f were bounded on each subinterval $[x_{k-1}, x_k]$ of $[a, b]$ determined by P, then f would certainly be bounded on $[a, b]$ itself for suppose

$$|f(x)| \leq M_k \text{ for } x \in [x_{k-1}, x_k], k = 1, 2, \cdots, n.$$

(This says that f is bounded on each subinterval of P.) Put

$$M = \max \{M_1, M_2, \cdots, M_n\}.$$

Then if $x \in [a, b]$, it follows that $x \in [x_{k-1}, x_k]$ for some $k = 1, 2, \cdots, n$ and hence $|f(x)| \leq M_k \leq M$; that is, f is bounded on $[a, b]$.

Now we show that the unbounded function f is not integrable. *f is not integrable over $[a, b]$* means that if A is any real number whatever, there exists an $\epsilon > 0$ (depending generally on A) such that no matter what partition P is given, there is a partition $P' \supset P$ and a choice of ξ_k's for which $|\sum (P',f) - A| \geq \epsilon$. Let $\epsilon = 1$, and let A be any real number. We claim that if P is any partition, we can choose ξ_k so that

$$\left| \sum_{k=1}^{n} f(\xi_k) \Delta x_k - A \right| \geq 1. \tag{7.1}$$

To see this, we first observe that f is unbounded on some interval, say $[x_{m-1}, x_m]$, determined by P. We suppose all the ξ's fixed except ξ_m. Now $\sum (P,f)$ can be decomposed as follows:

$$\sum (P,f) = \sum{}' f(\xi_k) \Delta x_k + f(\xi_m) \Delta x_m$$

where we use $\sum'$ to denote that the term with $k = m$ is omitted. With this notation the left member of (7.1) can be written

$$\left| f(\xi_m) \Delta x_m - A + \sum{}' \right|.$$

But $-A + \sum'$ is a fixed number (call it $-B$), and by the triangle inequality, $[|c - d| + |d| \geq |(c - d) + d| = |c|$; that is, $|c - d| \geq |c| - |d|]$, we have

$$|f(\xi_m) \Delta x_m - B| \geq |f(\xi_m) \Delta x_m| - |B|.$$

To make this last expression ≥ 1, we simply choose ξ_m so that

$$|f(\xi_m)| \geq \frac{1 + |B|}{|\Delta x_m|},$$

and it is possible to do this since f is unbounded on $[x_{m-1}, x_m]$. To complete the proof, we note that $P \supset P$ and $\exists \sum (P, f) \ni |\sum (P, f) - A| \geq 1$. ∎

7.2 LINEARITY OF THE INTEGRAL

In this section we assume that the interval $[a, b]$ is fixed and consider the integral $\int_a^b f(x)\,dx$ to be a function of f; that is, we want to study the dependence of the integral on the *integrand* f. Accordingly, we define

$$I(f) = \int_a^b f(x)\,dx,$$

emphasizing that f is to vary while a, b are fixed.

Example 7.2.

If $f(x) = x^2$, we have $I(x^2) = \int_a^b x^2\,dx = (b^3 - a^3)/3$.

If $f(x) = \sin x$, we have $I(\sin x) = \int_a^b \sin x\,dx = \cos a - \cos b$.

The reader has no doubt used the facts that "the integral of a sum is the sum of the integrals" and "the integral of a constant times a function is the constant times the integral of the function." (The derivative has analogous properties.) As a matter of fact, these properties occur so frequently that it is worthwhile to introduce the following.

Definition 7.4. If $L(f)$ is a real-valued function of the **function** f, then we call L a (real) *functional*. The functional L is a *linear functional* iff

(1) $L(f + g) = L(f) + L(g)$ (*L* is *additive*),

and

(2) $L(cf) = cL(f)$, where c is an arbitrary real number   (*L* is *homogeneous*).

Stated in the language of functionals, two familiar properties of an integral are embodied in the following theorem.

■ **Theorem 7.2.** $I(f) = \int_a^b f(x)\,dx$ is a linear functional.

Proof: We first show $I(f + g) = I(f) + I(g)$. By this statement we mean specifically that if f and g are integrable, then so is their sum and the above equality holds.

Since f is integrable, we have a number $I(f)$ such that for every $\epsilon > 0$, there is a partition P'_ϵ such that

$$P \supset P'_\epsilon \Rightarrow \left| \sum (P,f) - I(f) \right| < \frac{\epsilon}{2}. \tag{7.2}$$

Similarly, since g is integrable, corresponding to the same $\epsilon > 0$, we have a partition P''_ϵ such that

$$P \supset P''_\epsilon \Rightarrow \left| \sum (P,g) - I(g) \right| < \frac{\epsilon}{2}. \tag{7.3}$$

Consider the partition $P_\epsilon = P'_\epsilon \cup P''_\epsilon$. We claim that it is the partition we seek to prove the integrability of the sum $f + g$ for if $P \supset P_\epsilon$, then both implications in (7.2) and (7.3) yield for any choice of ξ_k compatible with P

$$\left| \sum (P, f + g) - [I(f) + I(g)] \right| = \left| \sum (P,f) + \sum (P,g) - I(f) - I(g) \right|$$
$$\leq \left| \sum (P,f) - I(f) \right| + \left| \sum (P,g) - I(g) \right|$$
$$< \epsilon.$$

This proves that the integral $I(f + g)$ of $f + g$ exists and is equal to $I(f) + I(g)$. This statement is, of course, nothing more than the familiar formula:

$$\int_a^b [f(x) + g(x)]\,dx = \int_a^b f(x)\,dx + \int_a^b g(x)\,dx.$$

It remains to show that if c is a real number and if $I(f)$ exists, then $I(cf)$ exists and we have

$$I(cf) = cI(f).$$

Here is the proof:

$$\left| \sum (P, cf) - cI(f) \right| = \left| c \sum (P,f) - cI(f) \right|$$

(write down the definition of $\sum (P, cf)$ to see this)

$$= |c| \left| \sum (P,f) - I(f) \right|.$$

The rest is clear since c is a constant; details are left to the reader.   ■

7.3 EXERCISES

1. Consider the set of all functions differentiable at the fixed point ξ. Let $L(f)$ be the functional defined on this set by associating with each function f the number $f'(\xi)$. Show that L is a linear functional.

2. Consider the set S of all convergent sequences of real numbers. Let $\{x_n\} \in S$. Define $L(\{x_n\}) = \lim x_n$. Show that L is a linear functional.

3. Consider the set S of all real-valued functions f which are continuous at a fixed point ξ. Let $L(f) = f(\xi)$. Is L a linear functional? Drop the requirement of continuity in the definition above, insisting only that ξ belong to the domain of f. Is the resulting functional a linear functional?

4. Let f be a function of a real variable. Define $L(f)(x) = xf(x)$. Note that L associates with each function f another function defined by $xf(x)$. In general, we say that $L(f)$ is a *linear operator* if L associates with each function f of a certain class another function $L(f)$ in such a way that $L(f + g) = L(f) + L(g)$ and $L(cf) = cL(f)$ where c is an arbitrary real number.

   (a) Is $L(f)(x) = xf(x)$ a linear operator?

   (b) Let a_k, $k = 0, 1, \cdots, n$ be real numbers; let D^n, n a positive integer, denote the operator $D^n(f) = d^n f/dx^n$. Write
   $$L = a_n D^n + a_{n-1} D^{n-1} + \cdots + a_1 D + a_0$$
   and define $L(f) = a_n d^n f/dx^n + a_{n-1} d^{n-1} f/dx^{n-1} + \cdots + a_1 \, df/dx + a_0 f$. Show that $L(f)$ is a linear operator.

   (c) Let L and M be two linear operators. Define a new operator N by the rule, "carry out the operation L first, then M," and write $ML = N$. Thus with L defined as in (a) above and with $M = D$, we have $ML \sin x = M(x \sin x) = x \cos x + \sin x$. Does $ML = LM$?

   (d) Consider $L = x^2 D^2 - \sin x \, D + 3x$. When L operates on $\sin x$, for example, we get
   $$L(\sin x) = x^2 D^2 \sin x - \sin x \, D \sin x + 3x \sin x$$
   $$= -x^2 \sin x - \sin x \cos x + 3x \sin x.$$
   Show that this operator L is a linear operator.

   (e) In (b) above, the a_k's were real numbers. Suppose they are functions of x and again $L = a_n D^n + \cdots + a_1 D + a_0$. Is the resulting operator a linear operator?

5. Assuming the integral $\int_a^b x \, dx$ exists, compute its value as follows:

   (a) Set up the sum $\Sigma (P, x)$ where P is the partition of $[a, b]$ obtained by dividing $[a, b]$ into n equal parts and using the areas of the inscribed rectangles as an approximation to the area "under the curve $y = x$."

(b) Pass to the limit as n tends to infinity.

6. Carry out the same procedure as in Exercise 6 for the function $f(x) = x^2$ on the interval $[a, b]$. You will need the formula

$$1^2 + 2^2 + 3^2 + \cdots + (n-1)^2 = n(n-1)(2n-1)/6$$

which can be verified by induction.

7. Consider the set $\mathcal{P} = \{P \mid P \text{ is a partition of } [a, b]\}$. Define the relation $S = \{(P, Q) \mid P, Q \in \mathcal{P}, P \text{ is a refinement of } Q\}$. Show that S is reflexive and transitive, but not symmetric.

7.4 RIEMANN'S CONDITION

As usual, let f have $[a, b]$ as its domain and let $P = \{a = x_0, x_1, x_2, \cdots, x_n = b\}$ be a partition of $[a, b]$. For each choice of numbers ξ_k, $x_{k-1} \leq \xi_k \leq x_k$, $k = 1, 2, \cdots, n$, the sum

$$\sum (P, f) = \sum_{k=1}^{n} f(\xi_k) \, \Delta x_k$$

is uniquely determined. We have pointed out that $|f(\xi_k) \, \Delta x_k|$ may be looked upon as the area of a rectangle with altitude $|f(\xi_k)|$ and base Δx_k. We now analyze the effect of singling out certain "altitudes for the approximating

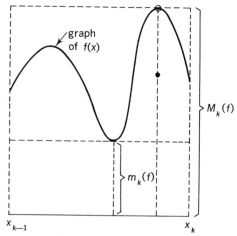

Fig. 7.2 The supremum $M_k(f)$ and infimum $m_k(f)$ of f on the interval $[x_{k-1}, x_k]$.

rectangles." There are two natural selections to look into. Let us focus our attention on the subinterval $[x_{k-1}, x_k]$ of the partition P (see Fig. 7.2). Consider the set of numbers $f(\xi)$ obtained when ξ varies over $[x_{k-1}, x_k]$; that is, consider the image of $[x_{k-1}, x_k]$ under f. We assume that f is bounded since we have already proved that if f is unbounded, then there is no hope for integrability of f (Theorem 7.1). It follows that the subset $\{f(\xi) \mid x_{k-1} \leq \xi \leq x_k\}$ is bounded above. Being a bounded set of real numbers, this set has a least upper bound or supremum. If we use this number as the altitude for the approximating rectangle and Δx_k as its base, we get a "circumscribed" rectangle as indicated in Fig. 7.2. Similarly, we are also interested in the infimum of the image of $[x_{k-1}, x_k]$ under f; here we get an "inscribed" approximating rectangle. In Fig. 7.2 we have illustrated the situation where $f \geq 0$. Note that if $f \leq 0$ on the interval in question, then the terms "circumscribed" and "inscribed" must be interchanged. With these intuitive considerations in mind, we lay down the following definition, abandoning all geometry.

Definition 7.5. $M_k(f) = \sup \{f(\xi) \mid x_{k-1} \leq \xi \leq x_k\}$
and
$$m_k(f) = \inf \{f(\xi) \mid x_{k-1} \leq \xi \leq x_k\}.$$

We call the corresponding sums taken over the partition P the *upper sum*

$$U(P, f) = \sum_{k=1}^{n} M_k(f) \, \Delta x_k,$$

and the *lower sum*

$$L(P, f) = \sum_{k=1}^{n} m_k(f) \, \Delta x_k,$$

respectively. The difference

$$\Omega_k(f) = M_k(f) - m_k(f)$$

is called the *oscillation* of f on $[x_{k-1}, x_k]$. These concepts assume f to be bounded.

Observe that if f happens to be continuous, M_k and m_k will be the maximum and minimum, respectively, of f on the closed interval $x_{k-1} \leq \xi \leq x_k$. But we do not want to pay the price in loss of generality for making such a stringent assumption and so the best we can do with f assumed only to be bounded is to speak of the sup and inf (see Theorem 5.2). Our point is this: $M_k(f)$ [or $m_k(f)$] is not necessarily the *value* of f at any point of the interval $[x_{k-1}, x_k]$. On the other hand, even though $M_k(f)$ may not be a value of f at some point of $[x_{k-1}, x_k]$, there are values of f arbitrarily close to $M_k(f)$. (Why?)

Here are a few interesting and useful results concerning upper and lower sums:

Since $m_k(f) \leq f(\xi_k) \leq M_k(f)$ for all $\xi_k \in [x_{k-1}, x_k]$, if we sum on $k = 1, 2, \cdots, n$, we have the following

Property 1: $L(P,f) \leq \sum (P,f) \leq U(P,f)$ (7.4)

for all P and every number in the set $\{\sum (P, f)\}$.

To determine what effect refining a partition has on the upper and lower sums, we let $P' \supset P$. We suppose the subinterval $[x_{k-1}, x_k]$ to have endpoints belonging to P and insert one additional point x, $x_{k-1} < x < x_k$ so that all three points x_{k-1}, x, x_k, are consecutive points of P' (see Fig. 7.3). It is clear

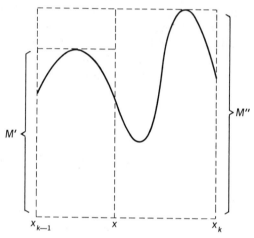

Fig. 7.3   An upper sum does not increase when the partition is refined.

that if M' and M'' denote the suprema of f on the intervals $[x_{k-1}, x]$ and $[x, x_k]$, respectively, while M_k denotes the supremum of f on the *entire* interval $[x_{k-1}, x_k]$, then

$$M' \leq M_k \quad \text{and} \quad M'' \leq M_k$$

which, in turn, imply

$$M'(x - x_{k-1}) \leq M_k(x - x_{k-1}) \quad \text{and} \quad M''(x_k - x) \leq M_k(x_k - x).$$

Adding, we get

$$M'(x - x_{k-1}) + M''(x_k - x) \leq M_k(x_k - x_{k-1}).$$

Finally, summing on $k = 1, 2, \cdots, n$, we obtain

$$U(P',f) \leq U(P,f).$$

This proves the following.

Property 2: $P' \supset P \Rightarrow U(P',f) \leq U(P,f).$ (7.5)

In words: Upper sums do not increase when the partition is refined. Analogous reasoning will establish the next property.

Property 3: $P' \supset P \Rightarrow L(P',f) \geq L(P,f).$ (7.6)

Finally, to compare arbitrary lower and upper sums, let P_1, P_2 be any two partitions and put $P = P_1 \cup P_2$. Then we have Property 4.

Property 4: $L(P_1,f) \leq L(P,f) \leq U(P,f) \leq U(P_2,f).$ (7.7)
          by (7.6)   by (7.4)   by (7.5)

This tells us that a lower sum is always dominated by (that is, is not greater than) an upper sum, regardless of the partitions involved.

It does not take much imagination to visualize the difference $U(P,f) - L(P,f)$ in approximating sums as the sum of the areas of certain "residual rectangles." That is to say,

$$U(P,f) - L(P,f) = \sum_{k=1}^{n} M_k(f)\,\Delta x_k - \sum_{k=1}^{n} m_k(f)\,\Delta x_k$$

$$= \sum_{k=1}^{n} [M_k(f) - m_k(f)]\,\Delta x_k \geq 0$$

can be interpreted as the sum of the areas of rectangles with altitude $M_k(f) - m_k(f)$ and base Δx_k. Note that in view of the definition of oscillation $\Omega_k(f)$ of f on $[x_{k-1}, x_k]$, we may write $U(P,f) - L(P,f) = \sum_{k=1}^{n} \Omega_k(f)\,\Delta x_k$. For a "decent" function we should expect the difference $U(P,f) - L(P,f)$ to tend to 0 as the partition P becomes finer and finer. There are, however, some "indecent" functions. An example follows.

Example 7.3.   (The Dirichlet function.)
   For $0 \leq x \leq 1$, let

$$f(x) = \begin{cases} 0, & \text{if } x \text{ is irrational,} \\ 1, & \text{if } x \text{ is rational.} \end{cases}$$

If P is any partition of $[0, 1]$, it is clear that $M_k(f) = 1$, $m_k(f) = 0$ for all $k = 1, 2, \cdots, n$. Hence $U(P,f) = 1$ and $L(P,f) = 0$ for all partitions P. Also, the oscillation of f on $[x_{k-1}, x_k]$ is 1; that is, $\Omega_k(f) = 1$. Thus $U(P,f) - L(P,f) = 1$, $\forall$ partitions P.

In order to exclude functions of this kind, let us agree to say that f *satisfies Riemann's condition* iff for every $\epsilon > 0$, there is a partition P_ϵ such that

$$P \supset P_\epsilon \Rightarrow U(P,f) - L(P,f) < \epsilon.$$

Now suppose that $U(P,f) - L(P,f) < \epsilon$ for some partition $P \supset P_\epsilon$. Recall that under refinement of P, $U(P,f)$ does not increase and $L(P,f)$ does not decrease. Hence we see that

$$P' \supset P \Rightarrow U(P',f) - L(P',f) \le U(P,f) - L(P,f) < \epsilon.$$

In other words, the inequality $U(P,f) - L(P,f) < \epsilon$ is preserved if P is replaced by a refinement of P. We therefore use the (apparently) simpler but equivalent condition as

Definition 7.6. f *satisfies Riemann's condition* iff

$$\forall \epsilon > 0, \exists P_\epsilon \ni U(P_\epsilon,f) - L(P_\epsilon,f) < \epsilon.$$

We now show that integrable functions, and only these, satisfy Riemann's condition. In order to do this, we shall need the fact that every upper sum can be approximated arbitrarily closely by an ordinary sum $\sum (P,f)$ (see Definition 7.2). This is the content of the lemma below.

Lemma. If $U(P,f)$ is an upper sum for f corresponding to the partition P, and if $\epsilon > 0$, then there exist $\xi_1, \xi_2, \cdots, \xi_n$ such that the corresponding sum $\sum (P,f)$ has the property $|\sum (P,f) - U(P,f)| < \epsilon$.

Proof: Let $\epsilon > 0$ be given and let P be any partition of $[a, b]$. Since $M_k(f) = \sup \{f(\xi) \mid \xi \in [x_{k-1}, x_k]\}$, there exists ξ_k such that

$$f(\xi_k) > M_k(f) - \frac{\epsilon}{b-a}, \qquad k = 1, 2, \cdots, n. \tag{7.8}$$

[A property of the supremum of a set (Theorem 2.9) was invoked.] Multiplying both members of (7.8) by Δx_k and summing on k, we obtain

$$\sum (P,f) > U(P,f) - \epsilon.$$

Since $U(P,f) \ge \sum (P,f)$ for all P, it follows that

$$-\epsilon < 0 \le U(P,f) - \sum (P,f) < \epsilon;$$

in other words,
$$\left| U(P,f) - \sum (P,f) \right| < \epsilon. \quad \blacksquare$$

We leave it to the reader to prove the dual statement for lower sums:

$$\left| L(P,f) - \sum{}^* (P,f) \right| < \epsilon.$$

(NOTE: The choice of ξ_k's will be different from above. This is the reason we denoted the corresponding sum by $\sum^* (P,f)$.)

We are now ready to prove the following theorem.

■ Theorem 7.3. f is integrable $\Leftrightarrow f$ satisfies Riemann's condition.

Proof: We first show integrability implies Riemann's condition. Let $\epsilon > 0$ be given. By hypothesis, $\exists P_\epsilon$ such that

$$P \supset P_\epsilon \Rightarrow \left| \sum (P,f) - A \right| < \frac{\epsilon}{4} \qquad (7.9)$$

where $A = \int_a^b f(x)\, dx$. According to the lemma (and its dual), there exist numbers $\sum (P,f)$ and $\sum^* (P,f)$ such that

$$\left| U(P,f) - \sum (P,f) \right| < \frac{\epsilon}{4} \quad \text{and} \quad \left| L(P,f) - \sum^* (P,f) \right| < \frac{\epsilon}{4}.$$

Using this, the triangle inequality, and (7.9),

$$\begin{aligned}
|U(P,f) - L(P,f)| &= \Big| U(P,f) - \sum (P,f) + \sum (P,f) - A + A \\
&\qquad - \sum^* (P,f) + \sum^* (P,f) - L(P,f) \Big| \\
&\leq \left| U(P,f) - \sum (P,f) \right| + \left| \sum (P,f) - A \right| \\
&\qquad + \left| A - \sum^* (P,f) \right| + \left| \sum^* (P,f) - L(P,f) \right| < \epsilon.
\end{aligned}$$

This proves the first part.

We now prove Riemann's condition implies integrability. We are given that for every $\epsilon > 0$, there exists a partition P_ϵ such that

$$P \supset P_\epsilon \Rightarrow 0 \leq U(P,f) - L(P,f) < \epsilon. \qquad (7.10)$$

If P_1 and P_2 are arbitrary partitions, we have according to (7.7)

$$L(P_1,f) \leq U(P_2,f). \qquad (7.11)$$

If we fix P_2 and allow P_1 to vary over all partitions, this inequality asserts that the set $L(P,f)$ has an upper bound, namely, $U(P_2,f)$. Therefore $L(P,f)$ has a supremum. Put

$$A = \sup \{ L(P,f) \mid P \text{ a partition of } [a, b] \}. \qquad (7.12)$$

Moreover, if we allow both P_1 and P_2 to vary in (7.11), we see that every upper sum $U(P_2,f)$ is an upper bound of the set of lower sums $L(P_1,f)$, so

$$A \leq U(P,f) \text{ for all } P. \qquad (7.13)$$

Collecting these inequalities, we have from (7.10), (7.12), (7.13), and (7.4):

$$(a) \ 0 \leq U(P,f) - L(P,f) < \epsilon$$

$$(b) \ L(P,f) \leq A \leq U(P,f)$$

$$(c) \ L(P,f) \leq \sum (P,f) \leq U(P,f).$$

Since (a) holds for all $P \supset P_\epsilon$, while (b) and (c) are valid for all partitions, if we rewrite (c) as

$$- U(P,f) \leq - \sum (P,f) \leq - L(P,f)$$

and add (b) to it, then invoke (a), we get

$$- \epsilon < L(P,f) - U(P,f) \leq A - \sum (P,f) \leq U(P,f) - L(P,f) < \epsilon.$$

With this, we have proved that for every $\epsilon > 0$, $\exists P_\epsilon \ni$

$$P \supset P_\epsilon \Rightarrow \left| A - \sum (P,f) \right| < \epsilon;$$

that is, f is integrable. The equivalence proof is now complete. ∎

7.5 EXERCISES

1. Prove that if $L(P,f)$ is a lower sum for f corresponding to the partition P and if $\epsilon > 0$, then there exist $\xi_1, \xi_2, \cdots, \xi_n$ such that the corresponding sum $\sum^* (P,f)$ has the property:

$$\left| \sum{}^* (P,f) - L(P,f) \right| < \epsilon.$$

2. Using the Dirichlet function f (see Example 7.3), find a partition P of $[0, 1]$, a corresponding sum $\sum (P,f)$ and a positive number ϵ such that $|L(P,f) - \sum (P,f)| \geq \epsilon$. (Note that the statement in Exercise 1 is valid for an arbitrary function; that is, "every lower sum can be approximated arbitrarily closely by an ordinary sum." The present example shows, however, that there are functions such that an ordinary sum may not be approximated by the corresponding lower sum.)

3. (a) Property 2 of upper sums asserts that upper sums do not increase when the partition is refined; that is,

$$P' \supset P \Rightarrow U(P',f) \leq U(P,f).$$

This suggests considering the *infimum* of the upper sums, which we call the *upper Darboux integral of f* [denoted by $\overline{\int_a^b} f(x)\, dx$]. Thus

$$\overline{\int_a^b} f(x)\, dx = \inf \, \{U(P, f) \,|\, P \text{ is an arbitrary partition of } [a, b]\}.$$

Prove that if f is an arbitrary bounded function, then $\overline{\int_a^b} f(x)\, dx$ exists.

(b) Similarly, Property 3 asserts that lower sums do not decrease when the partition is refined. We define the *lower Darboux integral of f* by

$$\underline{\int_a^b} f(x)\, dx = \sup \, \{L(P, f) \,|\, P \text{ is an arbitrary partition of } [a, b]\}.$$

Prove that if f is an arbitrary bounded function, then the lower Darboux integral of f exists.

(c) Prove that $\underline{\int_a^b} f(x)\, dx \leq \overline{\int_a^b} f(x)\, dx$.

(d) Show that f is integrable $\Leftrightarrow \underline{\int_a^b} f(x)\, dx = \overline{\int_a^b} f(x)\, dx$, and when the upper and lower integrals are equal, their common value is $\int_a^b f(x)\, dx$.

[HINT: To prove the implication $\Rightarrow$, assume that Riemann's condition holds (this is equivalent to assuming that f is integrable). Then for $\epsilon > 0, \exists P_\epsilon \ni$

$$P \supset P_\epsilon \Rightarrow U(P,f) < L(P,f) + \epsilon.$$

It follows that

$$P \supset P_\epsilon \Rightarrow \overline{\int_a^b} f(x)\, dx \leq U(P,f) < L(P,f) + \epsilon \leq \underline{\int_a^b} f(x)\, dx + \epsilon;$$

that is, $\overline{\int_a^b} f(x)\, dx \leq \underline{\int_a^b} f(x)\, dx$. In view of part (c) above, we then have $\underline{\int_a^b} f(x)\, dx = \overline{\int_a^b} f(x)\, dx$.

To prove the opposite implication $\Leftarrow$, let $\epsilon > 0$. We know $\exists P_\epsilon' \ni$

$$P \supset P_\epsilon' \Rightarrow U(P,f) < \overline{\int_a^b} f(x)\, dx + \epsilon. \quad \text{(Why?)}$$

Also, $\exists P_\epsilon'' \ni$

$$P \supset P_\epsilon'' \Rightarrow \underline{\int_a^b} f(x)\, dx - \epsilon < L(P,f).$$

Hence

$$P \supset P_\epsilon' \cup P_\epsilon'' \Rightarrow \underline{\int_a^b} f(x)\, dx - \epsilon < L(P,f) \leq \sum(P,f)$$

$$\leq U(P,f) < \overline{\int_a^b} f(x)\, dx + \epsilon.$$

But $\underline{\int_a^b} f(x)\, dx = \overline{\int_a^b} f(x)\, dx$, by hypothesis. Hence $\int_a^b f(x)\, dx$ exists and equals the common value of the upper and lower Darboux integrals.]

4. Let P be a partition of $[a, b]$. Define the *norm* $\|P\|$ *of* P by

$$\|P\| = \max\{|x_k - x_{k-1}|, k = 1, 2, \cdots, n\}.$$

Let f be defined on $[a, b]$. Show that the following condition (*) is equivalent to Riemann integrability (Definition 7.3):
(*) $\exists$ a number A such that

$$\forall \epsilon > 0, \exists \delta > 0 \ni \|P\| < \delta \Rightarrow \left|\sum(P,f) - A\right| < \epsilon.$$

[HINT: Consider the two conditions:

(1) $\epsilon > 0, \exists P_\epsilon \ni P \supset P_\epsilon \Rightarrow U(P,f) - L(P,f) < \dfrac{\epsilon}{3}.$

(2) $\epsilon > 0, \exists \delta > 0 \ni \|P'\| < \delta \Rightarrow U(P',f) - L(P',f) < \epsilon.$

To show $(2) \Rightarrow (1)$ is easy. The difficulty lies in proving $(1) \Rightarrow (2)$. Let $\epsilon > 0$. Then $P_\epsilon = \{x_0, x_1, \cdots, x_N\}$ is determined. Define

$$\delta = \min\left\{\frac{\epsilon}{3(N+1)(M-m)}, \min_k \Delta x_k\right\}$$

where $N + 1 = $ number of points in P_ϵ, $M = \sup f \neq m = \inf f$, and

$\Delta x_k = x_k - x_{k-1}$ with $x_k \in P_\epsilon$, $x_{k-1} \in P_\epsilon$. Let $P' = \{x'_0, x'_1, \cdots, x'_n\}$ be any partition with $\|P'\| < \delta$. Consider $[x'_{k-1}, x'_k]$. Either (1) $[x'_{k-1}, x'_k] \subset$ some subinterval of P_ϵ, or (2) it is not. In case (1), writing $M_k f$, $m_k f$ for $M_k(f)$, $m_k(f)$, respectively,

$$(M'_k f - m'_k f)\, \Delta x'_k \le (M_j f - m_j f)\, \Delta x_j \text{ for some } j = 1, 2, \cdots N.$$

In case (2),

$$\exists \text{ unique } x_j \in P_\epsilon \ni x'_{k-1} < x_j < x'_k$$

so that

$$(M'_k f - m'_k f)\, \Delta x'_k \le (M - m)\delta.$$

Hence

$$\sum_{k=1}^{n} (M'_k - m'_k)\, \Delta x'_k \le U(P_\epsilon, f) - L(P_\epsilon, f) + (M - m)\delta(N + 1)$$

$$\le \frac{\epsilon}{3} + (M - m)(N + 1)\frac{\epsilon}{3(M - m)(N + 1)} < \epsilon.]$$

7.6   LEBESGUE'S CRITERION FOR RIEMANN INTEGRABILITY

With the tools at our disposal it is not difficult to prove that continuity is a sufficient condition for (Riemann) integrability.

■ **Theorem 7.4.**   Every continuous function on a closed interval is integrable.

Proof: Let f be continuous on $[a, b]$. By Theorem 5.1, f is uniformly continuous on $[a, b]$. Therefore, for every $\epsilon > 0$, there is a $\delta > 0$ such that

$$|x - y| < \delta \Rightarrow |f(x) - f(y)| < \frac{\epsilon}{b - a}. \tag{7.14}$$

Our goal is to use this fact to show that f satisfies Riemann's condition and hence is integrable. To do this, we consider any partition P such that $\Delta x_k < \delta$ for all $k = 1, 2, \cdots, n$. We have

$$U(P, f) - L(P, f) = \sum_{k=1}^{n} [M_k(f) - m_k(f)]\, \Delta x_k. \tag{7.15}$$

Since f is continuous, f assumes a maximum and a minimum on each closed subinterval of the partition P; that is, for each $k = 1, 2, \cdots, n$, there exist points $x_k^*, y_k^* \in [x_{k-1}, x_k]$ such that $f(x_k^*) = M_k(f)$ and $f(y_k^*) = m_k(f)$. But $|x_k^* - y_k^*| < \delta$ and hence by (7.14)

$$|f(x_k^*) - f(y_k^*)| = |M_k(f) - m_k(f)| = M_k(f) - m_k(f) < \frac{\epsilon}{b - a}. \tag{7.16}$$

Substituting (7.16) into (7.15), we get

$$U(P,f) - L(P,f) < \sum_{k=1}^{n} \frac{\epsilon}{b-a} \Delta x_k = \frac{\epsilon}{b-a} \sum_{k=1}^{n} \Delta x_k = \epsilon,$$

proving the theorem. ∎

Although continuity is a sufficient condition for integrability, it is by no means necessary, as we shall see shortly.

In the early part of the present century, the mathematician Henri Lebesgue developed a more general theory of integration than the theory we are now discussing. One of the by-products of that theory was an elegant result now referred to as Lebesgue's criterion for Riemann integrability. To motivate this result, we first observe that a function can be discontinuous at a point and still be integrable.

Example 7.4. The function (see Fig. 7.4) defined by

$$f(x) = \begin{cases} 1, & \text{if } 0 \le x \le 1 \\ 0, & \text{if } 1 < x \le 2, \end{cases}$$

in spite of its discontinuity at $x = 1$, is integrable and $\int_0^2 f(x)\, dx = 1$.

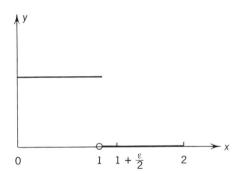

Fig. 7.4   In spite of its discontinuity at 1, the function whose graph is shown is integrable.

Let $\epsilon > 0$. Consider any partition P of $[0, 2]$ which contains the points 1 and $1 + \epsilon/2$. It is easy to verify that $U(P,f) - L(P,f) < \epsilon$, and consequently f satisfies Riemann's condition and is integrable.

On the other hand, if f is highly discontinuous, then it may fail to be integrable as shown by the following example.

Example 7.5. If f is the Dirichlet function (see Example 7.3), then f is discontinuous everywhere and f is not integrable.

Let r be any rational number, $0 \leq r \leq 1$. Then there is a sequence $x_n \to r$, with x_n irrational, $n = 1, 2, \cdots$. Since $f(x_n) = 0$ for all n, and $f(r) = 1$, $f(x_n)$ does not converge to $f(r)$. Hence f is discontinuous at every rational $r \in [0, 1]$. Analogously, f is discontinuous at every irrational. Hence f is discontinuous at every point of its domain.

To see that f is not integrable, review Example 7.3 and apply Theorem 7.3.

The last two examples suggest that we search for a compromise between the two extremes of continuity everywhere and discontinuity everywhere— that we seek a property which will imply integrability and be implied by it. Such is the Lebesgue criterion and it rests upon the concept of "continuity except on a set of measure zero" or "continuity almost everywhere." To be precise, we introduce the following.

Definition 7.7. Let S be a set of real numbers. S *has measure zero* iff for every $\epsilon > 0$, there is a sequence $\{I_n\}$ of open intervals such that

$$(1) \quad \bigcup_{n=1}^{\infty} I_n \supset S$$

and

$$(2) \quad \sum_{n=1}^{\infty} l(I_n) \leq \epsilon$$

where $l(I) = b - a$ denotes the length of the interval $I = (a, b)$. [This definition can be paraphrased: "S has measure zero if and only if S can be covered by open intervals of arbitrarily small total length."]

If a property holds except for the points of a set having measure zero, then we say that the property holds *almost everywhere*.

Some easy consequences of this definition follow.

Example 7.6. If S is finite, then S has measure zero.

Let $S = \{a_1, a_2, \cdots, a_n\}$ and let $\epsilon > 0$ be given. Intuitively, we think of drawing a segment of length ϵ and dividing it into n equal parts (Fig. 7.5).

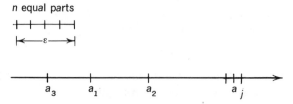

Fig. 7.5   A finite set of real numbers has measure zero.

We take the jth part and place it so that a_j is at its center. The n intervals determined in this way will have the required properties. Formally, we consider the collection of n neighborhoods:

$$N\left(a_k; \frac{\epsilon}{2n}\right), \, k = 1, 2, \cdots, n.$$

It is easy to see that

$$(1) \quad \bigcup_{k=1}^{n} N\left(a_k; \frac{\epsilon}{2n}\right) \supset \{a_1, a_2, \cdots, a_n\},$$

and since each neighborhood is merely an open interval of length ϵ/n,

$$(2) \quad \sum_{k=1}^{n} l\left(N\left(a_k; \frac{\epsilon}{2n}\right)\right) = \epsilon \leq \epsilon.$$

Example 7.7. Every denumerable set S has measure zero.

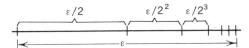

Fig. 7.6   A denumerable set of real numbers has measure zero.

Let $\epsilon > 0$ be given. Divide an interval of length ϵ (Fig. 7.6) into subintervals of lengths

$$\frac{\epsilon}{2}, \frac{\epsilon}{2^2}, \frac{\epsilon}{2^3}, \cdots, \frac{\epsilon}{2^n}, \cdots.$$

Since S is denumerable, we can write

$$S = \{a_1, a_2, \cdots, a_n, \cdots\}.$$

Use the interval of length $\epsilon/2^n$ to cover the point a_n. Details are left to the reader. (Note that as a special case of this result, the set of all rational numbers has measure zero.)

Example 7.8. If S_k has measure zero, $k = 1, 2, \cdots$, then $S = \bigcup_{k=1}^{\infty} S_k$ has measure zero.

Let $\epsilon > 0$ be given. Now $\epsilon/2^k$ is also a positive number, and since S_k has measure zero, $\exists$ intervals $I_k^1, I_k^2, \cdots, I_k^j, \cdots$, such that

$$\bigcup_{j=1}^{\infty} I_k^j \supset S_k$$

and

$$\sum_{j=1}^{\infty} l(I_k^j) \leq \epsilon/2^k.$$

This last statement is valid for every positive integer k. It follows that

$$\bigcup_{k=1}^{\infty} \bigcup_{j=1}^{\infty} I_k^j \supset \bigcup_{k=1}^{\infty} S_k = S$$

and

$$\sum_{k=1}^{\infty} \sum_{j=1}^{\infty} l(I_k^j) = \sum_{k=1}^{\infty} \frac{\epsilon}{2^k} = \epsilon \le \epsilon.$$

Hence the union of a denumerable number of sets of measure zero is itself of measure zero.

———————

There is an equivalent definition of measure zero which is useful. In Definition 7.7, we required that the covering intervals be open. It is obvious that if we have such open intervals satisfying conditions (1) and (2) for a set S, then we may replace them by *closed* intervals (by simply adjoining endpoints) without disturbing (1) and (2). On the other hand, suppose that S has the property that for every $\epsilon > 0$, we can find *closed* intervals satisfying (1) and (2). Now we can replace these by *disjoint* closed intervals leaving (1) and (2) intact (in case two closed intervals overlap, substitute, for them, their union). But there are at most a *denumerable* number of disjoint closed intervals (deleting the endpoints of the closed intervals, we look at the resulting disjoint open intervals and invoke Theorem 4.3). But the denumerable set of endpoints of these disjoint closed intervals can be enclosed in open intervals of arbitrarily small total length (see Example 7.7). This proves

■ **Theorem 7.5.** S has measure zero $\Leftrightarrow$ for every $\epsilon > 0$, there is a sequence $\{I_n\}$ of closed intervals such that

$$(1) \quad \bigcup_{n=1}^{\infty} I_n \supset S$$

and

$$(2) \quad \sum_{n=1}^{\infty} l(I_n) \le \epsilon$$

where $l(I) = b - a$ for $I = [a, b]$.

We are now in a position to state Lebesgue's criterion. It asserts that the bounded function f is Riemann integrable iff f is continuous except on a set having measure zero.

In order to make further progress toward proving this statement, we shall have to take a close look at what it means to say that a function f is discontinuous at a point ξ of its domain. Of course, this means $\lim_{x \to \xi} f(x) \ne f(\xi)$. In detail, f is *discontinuous at* ξ iff $\exists \epsilon > 0 \ni$ if δ is an arbitrary positive number, then $\exists x$ with $|x - \xi| < \delta \ni |f(x) - f(\xi)| \ge \epsilon$. In the language of neighborhoods of ξ, we can say f is discontinuous at ξ iff $\exists \epsilon > 0 \ni$ if $N(\xi; \delta)$ is an arbitrary neighborhood of ξ, then $\exists x \in N(\xi; \delta) \ni |f(x) - f(\xi)| \geq \epsilon$.

It is essential that we develop a convenient way to detect whether a given bounded function f is discontinuous at a given point ξ. To this end, consider any neighborhood $N(\xi; r)$ of ξ. We can associate with this neighborhood the real number

$$\Omega(f; N(\xi; r)) = \sup \{f(x) - f(y) \mid x, y \in N(\xi; r)\};$$

we call $\Omega(f; N)$ the *oscillation of f on N* (see Definition 7.5). Now consider the sequence of neighborhoods of ξ with radii tending to 0 (see Fig. 7.7):

$$N(\xi; 1), N\left(\xi; \frac{1}{2}\right), \cdots, N\left(\xi; \frac{1}{n}\right), \cdots \tag{7.17}$$

together with the corresponding sequence of oscillations

$$\Omega(f; N(\xi; 1)), \Omega\left(f; N\left(\xi; \frac{1}{2}\right)\right), \cdots, \Omega\left(f; N\left(\xi; \frac{1}{n}\right)\right), \cdots. \tag{7.18}$$

Since the sequence of sets in (7.17) is decreasing, that is,

$$N(\xi; 1) \supset N\left(\xi; \frac{1}{2}\right) \supset \cdots,$$

the sequence (7.18) of real numbers is monotonic nonincreasing. (This follows from the fact that $A \supset B$ implies $\sup A \geq \sup B$.) Moreover, the sequence

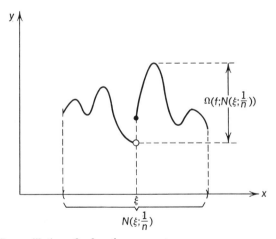

Fig. 7.7   The oscillation of a function on a set.

(7.18) is bounded below since $\Omega(f; N) \geq 0$ for all neighborhoods N. It follows that the sequence (7.18) has a limit (see Theorem 3.6). This paves the way to the following definition.

Definition 7.8. Let f be a bounded function. The *oscillation* $\omega(f; \xi)$ *of f at the point ξ* is defined by

$$\omega(f; \xi) = \lim_{n \to \infty} \Omega\left(f; N\left(\xi; \frac{1}{n}\right)\right)$$

where $\Omega(f; N(\xi; 1/n)) = \sup \{f(x) - f(y) \mid x, y \in N(\xi; 1/n)\}$ is the *oscillation of f on N*.

Example 7.9. Let f be defined by (see Fig. 7.8)

$$f(x) = \begin{cases} 1, & \text{if } 0 \leq x < 1 \\ 2, & \text{if } 1 \leq x \leq 2 \\ -1, & \text{if } 2 < x \leq 3. \end{cases}$$

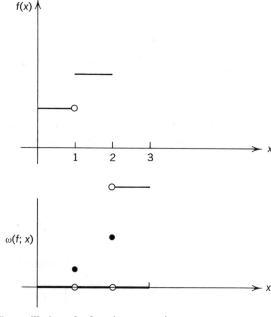

Fig. 7.8   The oscillation of a function at a point.

The oscillation function ω is then given by

$$\omega(f; x) = \begin{cases} 1, & \text{if } x = 1, \\ 3, & \text{if } x = 2, \\ 0, & \text{if } x \neq 1, 2. \end{cases}$$

Note how $\omega(f; x)$ "picks out" the points of discontinuity of f; that is, $\omega(f; x) \neq 0$ iff f is discontinuous at x. This is no coincidence, as we now prove.

■ **Theorem 7.6.** f is discontinuous at $\xi \Leftrightarrow \omega(f; \xi) > 0$.

Proof: By definition, f is discontinuous at ξ iff $\exists \epsilon > 0 \ni |f(x) - f(\xi)| \geq \epsilon$ for some x in each neighborhood $N(\xi; \delta)$. Now both $f(x) - f(\xi)$ and $f(\xi) - f(x)$ enter in the determination of $\Omega(f; N(\xi; \delta))$, hence so does $|f(x) - f(\xi)|$. Thus f is discontinuous at ξ iff $\exists \epsilon > 0 \ni \Omega(f; N(\xi; \delta)) = \sup \{f(x) - f(y) \mid x, y \in N\} \geq \epsilon$ for all δ. It follows that $\omega(f; \xi) = \lim_{n \to \infty} \Omega(f; N(\xi; 1/n)) \geq \epsilon$ iff f is discontinuous at ξ.   ∎

We are now in a position to prove Lebesgue's theorem.

■ **Theorem 7.7.**   (Lebesgue's criterion for Riemann integrability.) Let f be a bounded function on $[a, b]$. f is integrable $\Leftrightarrow f$ is continuous almost everywhere.

Proof: We first show f integrable $\Rightarrow f$ continuous almost everywhere.

Let ξ be a point of discontinuity of f. Then $\omega(\xi)$, the oscillation of f at ξ, is a positive number (Theorem 7.6). Therefore, there is some positive integer m such that $\omega(\xi) > 1/m$. Fix m. Consider the set E_m of all points of $[a, b]$ with the property of ξ; that is, put

$$E_m = \{x \mid \omega(x) > 1/m\}. \tag{7.19}$$

We will prove that E_m has measure zero. Let $\epsilon > 0$ and let P be a partition of $[a, b]$ such that

$$\sum_{k=1}^{n} \Omega_k(x_k - x_{k-1}) < \frac{\epsilon}{m} \tag{7.20}$$

where we have put $\Omega_k = M_k(f) - m_k(f)$. (Riemann's condition guarantees the existence of such a partition.) If $x \in E_m$, then x belongs to one of the subintervals of P. Consider only those terms $\Omega_k(x_k - x_{k-1})$ in the sum (7.20) such that $[x_{k-1}, x_k]$ contains points of E_m; denote their sum by $\sum' \Omega_k(x_k - x_{k-1})$. Since *every* term of the left member of (7.20) is ≥ 0, it follows that

$$\sum' \Omega_k(x_k - x_{k-1}) \leq \sum_{k=1}^{n} \Omega_k(x_k - x_{k-1}) < \frac{\epsilon}{m}. \tag{7.21}$$

The factor Ω_k in each term in $\sum'$ satisfies the inequality

$$\Omega_k \geq \omega(x) > \frac{1}{m} \tag{7.22}$$

where $x \in E_m$. Using (7.22) in (7.21), we conclude that

$$\left(\frac{1}{m}\right) \sum' (x_k - x_{k-1}) = \sum' \left(\frac{1}{m}\right)(x_k - x_{k-1}) < \frac{\epsilon}{m}. \tag{7.23}$$

But the subintervals involved in $\sum'$ contain all points of E_m and (7.23) tells us that the sum $\sum' (x_k - x_{k-1})$ of their lengths is less than ϵ. This means that E_m has measure zero.

If D_f denotes the set of all points of discontinuity of f, then

$$D_f = \{x \mid \omega(x) > 0\} = \bigcup_{m=1}^{\infty} E_m.$$

But E_m, $m = 1, 2, \cdots$ has measure 0, hence D_f has measure 0 (Example 7.8). This proves half the theorem.

To complete the proof, we have left to show that f bounded and continuous almost everywhere $\Rightarrow f$ integrable. Let $\epsilon > 0$. All we need do is show that f satisfies Riemann's condition, that is, find a partition P_ϵ such that $U(P_\epsilon, f) - L(P_\epsilon, f) < \epsilon$. Let $M = \sup f$, $m = \inf f$ on $[a, b]$. Since the set D_f of points of discontinuity of f has measure 0, we know that there is a sequence $\{I_n\}$ of open intervals with $\bigcup_{n=1}^{\infty} I_n \supset D_f$ such that $\sum_{n=1}^{\infty} l(I_n) < \epsilon/2(M - m)$. In addition, each point x of continuity of f is contained in a neighborhood $N(x; r)$ of x such that the oscillation of f on $N(x; r) < \epsilon/2(b - a)$. Replace each $N(x; r)$ by $N(x; r/2)$; note that the oscillation of f on $N(x; r/2)$ still satisfies the inequality $\Omega(f; N(x; r/2)) < \epsilon/2(b - a)$ and, moreover, the oscillation of f on the closed interval obtained by adjoining the endpoints of $N(x; r/2)$ to $N(x; r/2)$ also satisfies this inequality. Each point of $[a, b]$ is either a point of continuity or discontinuity of f and therefore belongs to an $N(x; r/2)$ or an I_n. The collection of I_n's and $N(x; r/2)$'s forms an open cover of $[a, b]$, and hence by the Heine-Borel theorem, a finite subcover exists. Consider the partition P_ϵ consisting of the endpoints of all intervals of this subcover. We claim that P_ϵ is the partition sought. For, form the corresponding sum $\sum_{k=1}^{n} \Omega_k(x_k - x_{k-1})$. Each open interval (x_{k-1}, x_k) is contained in some I_n or some $N(x; r/2)$. In the former case, the corresponding sum $\sum'$ of terms satisfies

$$\sum' \Omega_k(x_k - x_{k-1}) \le \sum' (M - m)(x_k - x_{k-1}) < (M - m) \frac{\epsilon}{2(M - m)} = \frac{\epsilon}{2}$$

while in the latter case the corresponding sum $\sum''$ satisfies

$$\sum'' \Omega_k(x_k - x_{k-1}) < \sum'' \frac{\epsilon}{2(b - a)} (x_k - x_{k-1}) \le \frac{\epsilon}{2(b - a)} (b - a) = \frac{\epsilon}{2}.$$

Consequently

$$\sum_{k=1}^{n} \Omega_k(x_k - x_{k-1}) < \epsilon,$$

that is, $U(P_\epsilon, f) - L(P_\epsilon, f) < \epsilon$ and the proof is complete. ∎

This theorem of Lebesgue is a very powerful result. Many of the consequences of Riemann integrability may be easily deduced from it. The key to its application consists in noting that it tells us that the class of Riemann integrable functions is precisely the class of functions which are bounded and continuous almost everywhere. Thus the question of whether or not a function f is Riemann integrable may be replaced by the question as to whether or not f is bounded and continuous almost everywhere.

Let R denote the set of Riemann integrable functions on the interval $[a, b]$ and write $f \in R$ iff f is Riemann integrable on $[a, b]$. If D_f denotes the set of points of discontinuity of f, and if $mD_f = 0$ denotes the statement that D_f has measure zero, then Lebesgue's theorem may be written in the concise form:

$$f \in R \Leftrightarrow mD_f = 0 \text{ and } f \text{ bounded.}$$

To illustrate an application of the theorem, suppose that $f \in R$ and we want to know if $|f| \in R$. This is the same as being told that f is bounded and continuous almost everywhere, and raising the question as to whether these properties are inherited by $|f|$. Clearly, boundedness of f implies boundedness of $|f|$. By the triangle inequality, we know that

$$\big|\, |f(x)| - |f(\xi)|\, \big| \le |f(x) - f(\xi)|$$

and consequently,

$$f \text{ continuous at } \xi \Rightarrow |f| \text{ continuous at } \xi.$$

This is equivalent to

$$|f| \text{ discontinuous at } \xi \Rightarrow f \text{ discontinuous at } \xi,$$

that is,

$$D_{|f|} \subset D_f.$$

But $mD_f = 0$, by hypothesis, and since every subset of a set of measure zero is itself of measure zero, it follows that $mD_{|f|} = 0$. Thus $|f| \in R$.

7.7 EXERCISES

1. Show that the function of Example 7.4 is integrable.
2. Complete details in the proof that every denumerable set has measure zero (see Example 7.7).
3. Prove that if $E_m = \{x \mid \omega(x) > 1/m\}$ and if $D_f = \{x \mid \omega(x) > 0\}$, then $D_f = \bigcup_{m=1}^{\infty} E_m$.
4. (a) Show that the set $S = \{x \mid 0 < x < 1\}$ is not a set having measure zero.
   (b) Show that the set $S = \{x \mid 0 < x < 1, x \text{ irrational}\}$ is not a set having measure zero.
5. Prove that if $A \subset B$, then $\Omega(f; A) \le \Omega(f; B)$. [Assume domain of $f \supset B$.]

6. Prove that the function

$$f(x) = \begin{cases} x \sin \dfrac{1}{x}, & \text{if } 0 < x \le 1 \\ 0, & \text{if } x = 0 \end{cases}$$

is integrable on $[0, 1]$.

7. (a) Prove that if f and g are integrable on $[a, b]$, and if $f(x) \le g(x)$ for all $x \in [a, b]$, then $\int_a^b f(x)\, dx \le \int_a^b g(x)\, dx$.

[HINT: Consider $h(x) = g(x) - f(x) \ge 0$. Show that $\int_a^b h(x)\, dx \ge 0$ and then use linearity of the integral.]

(b) If f is integrable on $[a, b]$ and if $m \le f(x) \le M$ for all $x \in [a, b]$, then $m(b - a) \le \int_a^b f(x)\, dx \le M(b - a)$. Moreover, if f is continuous on $[a, b]$, then $\exists \xi$, $a \le \xi \le b$, such that $\int_a^b f(x)\, dx = f(\xi)(b - a)$ (mean value theorem of integral calculus). Prove these statements.

8. If f and g are integrable on $[a, b]$, show that the product fg is integrable on $[a, b]$.

[HINT: Use Lebesgue's criterion.]

9. What conditions on f and g will insure integrability of the quotient f/g?

[HINT: Consider g bounded away from zero; that is, suppose $\exists k > 0$ such that $|g| \ge k$.]

10. Prove that if f is integrable on $[a, b]$, then so is $|f|$ and

$$\left| \int_a^b f(x)\, dx \right| \le \int_a^b |f(x)|\, dx.$$

[HINT: In the text we prove that Lebesgue's criterion implies integrability of $|f|$, having been given that f is integrable. Now appeal to Exercise 7(a).]

11. (a) Prove that if f is continuous on $[a, b]$, then $F(x) = \int_a^x f(t)\, dt$ is differentiable on $[a, b]$ and $F'(x) = f(x)$.

[HINT: Show that $F(x) - F(\eta) = \int_\eta^x f(t)\, dt$. Now apply Exercise 7(b) to the interval $[\eta, x]$.]

(b) Prove the *fundamental theorem of calculus:*

If f is integrable on $[a, b]$ and if F is differentiable on $[a, b]$ with $F' = f$, then

$$\int_a^b f(x)\, dx = F(b) - F(a).$$

12. Write a detailed analytic proof of Theorem 7.5.
13. (a) Show that no matter how $f(x) = x^{-1/2}$ is defined at $x = 0$, $\int_0^1 x^{-1/2}\,dx$ does not exist.

(b) Show that if $0 < h < 1$, $\int_h^1 x^{-1/2}\,dx$ exists and find its value using Exercise 11(b).

(c) Show that $\lim_{h \to 0^+} \int_h^1 x^{-1/2}\,dx$ exists. This is an *improper Riemann integral*. Compare with (a).

14. Show that if f is integrable on $[a, b]$ and if $[c, d] \subset [a, b]$, then f is integrable on $[c, d]$.

[HINT: Appeal to Lebesgue's theorem.]

Supplement to Chapter 7

The most immediate generalization of the (real) Riemann integral is to a complex-valued function defined on the real interval $a \leq t \leq b$. This can be accomplished by noting that a complex-valued function $f(t)$ can be decomposed into its real and imaginary parts:

$$f(t) = u(t) + iv(t). \tag{7.24}$$

Imitating Definition 7.3, we have

Definition 7.9. *f is integrable on $[a, b]$* iff there exists a complex number, denoted by $\int_a^b f(t)\,dt$ and called the *integral of f on $[a, b]$*, such that for every $\epsilon > 0$, there is a partition P_ϵ such that

$$P \supset P_\epsilon \Rightarrow \left| \sum (P, f) - \int_a^b f(t)\,dt \right| < \epsilon, \tag{7.25}$$

where $\sum (P, f)$ may be replaced by any number of the form $\sum_{k=1}^n f(\xi_k)\,\Delta t_k$ in which
$$P = \{t_0, t_1, \cdots, t_n\}, a = t_0 < t_1 < \cdots < t_n = b,$$
$$\xi_k \in [t_{k-1}, t_k], \Delta t_k = t_k - t_{k-1}.$$

In view of (7.24), we may write

$$\sum (P, f) = \sum_{k=1}^n u(\xi_k)\,\Delta t_k + i \sum_{k=1}^n v(\xi_k)\,\Delta t_k.$$

Thus if we put $\int_a^b f(t)\,dt = \alpha + \beta i$, condition (7.25) becomes

$$P \supset P_\epsilon \Rightarrow \left| \left(\sum_{k=1}^n u(\xi_k)\,\Delta t_k - \alpha \right) + i \left(\sum_{k=1}^n v(\xi_k)\,\Delta t_k - \beta \right) \right| < \epsilon.$$

But $|x + iy| < \epsilon$ implies both $|x| \leq |x + iy| < \epsilon$ and $|y| \leq |x + iy| < \epsilon$; conversely, $|x| < \epsilon/2$ and $|y| < \epsilon/2$ imply $|x + iy| \leq |x| + |y| < \epsilon/2 + \epsilon/2 = \epsilon$. We therefore arrive at Theorem 7.8.

■ **Theorem 7.8.** $\int_a^b [u(t) + iv(t)]\, dt$ exists iff $\int_a^b u(t)\, dt$ and $\int_a^b v(t)\, dt$ exist. Moreover, $\int_a^b [u(t) + iv(t)]\, dt = \int_a^b u(t)\, dt + i \int_a^b v(t)\, dt$.

This result states that a complex-valued function of a real variable is integrable if and only if its real and imaginary parts are integrable. In effect, it reduces the theory of the integral of a complex-valued function of a real variable to the case of a real-valued function of a real variable. In particular, uniqueness of the integral (when it exists) and necessity of boundedness of f for integrability of f follow immediately.

We leave it to the reader to prove the linearity of the integral: If f, g are complex-valued functions of the real variable t, $a \leq t \leq b$, if γ is any complex number, and if the integrals of f, g on $[a, b]$ exist, then the integrals $\int_a^b [f(t) + g(t)]\, dt$ and $\int_a^b \gamma f(t)\, dt$ exist and we have

$$(1) \quad \int_a^b [f(t) + g(t)]\, dt = \int_a^b f(t)\, dt + \int_a^b g(t)\, dt$$

and

$$(2) \qquad \int_a^b \gamma f(t)\, dt = \gamma \int_a^b f(t)\, dt.$$

Taking Theorem 7.8 into account, we conclude that the characterizations (see Introduction to Chapter 7) of integrable functions proved in Chapter 7 carry over intact to the complex function of a real variable case.

A further and more useful generalization can be obtained as follows. In our discussion above the interval $[a, b]$ may be considered to be the image of $[a, b]$ under the function z defined by

$$z(t) = x(t) + iy(t)$$

where $x(t) = t$ and $y(t) = 0$ for $a \leq t \leq b$. This is a special case of the situation where

$$z(t) = x(t) + iy(t)$$

is an arbitrary differentiable function of t on the interval $a \leq t \leq b$. In general, the image of $[a, b]$ under $z(t)$ will be a curve Γ in the plane; that is,

$$\Gamma = \{z(t) \mid a \leq t \leq b\}.$$

If f is defined on Γ, we may raise the question as to the existence of the *line integral* defined by

$$\int_\Gamma f(z)\, dz = \int_a^b f(z(t))z'(t)\, dt.$$

Since the integral on the right has an integrand $f(z(t))z'(t)$ which is a complex-valued function of a real variable t, we again encounter the situation of Theorem 7.8. Once again the characterizations of integrable functions found in Chapter 7 are valid.

7.8 EXERCISES

1. Show that $f(z) = u(z) + iv(z)$, where u and v are real, is bounded iff u and v are bounded.
2. (Change of variable in an integral.) Prove that if g has a continuous derivative g' on $I = [c, d]$, and if f is continuous on $g(I)$ with $g(c) = a$, $g(d) = b$, then

$$\int_a^b f(x)\, dx = \int_c^d f(g(t))g'(t)\, dt.$$

[HINT: Consider the function G defined for $x \in g(I)$ by

$$G(x) = \int_c^x f(g(t))g'(t)\, dt.$$

Why does $G(x)$ exist? Now define

$$F(x) = \int_a^x f(t)\, dt.$$

We are through if we can show that $F(g(d)) = G(d)$. Why? Invoke the result in Exercise 11 (b), Section 7.7, to get $G'(x) = f(g(x))g'(x)$. By the chain rule, the derivative of $F(g(x))$ is also $f(g(x))g'(x)$. Why? Hence the difference

$$F(g(x)) - G(x) = \text{const.}$$

Putting $x = c$, we evaluate: const. $= 0$. Why? Therefore, $F(g(x)) = G(x)$ for all $x \in g(I)$. In particular, $F(g(d)) = G(d)$, Q.E.D.]

3. (Invariance of the line integral $\int_\Gamma f(z)\, dz$ under change of parameter.) Show that if $t = t(\tau)$ has a derivative $t'(\tau) > 0$ and $t(\tau)$ maps the interval $c \le \tau \le d$ onto $a \le t \le b$, then

$$\int_a^b f(z(t))z'(t)\, dt = \int_c^d f(z(t(\tau)))z'(t(\tau))t'(\tau)\, d\tau.$$

(This shows that the line integral along a curve Γ is independent of the parametric representation of the curve.)

4. (a) Let S be a set of complex numbers. Give a definition of S *has measure zero* by referring to Definition 7.7, interpreting I_n to be an open interval in the plane and replacing *length* by *area*.
   (b) Show that every finite set of complex numbers has measure zero.
   (c) Show that every denumerable set of complex numbers has measure zero.
   (d) Show that if S_k, $k = 1, 2, \cdots$, has measure zero, then $\bigcup_{k=1}^\infty S_k$ has measure zero.

8

Sequences of Functions: An Existence Theorem in Differential Equations

INTRODUCTION

In Chapter 3 we introduced the concept of limit of a sequence of real numbers. At this time we shall be dealing with sequences of functions. In many problems of analysis it is fruitful to introduce a notion of "limit of a sequence of functions." Depending on the circumstances, it may be possible to do this in several ways. Usually, in a given situation, one definition of "limit of a sequence of functions" will be more serviceable than another. In our brief investigation, we shall be concerned with two such notions:

(1) "Pointwise convergence" of a sequence of functions.

(2) "Uniform convergence" of a sequence of functions. The concept of "uniform convergence" is valuable in providing sufficient conditions for the validity of interchanging various operations, for example, "passage to limit" and "integrate." The relevant theorems are proved in Section 8.1. Since many problems arise naturally or can be solved more readily in the context of certain sequences known as "series," the theorems are translated into the language of series in Section 8.3.

Finally, the contraction mapping theorem proved in Chapter 6 is general-ized to the abstract setting of a complete metric space and is used to prove an existence theorem in the theory of differential equations. In this applica-tion the notion of uniform convergence of a sequence of continuous functions plays an essential role.

8.1   UNIFORM CONVERGENCE

As a starting point, we take the following definition.

Definition 8.1.   Let $f_1, f_2, \cdots, f_n, \cdots$ be a sequence of real-valued func-tions, each with domain S. Suppose that for each $x \in S$, $\lim_{n\to\infty} f_n(x)$ exists. We may then define a function f by setting $f(x) = \lim_{n\to\infty} f_n(x)$. We call f the *pointwise limit* of the sequence $\{f_n\}$ and say that f_n *converges to* f.

Example 8.1.   Consider f_n defined by $f_n(x) = x^n$, $0 \le x \le \frac{1}{2}$, $n = 1, 2, \cdots$. Here the pointwise limit is f where $f(x) = \lim_{n\to\infty} x^n = 0$, $0 \le x \le \frac{1}{2}$. So in this case each term f_n of the sequence is continuous and the pointwise limit f is likewise continuous.

Example 8.2.   Consider f_n defined by $f_n(x) = x^n$, $0 \le x \le 1$, $n = 1, 2, \cdots$. Clearly, the pointwise limit of $\{f_n\}$ is the function f defined by

$$f(x) = \lim_{n\to\infty} x^n = \begin{cases} 0, & \text{if } 0 \le x < 1 \\ 1, & \text{if } x = 1. \end{cases}$$

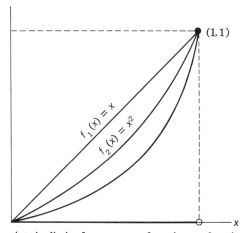

Fig. 8.1   The pointwise limit of a sequence of continuous functions need not be a continuous function.

We learn from this example that the pointwise limit of a sequence of continuous functions may be a discontinuous function (see Fig. 8.1).

We now raise the question:

Suppose $\{f_n\}$ is a sequence of continuous functions on $[a, b]$ and suppose

$$x \in [a, b] \Rightarrow \exists \lim_{n \to \infty} f_n(x) = f(x).$$

What condition can we impose on the sequence $\{f_n\}$ so as to guarantee that f will also be continuous?

This question can be interpreted as follows: To say that f is continuous at $\xi \in [a, b]$ is the same as stipulating that

$$\lim_{x \to \xi} f(x) = f(\xi),$$

hence that

$$\lim_{x \to \xi} [\lim_{n \to \infty} f_n(x)] = f(\xi). \tag{8.1}$$

But, by definition,

$$f(\xi) = \lim_{n \to \infty} f_n(\xi), \tag{8.2}$$

and by virtue of the assumed continuity of f_n at ξ, (8.2) may be written

$$f(\xi) = \lim_{n \to \infty} [\lim_{x \to \xi} f_n(x)]. \tag{8.3}$$

Substituting (8.3) into (8.1), we see that continuity of f at ξ is equivalent to the condition

$$\lim_{x \to \xi} [\lim_{n \to \infty} f_n(x)] = \lim_{n \to \infty} [\lim_{x \to \xi} f_n(x)]; \tag{8.4}$$

that is, it is equivalent to interchangeability of the limit processes indicated in (8.4).

Our present goal is to show that if the sequence $\{f_n\}$ of continuous functions "converges uniformly" to f, then f will also be continuous.

Definition 8.2. *The sequence $\{f_n\}$ converges uniformly to f on S iff*

$$\forall \epsilon > 0, \exists N \ni n > N \Rightarrow |f_n(x) - f(x)| < \epsilon, \forall x \in S.$$

Geometric interpretation should help in grasping this concept; refer to Fig. 8.2. There we find a graph representing f and about that graph we have drawn a "band of width 2ϵ"; that is, the graphs of $f + \epsilon$ and $f - \epsilon$ have been drawn in broken lines. If, corresponding to each positive ϵ, we can find a positive integer N (usually dependent on ϵ) in such a way that all functions in the "tail end of the sequence," that is, $f_{N+1}, f_{N+2}, \cdots$, have graphs which fall within this band, then we say $\{f_n\}$ converges uniformly to f.

The difference between pointwise convergence and uniform convergence is simply this: In the case of Definition 8.1, given an $\epsilon > 0$ and an $x \in [a, b]$, we require a corresponding N such that $|f_n(x) - f(x)| < \epsilon$ for all $n > N$. So N depends on *both* ϵ and x. In uniform convergence, however, given only an $\epsilon > 0$, we require a corresponding N such that $|f_n(x) - f(x)| < \epsilon$ for all $n > N$ *and* for all $x \in [a, b]$. Here N depends on ϵ only.

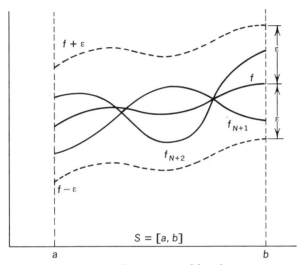

Fig. 8.2 Uniform convergence of a sequence of functions.

Obviously, if $\{f_n\}$ converges uniformly to f, then $\{f_n\}$ converges to f. The converse is false as shown by Examples 8.2 and 8.4.

Example 8.3. The sequence $\{f_n\}$ defined by $f_n(x) = x^2 - (x/n), 0 \le x \le 1$, $n = 1, 2, \cdots$, converges to the function f where

$$f(x) = \lim_{n \to \infty} f_n(x) = \lim_{n \to \infty} \left(x^2 - \frac{x}{n} \right) = x^2, \qquad 0 \le x \le 1.$$

Moreover, f_n converges uniformly to f. To prove this, we compute the distance

$$|f_n(x) - f(x)| = \left| \left(x^2 - \frac{x}{n} \right) - x^2 \right| = \frac{x}{n} \le \frac{1}{n}.$$

Now let $\epsilon > 0$ be given and choose $N > 1/\epsilon$. Then

$$n > N \Rightarrow n > \frac{1}{\epsilon} \Rightarrow |f_n(x) - f(x)| \le \frac{1}{n} < \epsilon$$

and this holds for all $x, 0 \le x \le 1$.

Example 8.4.   Consider f_n (see Fig. 8.3) where

$$f_n(x) = \begin{cases} 2nx, & \text{if } 0 \le x \le \dfrac{1}{2n} \\[2ex] -2nx + 2, & \text{if } \dfrac{1}{2n} < x \le \dfrac{1}{n} \\[2ex] 0, & \text{if } \dfrac{1}{n} < x \le 1. \end{cases}$$

It is easy to see that $f(x) = \lim_{n\to\infty} f_n(x) = 0, 0 \le x \le 1$. Thus f_n converges to 0. But the convergence is not uniform. According to Definition 8.2, to

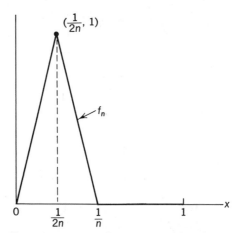

Fig. 8.3   Nonuniform convergence of a sequence of functions.

deny uniform convergence of $\{f_n\}$ to f we must find an $\epsilon_0 > 0$ such that, no matter what N is given, $\exists n > N$ and $\exists x_0 \in [0, 1] \ni |f_n(x_0) - f(x_0)| \ge \epsilon_0$. Compute the distance

$$\left| f_n\left(\frac{1}{2n}\right) - f\left(\frac{1}{2n}\right) \right| = \left| 2n\left(\frac{1}{2n}\right) - 0 \right| = 1.$$

Then all we need do is choose $x_0 = \dfrac{1}{2n}$, $\epsilon_0 = 1$ and $n = N + 1$.

Our first theorem asserts "continuity is hereditary under uniform convergence."

■ **Theorem 8.1.**   If $\{f_n\}$ is a sequence of continuous functions on $[a, b]$, and if $\{f_n\}$ converges uniformly to f, then f is continuous on $[a, b]$.

Proof: Let $\xi \in [a, b]$. We are to prove that f is continuous at ξ. Let $\epsilon > 0$.

$$\exists N \ni n > N \Rightarrow |f_n(x) - f(x)| < \frac{\epsilon}{3}, \qquad \forall x \in [a, b].$$

In particular,

$$|f_{N+1}(x) - f(x)| < \frac{\epsilon}{3}, \qquad \forall x \in [a, b].$$

Since f_{N+1} is continuous at ξ,

$$\exists \delta > 0 \ni |x - \xi| < \delta \Rightarrow |f_{N+1}(x) - f_{N+1}(\xi)| < \frac{\epsilon}{3}.$$

It follows that

$$|x - \xi| < \delta \Rightarrow |f(x) - f(\xi)| \leq |f(x) - f_{N+1}(x)| + |f_{N+1}(x) - f_{N+1}(\xi)|$$

$$+ |f_{N+1}(\xi) - f(\xi)| < \frac{\epsilon}{3} + \frac{\epsilon}{3} + \frac{\epsilon}{3} = \epsilon. \quad \blacksquare$$

■ **Theorem 8.2.** If $\{f_n\}$ is a sequence of Riemann integrable functions on $[a, b]$ and if $\{f_n\}$ converges uniformly to f on $[a, b]$, then f is Riemann integrable on $[a, b]$ and

$$\lim_{n \to \infty} \int_a^b f_n(x)\, dx = \int_a^b \lim_{n \to \infty} f_n(x)\, dx = \int_a^b f(x)\, dx.$$

Proof: To show that f is Riemann integrable, we use Lebesgue's criterion and show that $mD_f = 0$; that is, the set D_f of points of discontinuity of f has measure zero.

Let $x_0 \in D_f$. Then some f_n is discontinuous at x_0 for if all f_k, $k = 1, 2, \cdots$ were continuous at x_0, f would also be continuous at x_0 (Theorem 8.1). Thus

$$x_0 \in D_f \Rightarrow x_0 \in D_{f_n} \qquad \text{for some } n;$$

that is,

$$D_f \subset \bigcup_{k=1}^{\infty} D_{f_k}. \tag{8.5}$$

But $mD_{f_k} = 0$ for all $k = 1, 2, \cdots$ since f_k is Riemann integrable, $\forall k$. Consequently

$$m\left(\bigcup_{k=1}^{\infty} D_{f_k}\right) = 0$$

since the union of a denumerable number of sets of measure zero has measure zero. But then (8.5) says D_f is a subset of a set of measure zero. Hence $mD_f = 0$, and we conclude that f is Riemann integrable.

Because of uniform convergence of $\{f_n\}$ to f,

$$\forall \epsilon > 0, \exists N \ni n > N \Rightarrow |f_n(x) - f(x)| < \frac{\epsilon}{b - a}, \qquad \forall x \in [a, b].$$

Therefore,

$$\left| \int_a^b f_n(x)\, dx - \int_a^b f(x)\, dx \right| = \left| \int_a^b (f_n(x) - f(x))\, dx \right|$$

$$\le \int_a^b |f_n(x) - f(x)|\, dx \quad \text{(Section 7.7, Exercise 10)}$$

$$< \frac{\epsilon}{b-a} \int_a^b dx = \epsilon.$$

This proves $\lim_{n \to \infty} \int_a^b f_n(x)\, dx = \int_a^b f(x)\, dx.$ ∎

Example 8.5. The rational numbers belonging to the interval $[0, 1]$ form a denumerable set so there exists a sequence $r_1, r_2, r_3, \cdots$ whose range is the set of all rational numbers in $[0, 1]$. For $n = 1, 2, \cdots$, define the function f_n, domain $[0, 1]$, by

$$f_n(x) = \begin{cases} 1, & \text{if } x \in \{r_1, r_2, \cdots, r_n\} \\ 0, & \text{if } x \notin \{r_1, r_2, \cdots, r_n\}. \end{cases}$$

The sequence $\{f_n\}$ converges to f where

$$f(x) = \begin{cases} 1, & \text{if } x \text{ is rational,} \\ 0, & \text{if } x \text{ is irrational.} \end{cases}$$

Clearly $\int_0^1 f_n(x)\, dx = 0$ for all n; therefore $\lim_{n \to \infty} \int_0^1 f_n(x)\, dx = 0$. On the other hand, f is not even Riemann integrable. This example illustrates a shortcoming of the concept of integrability in Riemann's sense. Here we have a sequence $\{f_n\}$ of Riemann integrable functions, each element of which is *bounded by the same number* (that is, $|f_n(x)| \le 1$ for all x, $0 \le x \le 1$) and $\{f_n\}$ converges to f, yet f is not Riemann integrable. This deficiency in Riemann's concept of integration is removed in Lebesgue's approach to integration.*

Example 8.6. In Example 8.2, we saw that $x^2 - (x/n)$ converges uniformly to x^2, $0 \le x \le 1$. We verify Theorem 8.2 as follows:

$$\lim_{n \to \infty} \int_0^1 \left(x^2 - \frac{x}{n} \right) dx = \lim_{n \to \infty} \left(\frac{1}{3} - \frac{1}{2n} \right) = \frac{1}{3}.$$

---

* See, for example, *Real and Abstract Analysis* by E. Hewitt and K. Stromberg, Springer-Verlag, New York, 1965, p. 172.

Interchanging the operations of "passage to limit" and "integrate" (compare with above), we have

$$\int_0^1 \lim_{n \to \infty} \left(x^2 - \frac{x}{n} \right) dx = \int_0^1 x^2 \, dx = \frac{1}{3}.$$

To paraphrase Theorem 8.2: "Uniform convergence of integrands is a sufficient condition for the limit of a sequence of integrals to equal the integral of the limit." In view of this, we might expect an analogous result to hold for differentiation. This is not the case as illustrated in the next example.

Example 8.7.   Consider $f_n(x) = (\sin nx)/n$, $n = 1, 2, \cdots, 0 \le x \le 2\pi$. Since $|(\sin nx)/n| \le 1/n \to 0$, f_n converges uniformly to the function f where $f(x) = 0$, $0 \le x \le 2\pi$.

Now $f_n'(x) = \cos nx$, hence $\lim_{n \to \infty} f_n'(\pi)$ does not exist, so obviously $\lim_{n \to \infty} f_n'(x) \ne (\lim_{n \to \infty} f_n(x))'$, even though f_n converges uniformly.

In order to resolve the difficulty, we need two preliminary results.

■ **Theorem 8.3.**   (Cauchy criterion for uniform convergence). $\{f_n\}$ converges uniformly on S iff

$$\forall \, \epsilon > 0, \exists N \ni n, m > N \Rightarrow |f_m(x) - f_n(x)| < \epsilon, \forall \, x \in S. \qquad (8.6)$$

Proof: Suppose $\{f_n\}$ converges uniformly to f on S. Then,

$$\forall \, \epsilon > 0, \exists N \ni n > N \Rightarrow |f_n(x) - f(x)| < \frac{\epsilon}{2}, \forall \, x \in S.$$

If $m > N$ and $n > N$,

$$|f_m(x) - f_n(x)| \le |f_m(x) - f(x)| + |f(x) - f_n(x)| < \epsilon,$$

so the Cauchy condition (8.6) is necessary for uniform convergence.

Conversely, suppose (8.6) holds. Then by the Cauchy criterion for existence of a limit of a sequence (Theorem 6.11), we may define f where

$$f(x) = \lim_{n \to \infty} f_n(x), \qquad \forall \, x \in S.$$

Now we must show $\{f_n\}$ converges uniformly to f. Let $\epsilon > 0$. By hypothesis,

$$\exists N \ni n, m > N \Rightarrow |f_n(x) - f_m(x)| < \epsilon/2, \qquad \forall \, x \in S.$$

If we fix $n > N$ and let m tend to infinity, we find

$$|f_n(x) - f(x)| < \epsilon, \qquad \forall \, x \in S. \quad ■$$

Lemma.   If $\{g_n\}$ converges uniformly to g on S, and if $x \in S'$, and if $\lim_{t \to x} g_n(t) = a_n$, then $\{a_n\}$ converges and $\lim_{n \to \infty} a_n = \lim_{t \to x} g(t)$. [The last equality can be written $\lim_{n \to \infty} \lim_{t \to x} g_n(t) = \lim_{t \to x} \lim_{n \to \infty} g_n(t)$.]

Proof: Let $\epsilon > 0$. Since $\{g_n\}$ converges uniformly to g, $\exists N \ni n, m > N \Rightarrow$ $|g_n(t) - g_m(t)| < \epsilon, \forall t \in S$. If we let $t \to x$ (invoking the hypothesis $x \in S'$), the last inequality becomes $|a_n - a_m| \le \epsilon$, and therefore a_n converges. Put $\lim a_n = a$. We now estimate

$$|g(t) - a| \le |g(t) - g_n(t)| + |g_n(t) - a_n| + |a_n - a|. \qquad (8.7)$$

Choose n such that

$$|g(t) - g_n(t)| < \frac{\epsilon}{3}, \qquad \forall t \in S$$

and

$$|a_n - a| < \frac{\epsilon}{3};$$

this is possible since $\{g_n\}$ converges uniformly to g and $a_n \to a$. With n fixed, choose a neighborhood $N(x)$ such that

$$t \in N(x) \cap S \Rightarrow |g_n(t) - a_n| < \frac{\epsilon}{3};$$

such $N(x)$ exists by virtue of the hypothesis $\lim_{t \to x} g_n(t) = a_n$. Returning to (8.7), we have $\forall \epsilon > 0, \exists N(x) \ni t \in N(x) \cap S \Rightarrow |g(t) - a| < \epsilon$. ∎

(NOTE: In view of the discussion above culminating in (8.4), Theorem 8.1 could have been proved as an immediate consequence of this lemma.)

■ **Theorem 8.4.**   If the sequence $\{f_n'\}$ of derivatives exists and converges uniformly on $[a, b]$, and if for some $\xi \in [a, b]$, $\{f_n(\xi)\}$ converges, then there exists a function f such that $\{f_n\}$ converges uniformly to f on $[a, b]$ and $f'(x) = \lim_{n \to \infty} f_n'(x), \forall x \in [a, b]$.

Proof: Let $\epsilon > 0$. By hypotheses,

$$\exists N \ni n, m > N \Rightarrow |f_n(\xi) - f_m(\xi)| < \frac{\epsilon}{2}$$

and

$$|f_n'(t) - f_m'(t)| < \frac{\epsilon}{2(b - a)}, \qquad \forall t \in [a, b].$$

Applying the mean value theorem to the function $f_n - f_m$, we obtain

$$|f_n(x) - f_m(x) - f_n(t) + f_m(t)| = |(f_n - f_m)'(\bar{t})(x - t)|$$

$$< \frac{\epsilon}{2} \frac{|x - t|}{(b - a)} \le \frac{\epsilon}{2} \qquad (8.8)$$

($\bar{t}$ between x and t, $\bar{t} \in [a, b]$), $\forall x, t \in [a, b]$ and $\forall n, m > N$.

It follows from (8.8) that

$$|f_n(x) - f_m(x)| \leq |f_n(x) - f_m(x) - f_n(\xi) + f_m(\xi)| + |f_n(\xi) - f_m(\xi)|$$

$$< \frac{\epsilon}{2} + \frac{\epsilon}{2} = \epsilon, \ \forall \ n, m > N, \ \forall \ x \in [a, b].$$

In view of the Cauchy criterion for uniform convergence, it follows that $\{f_n\}$ converges uniformly on $[a, b]$. Let $f(x) = \lim_{n \to \infty} f_n(x)$, $a \leq x \leq b$ and return to (8.8). Dividing by $|x - t| \neq 0$, we get

$$\left| \frac{f_n(x) - f_n(t)}{x - t} - \frac{f_m(x) - f_m(t)}{x - t} \right| < \frac{\epsilon}{2(b - a)}. \tag{8.9}$$

If we define g_n by

$$g_n(t) = \frac{f_n(x) - f_n(t)}{x - t}, \tag{8.10}$$

then (8.9) simply says that the difference quotient g_n converges uniformly in t, for each fixed $x \neq t$, $x, t \in [a, b]$. Now $\{g_n\}$ converges pointwise:

$$\lim_{n \to \infty} g_n(t) = \lim_{n \to \infty} \frac{f_n(x) - f_n(t)}{x - t} = \frac{f(x) - f(t)}{x - t}.$$

Thus $\{g_n\}$ converges uniformly in t, for x fixed, to $[f(x) - f(t)]/(x - t)$. Also, from (8.10), $\lim_{t \to x} g_n(t) = f_n'(x)$. Invoking the lemma above (taking $S = [a, b] - \{x\}$), we conclude

$$\lim_{n \to \infty} \lim_{t \to x} g_n(t) = \lim_{t \to x} \lim_{n \to \infty} g_n(t),$$

or

$$\lim_{n \to \infty} f_n'(x) = f'(x), \qquad \forall \ x \in [a, b]. \quad \blacksquare$$

Theorem 8.4 gives sufficient conditions for $\lim_{n \to \infty} f_n'(x) = [\lim_{n \to \infty} f_n(x)]'$; that is, for the interchange of the operations of "passage to the limit" and "differentiation." The condition that the sequence $\{f_n(\xi)\}$ converge for some number ξ may seem to be superfluous; that this is not the case is illustrated in the next example.

Example 8.8.   The sequence $\{f_n\}$ defined by

$$f_n(x) = n, \qquad 0 \leq x \leq 1,$$

gives rise to the sequence $\{f_n'\}$ where

$$f_n'(x) = 0, \qquad 0 \leq x \leq 1.$$

It follows that $\{f_n'\}$ converges uniformly to the function F with $F(x) = 0$, $0 \leq x \leq 1$. However, it is clear that $\{f_n\}$ does not converge for any number x, $0 \leq x \leq 1$, since $|f_n(x)| \geq n$. Consequently,

$$[\lim_{n \to \infty} f_n(x)]' \neq \lim_{n \to \infty} f_n'(x)$$

for the left member is meaningless.

8.2 EXERCISES

1. (a) Find $f(x) = \lim f_n(x)$ if

$$f_n(x) = \begin{cases} 1 - nx, & \text{if } 0 \le x \le \dfrac{1}{n} \\ 0, & \text{if } \dfrac{1}{n} < x \le 1. \end{cases}$$

   (b) Show that $\{f_n\}$, defined in (a), does not converge uniformly to f.

   [HINT: Use the contrapositive of Theorem 8.1.]
2. Define f_n, $n = 1, 2, 3, \cdots$, by

$$f_n(x) = \begin{cases} 2n^2x, & \text{if } 0 \le x \le \dfrac{1}{2n} \\ 2n^2\left(\dfrac{1}{n} - x\right), & \text{if } \dfrac{1}{2n} < x < \dfrac{1}{n} \\ 0, & \text{if } \dfrac{1}{n} \le x \le 1. \end{cases}$$

   (a) Find $f(x) = \lim_{n \to \infty} f_n(x)$.
   (b) Show that $\left\{\int_0^1 f_n(x)\, dx\right\}$ does not converge to $\int_0^1 f(x)\, dx$.
   (c) Does $\{f_n\}$ converge uniformly to f?
3. Define f_n, $n = 1, 2, 3, \cdots$, by $f_n(x) = \lim_{m \to \infty} (\cos n!\pi x)^{2m}$.
   (a) Show that if x is rational, $\lim_{n \to \infty} f_n(x) = 1$.

   [HINT: If $x = a/b$, a, b integers, $n!x$ is an integer for n large enough, so $(\cos n!\pi x)^{2m} = 1$.]
   (b) Show that if x is irrational, $\lim_{n \to \infty} f_n(x) = 0$.

   [HINT: If $n!x$ is not an integer, $|\cos n!\pi x| < 1$, and so $f_n(x) = 0$.]
   (c) Is f_n integrable over $[0, 2\pi]$? How about $\lim_{n \to \infty} f_n$?
4. Let $f_n(x) = \sqrt[n]{x}$, $0 \le x \le 1$, $n = 1, 2, 3, \cdots$.
   (a) Find the pointwise limit of $\{f_n\}$.
   (b) Does $\{f_n\}$ converge uniformly?
5. Assume f to be differentiable. Show that f' is the pointwise limit of a sequence of continuous functions.

   [HINT: Consider $f_n(x) = [f(x + (1/n)) - f(x)]/(1/n)$.]

6. Suppose $\{f_n\}$ converges uniformly to f. Suppose further that f_n, $n = 1, 2, 3, \cdots$ has the Darboux property (Definition 5.4). Can we conclude that f inherits this property? (Prove or give a counter-example.)

7. (a) Give an example to show that even if $\{f_n\}$ converges uniformly to f and all graphs involved have length, it does not follow that length (lim f_n) = lim (length f_n).

[HINT: Let f_n be the union of the semicircles in Fig. 8.4.]

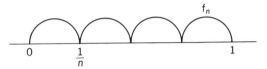

Fig. 8.4   Uniform convergence of $\{f_n\}$ does not imply length (lim f_n) = lim (length f_n).

(b) What is a sufficient condition for

$$\lim_{n\to\infty} \int_a^b \sqrt{1 + f_n'^2(x)}\, dx = \int_a^b \lim_{n\to\infty} \sqrt{1 + f_n'^2(x)}\, dx?$$

8. Though much more is assumed than in Theorem 8.4, the following theorem is much easier to prove and is adequate for many applications: If $\{f_n\}$ is a sequence of functions differentiable on $[a, b]$ and $\{f_n\}$ converges pointwise to f, and if $\{f_n'\}$ is integrable and $\{f_n'\}$ converges uniformly on $[a, b]$ to a continuous function g, then f is differentiable and

$$\lim_{n\to\infty} f_n'(x) = (\lim_{n\to\infty} f_n(x))' = f'(x).$$

[HINT: Apply Theorem 8.2 to the sequence $\{f_n'\}$ on $[a, x]$:

$$\int_a^x g(t)\, dt = \lim_{n\to\infty} \int_a^x f_n'(t)\, dt = \lim_{n\to\infty} [f_n(x) - f_n(a)] = f(x) - f(a).$$

Hence $f'(x) = g(x) = \lim_{n\to\infty} f_n'(x)$. Why?]

9. (a) Consider

$$f_n(x) = \frac{1}{nx + 1}, \qquad 0 \le x \le 1, \qquad n = 1, 2, 3, \cdots.$$

Find $\lim_{n\to\infty} f_n(x)$ and determine whether the convergence is uniform.

(b) Substitute $0 < x < 1$ in part (a) and investigate the same question.

10. Prove: If $\{f_n\}$ is a sequence of continuous functions on $[a, b]$, and if $\lim_{m,n\to\infty} \{\sup_{a \le x \le b} |f_n(x) - f_m(x)|\} = 0$, then $\{f_n\}$ converges uniformly to a continuous function f.

[HINT: Use the definition: If $\{a_{mn}\}$ is a *double sequence*, that is, a real-valued function on the Cartesian product $N \times N$ (N denotes the set of all natural numbers), we write $\lim_{m,n\to\infty} a_{mn} = a$ iff $\forall \epsilon > 0$, $\exists N \ni n, m > N \Rightarrow |a_{mn} - a| < \epsilon$. Invoke Theorems 8.3 and 8.1.]

8.3 INFINITE SERIES

In many applications of mathematics we have to deal with sequences each term of which is given to us as a certain sum. Such sequences are called "infinite series" or simply "series." Since we shall be concerned in Chapter 9 with series of complex numbers and the concepts and theorems which we introduce are no more difficult than for series of real numbers and indeed, the complex number case is a generalization of the ideas for the real number situation, we take complex numbers for the setting.

Definition 8.3. Let $\{a_k\}$ be a sequence of complex numbers. By the *infinite series* or simply *series* $\sum_{k=1}^{\infty} a_k$ is meant the sequence $\{s_n\}$ of partial sums defined by

$$s_n = \sum_{k=1}^{n} a_k.$$

When the sequence $\{s_n\}$ has a limit, $\lim_{n\to\infty} s_n = s$, we call s the *sum* of the series and sometimes use the symbol $\sum_{k=1}^{\infty} a_k$ to denote the number s. We say the series *converges* to s. If the sequence $\{s_n\}$ does not converge, we say the series $\sum_{k=1}^{\infty} a_k$ *diverges*. (There is little risk in confusing the sequence $\{s_n\}$ for its limit, and this convention is justified many times over by the simplicity in notation which is thereby obtained.)

We emphasize that a series is nothing more than a sequence, and therefore many theorems dealing with sequences apply to series. In particular, if a series has a sum (that is, limit), then it has only one and its partial sums (that is, terms) are bounded (see Theorems 3.1 and 3.2). The Cauchy criterion for existence of a limit of a sequence is applicable (Theorem 6.11): it tells us that the series $\sum_{k=1}^{\infty} a_k$ converges iff $\forall \epsilon > 0$, $\exists N \ni n > N \Rightarrow |s_{n+k} - s_n| < \epsilon$ for all positive integers k. But $s_{n+k} - s_n = a_{n+1} + \cdots + a_{n+k}$, and hence the following theorem.

■ **Theorem 8.5.** (Cauchy criterion for convergence of a series). The series $\sum_{k=1}^{\infty} a_k$ converges iff $\forall \epsilon > 0, \exists N \ni n > N \Rightarrow |a_{n+1} + \cdots + a_{n+k}| < \epsilon$ for all k.

Example 8.9. The harmonic series $\sum_{k=1}^{\infty} (1/k)$ diverges. For, estimating the sum of n successive terms, we have

$$\frac{1}{n+1} + \frac{1}{n+2} + \cdots + \frac{1}{n+n} > \frac{1}{n+n} + \frac{1}{n+n} + \cdots + \frac{1}{n+n}$$

$$= n\left(\frac{1}{2n}\right) = \frac{1}{2}.$$

Therefore, if we take $\epsilon = \frac{1}{2}$, and let N be any positive integer, there is an integer greater than N, namely $2N$, such that the absolute value of the sum of $2N$ terms

$$\left|\frac{1}{2N+1} + \cdots + \frac{1}{2N+2N}\right| > \frac{1}{2},$$

so that by Theorem 8.5 we conclude that $\sum_{k=1}^{\infty} (1/k)$ diverges.

Corollary. If the series $\sum_{k=1}^{\infty} a_k$ converges, then $\lim_{n \to \infty} a_n = 0$

Proof: In Theorem 8.5, take $k = 1$ to get

$$\forall \epsilon > 0, \exists N \ni n > N \Rightarrow |a_{n+1}| < \epsilon. \quad \blacksquare$$

The converse is, of course, false (see Example 8.9).

We recall from elementary calculus the concept of "absolute convergence."

Definition 8.4. The series $\sum_{k=1}^{\infty} a_k$ is said to *converge absolutely* iff $\sum_{k=1}^{\infty} |a_k|$ converges. If $\sum_{k=1}^{\infty} a_k$ converges, but not absolutely, then we say that $\sum_{k=1}^{\infty} a_k$ is *conditionally convergent*.

Theorem 8.5 and the triangle inequality are all we need to prove the following.

■ Theorem 8.6. If $\sum_{k=1}^{\infty} a_k$ converges absolutely, then $\sum_{k=1}^{\infty} a_k$ converges.

Proof: By hypothesis and Theorem 8.5, for every $\epsilon > 0$,

$$\exists N \ni n > N \Rightarrow |a_{n+1}| + \cdots + |a_{n+k}| < \epsilon, \qquad \forall k.$$

It follows from the triangle inequality that

$$n > N \Rightarrow |a_{n+1} + \cdots + a_{n+k}| \le |a_{n+1}| + \cdots + |a_{n+k}| < \epsilon, \qquad \forall k. \quad \blacksquare$$

The importance of the concept of absolute convergence lies in the fact that if a series has this property its terms may be rearranged without affecting the convergence of the series and, moreover, the sum is unchanged in the process, an analog of commutativity for finite sums (see Section 8.4, Exercise 1).

It is worthwhile to point out the explicit statement one gets by applying the definition of uniform convergence of a sequence of functions to the special case of a series.

Definition 8.5.   Let $\{f_k\}, k = 1, 2, \cdots$ be a sequence of complex-valued functions with domain S. *The series $\sum_{k=1}^{\infty} f_k$ of functions converges uniformly to the function f on S iff*

$$\forall \epsilon > 0, \qquad \exists N \ni n > N \Rightarrow \left| \sum_{k=1}^{n} f_k(x) - f(x) \right| < \epsilon, \qquad \forall x \in S.$$

Remark

In view of the Cauchy criterion for uniform convergence (Theorem 8.3), the following condition is equivalent to the condition of Definition 8.5:

$$\forall \epsilon > 0, \qquad \exists N \ni n > N \Rightarrow |f_n(x) + f_{n+1}(x) + \cdots + f_{n+k}(x)| < \epsilon,$$

$\forall x \in S, \forall$ positive integer k.

This leads us to a useful sufficient condition for uniform convergence, known as "the Weierstrass test."

■ **Theorem 8.7.**   If $\{f_k\}$ is a sequence of functions on S and if $|f_k(x)| \le M_k$ for all $x \in S$ and all $k = 1, 2, \cdots$, and if $\sum_{k=1}^{\infty} M_k$ converges, then the series $\sum_{k=1}^{\infty} f_k$ converges uniformly on S.

Proof: Since $\sum_{k=1}^{\infty} M_k$ converges, the Cauchy criterion is applicable:

$$\epsilon > 0, \qquad \exists N \ni n > N \Rightarrow |M_n + M_{n+1} + \cdots + M_{n+k}| < \epsilon, \qquad \forall k.$$

By our hypothesis, then,

$$|f_n(x) + f_{n+1}(x) + \cdots + f_{n+k}(x)| \le |f_n(x)| + |f_{n+1}(x)| + \cdots + |f_{n+k}(x)|$$
$$\le M_n + M_{n+1} + \cdots + M_{n+k}$$
$$= |M_n + M_{n+1} + \cdots + M_{n+k}| < \epsilon$$

for all $n > N$, and for all k. Now appeal to the remark under Definition 8.5.   ∎

Example 8.10.   Consider the series $\sum_{k=1}^{\infty} (-1)^{k+1} x/k, 0 \le x \le 1$. This series converges uniformly to the function f where $f(x) = x \log 2$ for, $1 - \frac{1}{2} + \frac{1}{3} - \cdots = \log 2$ and therefore

$$\left| (-1)^n \frac{x}{n} + (-1)^{n+1} \frac{x}{n+1} \cdots (-1)^{n+k} \frac{x}{n+k} \right| < \epsilon,$$

for $0 \le x \le 1$, and n sufficiently large and all k. However, the series does not converge absolutely for any $x \ne 0$. This shows that the converse of Theorem 8.7 is false.

Example 8.11.   Let $\{x\}$ denote the distance between the real number x and the nearest integer to x. Consider the series $\sum_{k=1}^{\infty} \{10^k x\}/10^k$.

We leave it to the reader to show that each term $\{10^k x\}/10^k$ is continuous in x and that the series converges uniformly in x. Hence it defines a continuous function f (see Section 8.4, Exercise 2). This function, discovered by B. L. van der Waerden, is differentiable nowhere!*

We learned earlier that if f, g are differentiable at each point of $[a, b]$, then the sum $f + g$ is differentiable on $[a, b]$ and, in fact

$$(f + g)' = f' + g'.$$

This result is readily extended, by finite induction, to any finite set of differentiable functions; that is,

$$(f_1 + f_2 + \cdots + f_n)' = f_1' + f_2' + \cdots + f_n'. \tag{8.11}$$

Theorem 8.4 provides a sufficient condition for further generalization of the formula (8.11):

■ **Theorem 8.8.**   If the sequence $\{s_n'\} = \{f_1' + f_2' + \cdots + f_n'\}$ of derivatives exists and converges uniformly on $[a, b]$, and if for some $\xi \in [a, b]$, $\{s_n(\xi)\}$ converges, then there exists a function s such that $\{s_n\}$ converges uniformly to s on $[a, b]$ and $s'(x) = \lim_{n \to \infty} s_n'(x)$, $\forall\, x \in [a, b]$ [in other words, $(f_1 + f_2 + \cdots)' = f_1' + f_2' + \cdots$].

Proof: Already given in Theorem 8.4.   ∎

The analogous question for integrals is answered by the following.

■ **Theorem 8.9.**   If $s_n = f_1 + f_2 + \cdots + f_n$ and $\{s_n\}$ is a sequence of Riemann integrable functions on $[a, b]$, and if $\{s_n\}$ converges uniformly to s on $[a, b]$, then s is Riemann integrable on $[a, b]$ and

$$\lim_{n \to \infty} \int_a^b s_n(x)\, dx = \int_a^b \lim_{n \to \infty} s_n(x)\, dx = \int_a^b s(x)\, dx;$$

---

*It is discussed in *Functional Analysis* by F. Riesz and B. Sz.-Nagy, Ungar Publishing Company, New York, 1955.

that is,

$$\sum_{k=1}^{\infty} \int_a^b f_k(x)\,dx = \int_a^b \sum_{k=1}^{\infty} f_k(x)\,dx.$$

Proof: Same as in Theorem 8.2. ∎

Example 8.12. It is clear that $\sum_{k=0}^n x^k = 1 + x + \cdots + x^n = \dfrac{1 - x^{n+1}}{1 - x}$, if $x \neq 1$. Therefore, if $|x| < 1$,

$$\lim_{n\to\infty} \frac{1 - x^{n+1}}{1 - x} = \frac{1}{1 - x}.$$

This justifies writing

$$|x| < 1 \Rightarrow \sum_{k=0}^{\infty} x^k = (1 - x)^{-1}. \tag{8.12}$$

We now show that if ξ is fixed with $|\xi| < 1$, then $\sum_{k=0}^{\infty} x^k$ converges uniformly if $|x| \leq |\xi|$. Indeed, let $|\xi| < |\eta| < 1$. Since $\sum_{k=0}^{\infty} \eta^k$ converges, the kth term of the series tends to 0; that is, $\lim_{k\to\infty} \eta^k = 0$, and therefore

$$\exists M \ni |\eta|^k \leq M \quad \text{for all } k.$$

Now

$$|x|^k = |\eta|^k \left|\frac{x}{\eta}\right|^k \leq M \left|\frac{\xi}{\eta}\right|^k.$$

If we put $M_k = M|\xi/\eta|^k$ and take into account the fact that $|\xi/\eta| < 1$ so that we know that the series $\sum_{k=0}^{\infty} M_k$ converges, then by the Weierstrass test (Theorem 8.7), we conclude that $\sum_{k=0}^{\infty} x^k$ converges uniformly if $|x| \leq |\xi| < 1$.

Moreover, we can show that the series $\sum_{k=1}^{\infty} k x^{k-1}$ obtained by termwise differentiation of $\sum_{k=0}^{\infty} x^k$ also converges uniformly for $|x| \leq |\xi| < 1$, to $(1 - x)^{-2}$. To see this, let $|x| \leq |\xi| < |\eta| < 1$. As before,

$$\exists M \ni |\eta|^k \leq M \quad \text{for all } k.$$

Then

$$|k x^{k-1}| = |\eta|^k k \left|\frac{x}{\eta}\right|^{k-1} \left|\frac{1}{\eta}\right|,$$

or

$$|k x^{k-1}| \leq \frac{Mk}{|\eta|} \left|\frac{\xi}{\eta}\right|^{k-1} \tag{8.13}$$

Applying the ratio test to the series whose kth term u_k is the right member of (8.13), we have

$$\left|\frac{u_{k+1}}{u_k}\right| = \frac{k+1}{k} \left|\frac{\xi}{\eta}\right|,$$

so that

$$\lim_{k \to \infty} \left| \frac{u_{k+1}}{u_k} \right| = \left| \frac{\xi}{\eta} \right| < 1,$$

showing that the series $\sum_{k=1}^{\infty} u_k = \sum_{k=1}^{\infty} \frac{Mk}{|\eta|} \left| \frac{\xi}{\eta} \right|^{k-1}$ converges. Hence, from (8.13) and the comparison test, $\sum_{k=1}^{\infty} kx^{k-1}$ converges absolutely if $|x| \le |\xi| < 1$.

Using the same idea as earlier, we can now show that the convergence of $\sum_{k=1}^{\infty} kx^{k-1}$ is uniform, if $|x| \le |\xi| < 1$. For, let $|x| \le |\xi| < |\eta| < 1$. Then convergence of $\sum_{k=1}^{\infty} k\eta^{k-1}$ yields:

$$\exists M' \ni k|\eta|^{k-1} \le M' \quad \text{for all } k.$$

Thus

$$|kx^{k-1}| = k|\eta|^{k-1} \left| \frac{x}{\eta} \right|^{k-1} \le M' \left| \frac{\xi}{\eta} \right|^{k-1}.$$

Again by the Weierstrass test, we conclude that $\sum_{k=1}^{\infty} kx^{k-1}$ converges uniformly if $|x| \le |\xi| < 1$.

Invoking Theorem 8.8, we conclude that termwise differentiation of $\sum_{k=1}^{\infty} x^k$ is valid for $|x| \le |\xi| < 1$. But if $|x| < 1$, there always exists a ξ such that $|x| \le |\xi| < 1$. Therefore, from (8.12) we get

$$|x| < 1 \Rightarrow \left(\sum_{k=1}^{\infty} x^k \right)' = \sum_{k=1}^{\infty} (x^k)' = (1 - x)^{-2},$$

or

$$|x| < 1 \Rightarrow \sum_{k=1}^{\infty} kx^{k-1} = (1 - x)^{-2}.$$

8.4 EXERCISES

1. Prove that if the series $\sum_{k=1}^{\infty} a_k$ converges absolutely, then any rearrangement of the series is convergent and has the same sum.

   (NOTE: A *rearrangement* of the series $\sum_{k=1}^{\infty} a_k$ is a series $\sum_{k=1}^{\infty} a_{f(k)}$ where f is a one-to-one function on the natural numbers onto the natural numbers.)

2. The "van der Waerden example" of a continuous everywhere, differentiable nowhere, function f is defined by

   $$f(x) = \sum_{k=1}^{\infty} \frac{\{10^k x\}}{10^k}$$

   where $\{x\}$ is defined to be the distance between the real number x and the nearest integer to x. Show that f is continuous by proving:

(a) $\{10^k x\}/10^k$ is continuous in x.

(b) The series $\sum_{k=1}^{\infty} \{10^k x\}/10^k$ converges uniformly (use Theorem 8.7).

3. Prove that if $\sum_{k=1}^{\infty} u_n$ and $\sum_{n=1}^{\infty} v_n$ are convergent series, then $\sum_{n=1}^{\infty} (u_n + v_n)$ is also convergent and $\sum_{n=1}^{\infty} (u_n + v_n) = \sum_{n=1}^{\infty} u_n + \sum_{n=1}^{\infty} v_n$.

4. Prove: $\sum_{n=1}^{\infty} u_n$ converges and c a complex number $\Rightarrow \sum_{n=1}^{\infty} cu_n$ converges and $\sum_{n=1}^{\infty} cu_n = c \sum_{n=1}^{\infty} u_n$.

5. Show that if $u_n \geq 0$, $n = 1, 2, \cdots$, then $\sum_{n=1}^{\infty} u_n$ converges iff it is bounded above.

6. Prove the comparison test:

If $|u_n| \leq v_n$ and if $\sum_{n=1}^{\infty} v_n$ converges, then $\sum_{n=1}^{\infty} u_n$ converges.

[HINT: $|\sum_{m=n}^{n+k} u_m| \leq \sum_{m=n}^{n+k} |u_m| \leq \sum_{m=n}^{n+k} v_m < \epsilon$ if n is large enough.]

7. Prove the ratio test:

If $u_n > 0$ for all n and if $\lim_{n \to \infty} u_{n+1}/u_n = r$, then

(a) $\sum_{n=1}^{\infty} u_n$ converges if $r < 1$

(b) $\sum_{n=1}^{\infty} u_n$ diverges if $r > 1$.

[HINT FOR (a): Let $r < s < 1$. $\exists N \ni n > N \Rightarrow u_{n+1}/u_n \leq s$, so that $u_{N+2} \leq su_{N+1}, u_{N+3} \leq su_{N+2} \leq s^2 u_{N+1}, \cdots$. But $\sum_{k=0}^{\infty} u_{N+1} s^k = u_{N+1} \sum_{k=0}^{\infty} s^k$ converges. Now use Exercise 6.]

8.5 APPLICATION TO DIFFERENTIAL EQUATIONS

In this section we prove a famous theorem in the area of mathematics known as differential equations. In this work we need the concept of continuity for a real-valued function f whose domain $D = \{(x, y) \mid a \leq x \leq b, c \leq y \leq d\}$ is a rectangle in the plane. If we write $z = (x, y)$, $w = (u, v)$, and define the distance $|z - w|$ between z and w in the usual plane analytic geometry way

$$|z - w| = \sqrt{(x - u)^2 + (y - v)^2},$$

then the concept of continuity may be developed in the same way as for functions of one real variable. In particular, a neighborhood $N(z; r)$ of z with radius r is the set

$$N(z; r) = \{w \mid |z - w| < r\}$$

and f is continuous at $z_0 \in D$ iff for every neighborhood $N(f(z_0); \epsilon)$ there exists $N(z_0; \delta) \ni z \in N(z_0; \delta) \cap D \Rightarrow f(z) \in N(f(z_0); \epsilon)$. Further details will be found in the supplements to Chapters 3, 4, and 5.

We are interested in proving an existence theorem known as "Picard's theorem." The problem is formulated as follows: Does there exist a function y whose derivative dy/dx is a prescribed function f of x and $y(x)$ and whose value $y(x_0)$ at a fixed point x_0 is also prescribed? More concisely, does the initial value problem

$$\begin{cases} \dfrac{dy}{dx} = f(x, y) \\ y(x_0) = y_0 \end{cases} \tag{8.14}$$

have a solution y? To be precise, we introduce the following definition.

Definition 8.6.   Let f be a real-valued function defined on a rectangle $D = \{(x, y) \mid a \leq x \leq b, c \leq y \leq d\}$ and let $(x_0, y_0) \in D$. *A solution of the initial value problem*

$$\begin{cases} \dfrac{dy}{dx} = f(x, y) \\ y(x_0) = y_0 \end{cases} \tag{8.15}$$

is a differentiable function ϕ on (a, b) such that $\phi(x_0) = y_0$ and $\phi'(x) = f(x, \phi(x))$, $a < x < b$.

Example 8.13.   The initial value problem

$$\begin{cases} \dfrac{dy}{dx} = -\dfrac{x}{y} \\ y(0) = 1 \end{cases}$$

has a solution y where $y(x) = \sqrt{1 - x^2}$, $-1 < x < 1$, as is easily verified:

$$\frac{dy(x)}{dx} = \frac{1}{2}(1 - x^2)^{-1/2}(-2x) = -\frac{x}{\sqrt{1 - x^2}} = -\frac{x}{y(x)}$$

and $y(0) = 1$. Note that on $D = \{(x, y) \mid |x| < 1, |y - 1| < \frac{1}{2}\}$, $f(x, y) = -x/y$ satisfies a Lipschitz condition with respect to y; that is,

$$|f(x, y_1) - f(x, y_2)| = \left| \frac{x}{y_1} - \frac{x}{y_2} \right| = |x| \left| \frac{y_2 - y_1}{y_1 y_2} \right| \leq 4|y_2 - y_1|.$$

Also, f is continuous on D. To see this, we begin with the computation

$$\left| -\frac{x}{y} - \left(-\frac{x_0}{y_0} \right) \right| = \left| -\frac{x}{y} + \frac{x_0}{y_0} \right| = \left| \frac{-xy_0 + x_0 y}{y y_0} \right|$$

$$= \left| \frac{-xy_0 + x_0 y_0 - x_0 y_0 + x_0 y}{y y_0} \right|$$

$$= \frac{1}{|y y_0|} \left| [y_0(x_0 - x) + x_0(y - y_0)] \right|.$$

We must show that this quantity can be made small provided x and y are "close" to x_0 and y_0, respectively. The bracketed expression is the inner product or dot product of the vectors (x_0, y_0) and $(y - y_0, x_0 - x)$, and hence by the Cauchy-Schwarz inequality (Theorem 3.10), we obtain

$$\left| \frac{x_0}{y_0} - \frac{x}{y} \right| \le \frac{1}{|yy_0|} \sqrt{x_0^2 + y_0^2} \sqrt{(x_0 - x)^2 + (y - y_0)^2}. \tag{8.16}$$

Now since $(x_0, y_0) \in D$,

$$\sqrt{x_0^2 + y_0^2} \le |x_0| + |y_0| \le 1 + \tfrac{3}{2} = \tfrac{5}{2},$$

and if $(x, y) \in D$,

$$\frac{1}{|yy_0|} \le \frac{1}{\frac{1}{2}^2} = 4.$$

Therefore, for points $(x, y) \in D$, we have from (8.16)

$$\left| \frac{x_0}{y_0} - \frac{x}{y} \right| \le 10\sqrt{(x_0 - x)^2 + (y - y_0)^2}.$$

Let $\epsilon > 0$. Define $\delta = \epsilon/11$ and consider the neighborhood $N((x_0, y_0); \delta) = \{(x, y) \mid (x_0 - x)^2 + (y - y_0)^2 < \delta^2\}$. Then

$$(x, y) \in D \cap N((x_0, y_0); \delta) \Rightarrow \left| \frac{x_0}{y_0} - \frac{x}{y} \right| < 10\left(\frac{\epsilon}{11}\right) < \epsilon$$

and this proves that f is continuous on D. We shall see below (Picard's Theorem) that the initial value problem of this example has only one solution.

Definition 8.7.   Let f be a function of two variables; that is, let the domain of f be the Cartesian product $S \times T$. *f satisfies a Lipschitz condition with respect to T* iff there exists a constant M such that

$$|f(x, y_1) - f(x, y_2)| \le M|y_1 - y_2|$$

for every $x \in S$ and all $y_1, y_2 \in T$.

Remark
When there is no danger of confusion, we will say $f(x, y)$ is Lipschitzian with respect to y. It is clear from the definition that if f is Lipschitzian with respect to y, and if x is arbitrary but fixed, f will be a continuous function of y. However, this does not mean that f will be continuous (in x and y) as our next example shows.

Example 8.14.   Consider the function f defined by

$$f(x, y) = \begin{cases} y \sin \dfrac{1}{x}, & \text{if } x \ne 0 \\[2mm] 0, & \text{if } x = 0. \end{cases}$$

Clearly, if $x \neq 0$,

$$|f(x, y_1) - f(x, y_2)| = \left|\sin \frac{1}{x}\right| |y_1 - y_2| \leq |y_1 - y_2|.$$

Thus for arbitrary x

$$|f(x, y_1) - f(x, y_2)| \leq |y_1 - y_2|;$$

that is, f is Lipschitzian with respect to y. On the other hand, f is discontinuous at every point $(0, y)$ of the y axis except the origin, for $f(0, y) = 0$ while

$$\lim_{x \to 0} f(x, y) = \lim_{x \to 0} y \sin \frac{1}{x}$$

does not exist unless $y = 0$.

Example 8.15. The function f defined by $f(x, y) = \sqrt{y}$, $y \geq 0$, is not Lipschitzian on any rectangle containing a point of the form $(x, 0)$. For if there were a constant M such that

$$|\sqrt{y_1} - \sqrt{y_2}| \leq M|y_1 - y_2|,$$

it would follow that for $y_1 - y_2 \neq 0$,

$$\left|\frac{\sqrt{y_1} - \sqrt{y_2}}{y_1 - y_2}\right| \leq M$$

or

$$\frac{1}{\sqrt{y_1} + \sqrt{y_2}} \leq M.$$

Taking $y_1 = 0$ and letting $y_2 \to 0$, we arrive at a contradiction. Note that the initial value problem

$$\frac{dy}{dx} = \sqrt{y}, \qquad y(0) = 0$$

has two solutions: $y(x) = 0$ and $y(x) = x^2/4$.

The existence theorem that we shall prove states, roughly speaking, that if the given function f in the initial value problem (8.15) is a continuous function (of x and y) and is Lipschitzian in y, then (8.15) has a unique solution. The plan of the proof runs as follows:

(1) The initial value problem (8.15) will be shown to be equivalent to a certain *integral equation*.

(2) A generalization of the contraction mapping theorem (Theorem 6.10) will be proved and shown to be applicable to the integral equation.

■ **Theorem 8.10.**   The initial value problem (8.15) is equivalent to the problem of solving the integral equation (f is a given continuous function)

$$\phi(x) = y_0 + \int_{x_0}^{x} f(t, \phi(t))\, dt \tag{8.17}$$

for continuous ϕ.

Proof: Suppose there exists a solution ϕ to (8.15). Then

$$\frac{d\phi(x)}{dx} = f(x, \phi(x)) \quad \text{and} \quad \phi(x_0) = y_0,$$

according to Definition 8.6 (in particular, ϕ is continuous). It follows from the fundamental theorem of calculus (Section 7.7, Exercise 11) that

$$\int_{x_0}^{x} f(t, \phi(t))\, dt = \phi(x) - \phi(x_0)$$

and therefore, (8.17) holds.

Conversely, if ϕ is a continuous solution of (8.17), then we compute

$$\begin{aligned}
\frac{\phi(x+h) - \phi(x)}{h} &= \frac{1}{h}\left[\int_{x_0}^{x+h} f(t, \phi(t))\, dt - \int_{x_0}^{x} f(t, \phi(t))\, dt \right]\\
&= \frac{1}{h}\int_{x}^{x+h} f(t, \phi(t))\, dt\\
&= \frac{f(t^*, \phi(t^*))h}{h},
\end{aligned}$$

where t^* is a point between x and $x + h$ (Section 7.7, Exercise 7),

$$= f(t^*, \phi(t^*)).$$

Passing to the limit as $h \to 0$ (the limit of the right member exists since ϕ, f are continuous), we get

$$\frac{d\phi(x)}{dx} = f(x, \phi(x)).$$

Also, from (8.17), $\phi(x_0) = y_0 + \int_{x_0}^{x_0} f(t, \phi(t))\, dt = y_0$, meaning that ϕ is a solution of (8.15).   ■

Remark

Note how neatly the initial condition $y(x_0) = y_0$ of (8.15) is absorbed in the integral equation formulation (8.17).

The second part of our plan is more involved. In order to generalize the contraction mapping theorem, we study the proof (Theorem 6.10), picking out the properties essential to the argument. First of all, the theorem makes an assertion about a function—defined on a set S—which carries a pair of objects at a certain *distance* apart into a pair of objects of the same kind at a (uniformly) lesser distance apart. This distance must satisfy a triangle inequality and the set S must have the property that every "Cauchy sequence" has a limit in S. Our generalization thus begins as follows.

Definition 8.8. A *metric space* is a set S together with a function d defined on $S \times S$ satisfying the following conditions:

    (1) $d(f, g) \geq 0$ for all $f, g \in S$ and $d(f, g) = 0$ iff $f = g$.
    (2) $d(f, g) = d(g, f)$ for all $f, g \in S$.
    (3) $d(f, g) + d(g, h) \geq d(f, h)$ for all $f, g, h \in S$.

$d(f, g)$ is called the *distance* between f and g. (Compare with Section 2.6 and Theorem 3.8.)

Definition 8.9. Let $\{f_n\}$ be a sequence of elements of a metric space S. $\{f_n\}$ is a *Cauchy sequence* iff for every $\epsilon > 0$, $\exists N \ni n > N \Rightarrow d(f_n, f_{n+k}) < \epsilon$ for all positive integers k. (Compare with Definition 6.6.)

Definition 8.10. The sequence $\{f_n\}$ of elements of a metric space S *converges* to an element $f \in S$ iff $\forall \epsilon > 0$, $\exists N \ni n > N \Rightarrow d(f_n, f) < \epsilon$. When f_n converges to f, we write $f = \lim f_n$ or $f_n \rightarrow f$ and call f the *limit* of the sequence $\{f_n\}$.

Definition 8.11. A metric space S is called *complete* iff every Cauchy sequence of elements of S has a limit belonging to S.

(NOTE: Theorem 6.11 may therefore be paraphrased: The real numbers with $d(a, b) = |a - b|$ form a complete metric space.)

Definition 8.12. A function A with domain a metric space S, range a subset of S, is called a *contraction mapping* iff there exists a number M, $0 < M < 1$, such that

$$d(Af, Ag) \leq Md(f, g)$$

where Af denotes the value of the function A at f [to avoid awkward notation we will write Af instead of $A(f)$].

Definition 8.13. A function A on S with range contained in S is said to have a *fixed point f* iff $Af = f$.

We now have the concepts necessary to state our generalized theorem.

■ **Theorem 8.11.** (Contraction mapping theorem.) If A is a contraction mapping of a complete metric space S into itself, then A has one and only one fixed point (that is, the equation $Af = f$ has a unique solution). Moreover, if f is the fixed point of A, then $f = \lim A^n g$ where $g \in S$ is arbitrary and $A^0 g = g$, $A^n g = A^{n-1}(Ag)$, $n = 1, 2, \cdots$.

Proof: (Compare with Theorem 6.10.) Let $g_0 \in S$. Set $g_1 = Ag_0$, $g_2 = Ag_1 = A^2 g_0$, $\cdots$, $g_n = Ag_{n-1} = A^n g_0$. The sequence $\{g_n\}$ is a Cauchy sequence, for

$$d(g_{n+k}, g_n) = d(A^{n+k} g_0, A^n g_0) \le M^n d(A^k g_0, g_0) = M^n d(g_k, g_0)$$
$$\le M^n [d(g_0, g_1) + d(g_1, g_2) + \cdots + d(g_{k-1}, g_k)]$$
$$\le M^n d(g_0, g_1)[1 + M + M^2 + \cdots + M^{k-1}]$$

$$\le M^n d(g_0, g_1) \frac{1}{1 - M}.$$

Since $0 < M < 1$, this last expression tends to 0 as $n \to \infty$, hence $\{g_n\}$ is a Cauchy sequence. Since S is complete, there exists an element $f \in S$ such that $f = \lim g_n = \lim A^n g_0$.

Next we show f is a fixed point of A. In fact, $g_n \to f$ implies $d(Ag_n, Af) < Md(g_n, f) < \epsilon$ for n sufficiently large, that is, $g_n \to f \Rightarrow Ag_n \to Af$. In other words, $g_n \to f \Rightarrow \lim Ag_n = Af = A \lim g_n$ (for this reason we say A is *continuous* at f). Therefore,

$$Af = A(\lim g_n) = \lim Ag_n = \lim g_{n+1} = f,$$

showing that f is a fixed point of A.

Finally, to prove uniqueness of the fixed point, suppose $Af = f$ and $Ag = g$. Then $d(f, g) = d(Af, Ag) < Md(f, g)$ and this implies $d(f, g) = 0$ which, in turn, implies $f = g$. ∎

We are now ready for the application to differential equations.

■ Theorem 8.12. (Picard's Theorem.)

If f is continuous on $G = \{(x, y) \mid |x - x_0| \le r, |y - y_0| \le s, r, s > 0\}$ and if f satisfies a Lipschitz condition with respect to its second variable, that is, $\exists M \ni |f(x, u) - f(x, v)| \le M|u - v|, \forall (x, u), (x, v) \in G$, then the initial value problem

$$\begin{cases} \dfrac{dy}{dx} = f(x, y) \\ y(x_0) = y_0 \end{cases} \tag{8.14}$$

has a unique solution ϕ on some neighborhood of x_0; that is, $\exists \delta > 0$ and $\exists$ function ϕ with domain $D = \{x \mid |x - x_0| < \delta\}$ such that ϕ satisfies (8.14) and ϕ is the only function with domain D that satisfies (8.14).

Proof: Since f is continuous on G and G is a closed and bounded set, f has a maximum K on G (see Theorem 5.2 and Supplement to Chapter 5).

Define

$$\delta = \min\left\{r, s, \frac{s}{K}, \frac{1}{2M}\right\}. \tag{8.18}$$

Then the set

$$G^* = \{(x, y) \mid |x - x_0| \leq \delta, |y - y_0| \leq K\delta\}$$

has the obvious property $G^* \subset G$. Therefore $(x, y) \in G^* \Rightarrow f(x, y)$ is meaningful. We now define C to be the set of all continuous functions ϕ defined on the closed interval $[x_0 - \delta, x_0 + \delta]$ such that $|\phi(x) - y_0| \leq K\delta$. In set-theoretic language

$$C = \{\phi \mid \phi \text{ is a continuous function of } x, |x - x_0| \leq \delta, \text{ and } |\phi(x) - y_0| \leq K\delta\}.$$

(Note that $f(x, \phi(x))$ makes sense.) We introduce a distance $d(\phi_1, \phi_2)$ for $\phi_1, \phi_2 \in C$, by setting

$$d(\phi_1, \phi_2) = \max_x \{|\phi_1(x) - \phi_2(x)| \mid |x - x_0| \leq \delta\}.$$

This definition is justified on the grounds that $|\phi_1 - \phi_2|$ is a continuous function on a finite closed interval, hence it has a maximum. The proof that all three axioms of a metric space (Definition 8.8) are fulfilled will be left to the reader (Section 8.6, Exercise 1).

The completeness of this metric space follows from the fact that if $\{\phi_n\}$ is a Cauchy sequence of elements of C, then for every $\epsilon > 0$,

$$\exists N \ni n > N \Rightarrow d(\phi_n, \phi_{n+k}) = \max_x |\phi_n(x) - \phi_{n+k}(x)| < \epsilon \qquad \text{for all } k,$$

and therefore for all x with $|x - x_0| \leq \delta$,

$$|\phi_n(x) - \phi_{n+k}(x)| \leq \max_x |\phi_n(x) - \phi_{n+k}(x)| < \epsilon$$

which tells us that $\{\phi_n\}$ converges uniformly for $|x - x_0| \leq \delta$ (see Section 8.1, Theorem 8.3). The uniformly convergent sequence $\{\phi_n\}$ of continuous functions consequently has a limit ϕ which is continuous (Theorem 8.1). To check that $\phi \in C$, we note that

$$|\phi_n(x) - y_0| \leq K\delta \Rightarrow \lim_{n \to \infty} |\phi_n(x) - y_0| \leq K\delta \Rightarrow |\phi(x) - y_0| \leq K\delta$$

(see Section 5.2, Exercise 1). Therefore C is a complete metric space.

Consider the mapping A of C which carries $\phi \in C$ into the function $A\phi$ defined by (compare with 8.17)

$$A\phi(x) = y_0 + \int_{x_0}^x f(t, \phi(t))\, dt. \tag{8.19}$$

[To illustrate, in Example 8.13 where $f(x, y) = -x/y$, $x_0 = 0$, $y_0 = 1$, the function ϕ defined by $\phi(x) = x^2 + 1$ is transformed into $A\phi$ where

$$A\phi(x) = 1 - \int_0^x \frac{t}{t^2 + 1}\, dt = 1 - \frac{1}{2}\log(t^2 + 1)\Big|_0^x = 1 - \frac{1}{2}\log(x^2 + 1).]$$

A is a contraction mapping of C into itself for, let $\phi \in C$. Then, by definition of $\phi \in C$, ϕ is a continuous function of x, $|x - x_0| \leq \delta$, and $|\phi(x) - y_0| \leq K\delta$. We will first show that A is a mapping of C into C; that is, $A\phi \in C$. That $A\phi$ is a continuous function of x, $|x - x_0| \leq \delta$, is easy to verify (Section 8.6, Exercise 1) so we omit this. Also, from (8.19) and definition of K,

$$|A\phi(x) - y_0| = \left| \int_{x_0}^{x} f(t, \phi(t)) \, dt \right| \leq K|x - x_0| \leq K\delta$$

which shows that $A\phi \in C$. Hence $AC \subset C$. In addition, if $x > x_0$ (this last restriction not an essential one),

$$|A\phi_1(x) - A\phi_2(x)| = \left| \int_{x_0}^{x} [f(t, \phi_1(t)) - f(t, \phi_2(t))] \, dt \right|$$

$$\leq \int_{x_0}^{x} |f(t, \phi_1(t)) - f(t, \phi_2(t))| \, dt$$

$$\leq \int_{x_0}^{x} M|\phi_1(t) - \phi_2(t)| \, dt \quad (f \text{ is Lipschitzian})$$

$$\leq M|x - x_0| \max_x |\phi_1(x) - \phi_2(x)|$$

$$\leq M \delta d(\phi_1, \phi_2).$$

However, the right member is independent of x and this justifies writing

$$\max_x |A\phi_1(x) - A\phi_2(x)| \leq M \delta d(\phi_1, \phi_2)$$

or

$$d(A\phi_1, A\phi_2) \leq M \delta d(\phi_1, \phi_2).$$

Using (8.18) we conclude that $\delta \leq \frac{1}{2}M$, so that $d(A\phi_1, A\phi_2) \leq \frac{1}{2}d(\phi_1, \phi_2)$. In other words, A is a contraction mapping of C into C. Invoking Theorem 8.11, we see that $A\phi = \phi$ has a unique solution. The equality $A\phi = \phi$, however, is precisely (8.17). ∎

It should be noted that the method of proof used in the contraction mapping theorem, at least theoretically, suggests how to estimate the solution of $A\phi = \phi$. We begin with any element g_0 of C and compute successive iterates: $Ag_0, A^2g_0, \cdots$. Of course, the convergence may be so slow that the procedure becomes infeasible.

8.6 EXERCISES

1. (a) Show that the space $C = \{\phi \mid \phi$ is a continuous function of x, $|x - x_0| \leq \delta$, and $|\phi(x) - y_0| \leq K\delta\}$ with $d(\phi_1, \phi_2) = \max_x \{|\phi_1(x) - \phi_2(x)|\}$ $\phi_1, \phi_2 \in C$, is a metric space.

(b) Show that $A\phi$, for $\phi \in C$, defined by

$$A\phi(x) = y_0 + \int_{x_0}^{x} f(t, \phi(t)) \, dt, \qquad |x - x_0| \leq \delta,$$

is a continuous function of x.

2. Prove that the set $S = \{(x, y) \mid x, y \text{ real numbers}\}$ with the function d on $S \times S$ defined by $d((x_1, y_1), (x_2, y_2)) = |x_1 - x_2| + |y_1 - y_2|$ is a metric space. This metric space is described intuitively as "only East-West, North-South roads for transportation." Explain. Is this space complete?

3. Show that the set $S = \{f \mid f \text{ is Riemann integrable on } [a, b]\}$ with $d(f, g) = \int_a^b |f(x) - g(x)| \, dx$ for $f, g \in S$ is a metric space which is not complete.

[HINT: To show that this metric space is not complete, see Example 8.5.]

4. If S is any metric space, if $f \in S$, and if $r > 0$, we define the *neighborhood* $N(f; r)$ *of* f *having radius* r by $N(f; r) = \{g \mid g \in S, d(f, g) < r\}$. Describe $N(0; 1)$ in each case:
   (a) The space C of Exercise 1(a).
   (b) The space S of Exercise 2.
   (c) The space S of Exercise 3.

5. Show that the function f defined by $f(x, y) = x + y$, where x, y are real numbers, is a continuous function. How about $x - y$? xy? $\sqrt{x^2 + y^2}$?

6. Solve the initial value problem:

$$\frac{dy}{dx} = x^2 + y, \qquad y(0) = 0.$$

7. Consider the initial value problem:

$$\frac{dy}{dx} = x^2 + y^2, \qquad y(0) = 0.$$

Compute $A\phi$, $A^2\phi$, $A^3\phi$, where A is defined by (8.19) (Section 8.5). Start with $\phi = 0$.

9

Fourier Series

INTRODUCTION

As another application of some of the theory which we have developed, in this chapter we focus our attention on an area of analysis which has had a profound influence on the development of analysis itself. The concept of Fourier series had its origin in the study of the conduction of heat. This problem is only one of a large class of similar problems in mathematical physics. The central concept of Fourier series is the forerunner of what is known today as *harmonic analysis*, an area of mathematics which continues to elicit vigorous mathematical research.

A simple problem in the conduction of heat ("Dirichlet's problem") is used to motivate the concept of Fourier series of a function. Two key results (the Riemann-Lebesgue lemma and Riemann's localization theorem) are subsequently proved and used to show that a sufficient condition for the Fourier series (evaluated at x) of a function f to converge to $f(x)$ is that f be Lipschitzian at x. Next we prove the important theorem of Fejér: For continuous functions, the sequence of arithmetic means of the partial sums of the Fourier series of f converges uniformly to f. As a consequence of this theorem, we prove a famous result due to Weierstrass. Weierstrass's approximation theorem, roughly speaking, says that an arbitrary continuous function can be approximated uniformly by a polynomial. We return to Fourier series and, by means of an application of a general result on series due to Frobenius, complete the solution of the Dirichlet problem.

Throughout the chapter we shall be concerned with complex-valued functions, usually with domain an interval of real numbers, although occasionally the domain too will be a set of complex numbers. It should be emphasized in this connection that the usual rules for differentiation and integration (both definite and indefinite) are valid for complex-valued functions of a real variable. This follows from the fact that if f is a complex-valued function defined on $[a, b]$, then

$$f(t) = x(t) + iy(t),$$

where x and y are real-valued functions of the real variable $t \in [a, b]$. Since the formal definition of the derivative is the same as for real functions, we have

$$f'(t) = \lim_{h \to 0} \frac{f(t+h) - f(t)}{h} = \lim_{h \to 0} \left[\frac{x(t+h) + iy(t+h) - x(t) - iy(t)}{h} \right]$$

$$= \lim_{h \to 0} \left[\frac{x(t+h) - x(t)}{h} + i \frac{y(t+h) - y(t)}{h} \right]$$

$$= x'(t) + iy'(t)$$

provided, of course, x' and y' exist. In particular, if we define the complex exponential $e^{i\alpha t}$, α a real constant, $t \in [a, b]$, by

$$e^{i\alpha t} = \cos \alpha t + i \sin \alpha t, \tag{9.1}$$

then

$$\frac{de^{i\alpha t}}{dt} = -\alpha \sin \alpha t + i\alpha \cos \alpha t$$

$$= i\alpha(\cos \alpha t + i \sin \alpha t)$$

$$= i\alpha e^{i\alpha t}.$$

Further details will be found in the Supplements to Chapters 5 and 6. Although we cannot afford the digression necessary to define rigorously the trigonometric functions and develop the familiar properties of these functions, the reader should be made aware that the geometric definitions given in elementary mathematics courses are imprecise.*

---

* There are several different ways of approaching this problem; the interested reader should consult, for example, *Principles of Mathematical Analysis* by W. Rudin, 2d ed., New York, McGraw-Hill Book Company, 1964, or *Complex Analysis* by L. Ahlfors, New York, McGraw-Hill Book Company, 1953.

9.1 THE DIRICHLET PROBLEM

A basic problem in the theory of conduction of heat finds its solution in the theory of Fourier series. As a matter of fact, the subject of Fourier series was given a great impetus with the publication of the book *Théorie Analytique de la Chaleur* (Analytic Theory of Heat) by J. B. J. Fourier in 1822. In physical terms, a motivating problem can be described as follows. Each point on the boundary of a unit circular disk is maintained at a certain temperature. It is understood that the temperature may vary from point to point on the boundary, but at any particular point it is fixed. Presumably such conditions are maintained through some physical arrangement, but this aspect is of no concern to us. The system is allowed to reach a "state of equilibrium" or "steady-state condition." The question is now raised as to the temperature distribution throughout the disk; that is, we select an arbitrary point of the disk and inquire as to the temperature at that point.

As far as mathematics is concerned, as yet no precise problem has been formulated. A mathematical model must be found which embodies the salient features of the physical description given above. We shall not go into detail in explaining how the transition from the physical criteria (discussed above) to the mathematical model (defined below) is effected; the interested reader should consult existing literature on the subject.*

Basic assumptions of heat conduction lead to the partial differential equation for the temperature function u of (r, θ) (polar coordinates) which we seek:

$$\frac{\partial^2 u}{\partial r^2} + \frac{1}{r}\frac{\partial u}{\partial r} + \frac{1}{r^2}\frac{\partial^2 u}{\partial \theta^2} = 0, \qquad r \neq 0. \tag{9.2}$$

This equation is known as Laplace's equation (in polar coordinate form). Two further conditions are imposed on the function u, arising essentially out of peculiarities of polar coordinates. Since (9.2) does not apply to $r = 0$, we impose the reasonable assumption (from both the physical and mathematical points of view) that

$$u \text{ is a continuous function of } (r, \theta),\ 0 \le r \le 1,\ \theta \text{ real.} \tag{9.3}$$

Bearing in mind that (9.2) places no restriction on u insofar as $r = 0$ is concerned, it is not surprising that there are functions u which satisfy (9.2) but are not continuous at $r = 0$. In other words, (9.3) is not implied by (9.2). This is illustrated by Example 9.1.

---

* For example, *An Introduction to Fourier Series and Integrals* by R. Seeley, New York, W. A. Benjamin, Inc., 1966.

Example 9.1. The function u defined by

$$u(r, \theta) = \begin{cases} 1, & \text{if } r \neq 0, \\ 0, & \text{if } r = 0 \end{cases}$$

satisfies (9.2) but is not continuous at $(0, 0)$ since the sequence $\{(1/n, 1/n)\}$ converges to $(0, 0)$, $\{u(1/n, 1/n)\}$ converges to 1, but $u(0, 0) = 0$.

Recognizing that (r, θ) and $(r, \theta + 2\pi)$ represent the same point, we must obviously insist that

$$u(r, \theta) = u(r, \theta + 2\pi). \tag{9.4}$$

Finally, the following requirement simply states that the boundary temperatures are specified by a given function f:

$$u(1, \theta) = f(\theta). \tag{9.5}$$

In connection with this last condition, we note that a complete specification of the boundary temperatures would be embodied in a function f with domain $0 \leq \theta < 2\pi$. Such a given function could be replaced by a function g defined to be the set $\{(\theta, g(\theta)) \mid \theta \text{ real}, g(\theta + 2\pi) = f(\theta)\}$; that is, we lose no generality in assuming that f is periodic with period 2π. This is done in order that (9.4) will be valid for all real θ. In summary:

The heat conduction problem (known as "Dirichlet's problem") is to find a function u such that (9.2) to (9.5) hold, where f is a given function with period 2π.

In what follows we shall be considering complex-valued functions u which satisfy some or all of the conditions, (9.2) to (9.5), above. Now, in order that a solution to the Dirichlet problem will admit a physical interpretation, it will have to be a real-valued function of a complex variable since it purports to answer the question: What is the *temperature* [real number $u(r, \theta)$] at the *point* (r, θ) (complex number)? Suppose, however, that we could succeed in finding a complex-valued function u which satisfies the conditions, (9.2) to (9.5). We could then decompose u into its real and imaginary parts, writing

$$u(r, \theta) = \alpha(r, \theta) + i\beta(r, \theta)$$

where each of α and β is a real-valued function of (r, θ). It is then a simple exercise to check that if u satisfies (9.2) to (9.5), it follows that each of α and β satisfies (9.2) to (9.5) (Section 9.3, Exercise 2). Thus a complex-valued function with properties (9.2) to (9.5) will have real and imaginary parts satisfying (9.2) to (9.5), and either of these can be interpreted physically.

Consider the function u defined by

$$u(r, \theta) = re^{i\theta}. \tag{9.6}$$

It is easy to check that (9.6) satisfies conditions (9.2) to (9.4). More generally, if m is any positive integer, the function defined by

$$u(r, \theta) = r^m e^{im\theta} \tag{9.7}$$

satisfies (9.2) to (9.4). We leave it to the reader to verify this (Section 9.3, Exercise 1). If m is a negative integer, then

$$r^m e^{im\theta}$$

is unbounded as $r \to 0$; that is

$$\left| r^m e^{im\theta} \right| = \left| r^m \right|$$

becomes arbitrarily large as r tends to 0. This means, of course, that for every $M > 0$, $\exists N(0; R) \ni r \in N(0; R) \Rightarrow |r^m| \geq M$. On the other hand, condition (9.3) implies that $|u|$ has a maximum since it is continuous on the compact set $\{(r, \theta) \mid 0 \leq r \leq 1, 0 \leq \theta \leq 2\pi\}$ and hence we cannot hope for $r^m e^{im\theta}$ to satisfy (9.3) when m is a negative integer. If, however, we consider

$$u(r, \theta) = r^{|m|} e^{im\theta}, \qquad m \text{ an integer}, \tag{9.8}$$

then it is a simple computational exercise to verify that (9.8) does indeed satisfy (9.2) to (9.4).

Now one of the most important facts concerning the conditions (9.2) to (9.5) is the linear nature of those conditions; that is, if $u_1, u_2, \cdots, u_n$ are functions satisfying (9.2) to (9.5), then any linear combination

$$\sum_{k=-1}^{n} c_k u_k$$

(where the c_k, $k = 1, 2, \cdots, n$, are complex numbers) also satisfies the same conditions. The proof of this statement is straightforward and is left to the reader (Section 9.3, Exercise 3). Thus (9.2) to (9.4) is satisfied by

$$u(r, \theta) = \sum_{k=-n}^{n} c_k r^{|k|} e^{ik\theta}. \tag{9.9}$$

In order that (9.5) hold, however, it would be necessary from (9.9) that

$$u(1, \theta) = \sum_{k=-n}^{n} c_k e^{ik\theta} = f(\theta).$$

Unfortunately, this represents a severe restriction on the "arbitrarily given function" f. In fact, since $\sum_{k=-n}^{n} c_k e^{ik\theta}$ is clearly a continuous function of θ, evidently if f is discontinuous the equality $\sum_{k=-n}^{n} c_k e^{ik\theta} = f(\theta)$ is not valid. [Of course, (9.3) and (9.5) imply f is continuous. But in more advanced problems we want to relax (9.3) so that discontinuous f may be considered.] In a natural attempt to alleviate this restriction, we are led to consider a *series* of the form

$$\sum_{k=-\infty}^{\infty} c_k e^{ik\theta}. \tag{9.10}$$

That a larger class of functions can be described by a series of the form (9.10) than by a finite sum of the form

$$\sum_{k=-n}^{n} c_k e^{ik\theta} \tag{9.11}$$

is obvious since (9.11) is a special case of (9.10) (put $c_k = 0$ for $|k| > n$ to see this). What may not be quite so obvious is that certain discontinuous functions may be represented by (9.10) as will be illustrated in Example 9.6.

These considerations suggest an approach to solving the Dirichlet problem: We try to determine the numbers c_k so that for all real θ we shall have

$$\sum_{k=-\infty}^{\infty} c_k e^{ik\theta} = f(\theta); \tag{9.12}$$

the function u defined by (9.9) is then determined by the same c_k with the expectation that its limit as $n \to \infty$ will furnish a solution to the problem.

We shall return to the Dirichlet problem later (Section 9.8). Our primary purpose in formulating that problem here was to indicate the leading role played by the series in the left member of (9.12).

9.2   FOURIER SERIES OF AN INTEGRABLE FUNCTION

With the motivation given above, we are led to the following definition.

Definition 9.1.   A *trigonometric polynomial* is a finite sum of the form

$$f(x) = \sum_{k=-n}^{n} c_k e^{ikx} \tag{9.13}$$

where the c_k, $k = 0, \pm1, \pm2, \cdots, \pm n$, are complex numbers and x is real.

Remark 1
Since

$$c_k(\cos kx + i \sin kx) + c_{-k}[\cos(-kx) + i \sin(-kx)]$$
$$= (c_k + c_{-k}) \cos kx + i(c_k - ic_{-k}) \sin kx$$
$$= (c_k + c_{-k}) \cos kx + (c_{-k} + ic_k) \sin kx,$$

it follows that every trigonometric polynomial can be written in the form

$$A_0 + \sum_{k=1}^{n} (A_k \cos kx + B_k \sin kx)$$

where $A_0, A_1, \cdots, A_n, B_1, \cdots, B_n$ are complex numbers. The well-known deMoivre formula:

$$(\cos \theta + i \sin \theta)^n = \cos n\theta + i \sin n\theta$$

together with the binomial theorem enable one to express the trigonometric functions of the integral multiples of θ as polynomials in $\cos \theta$, $\sin \theta$. These facts account for the name "trigonometric polynomial" since (9.13) is simply a polynomial in the trigonometric variables $\sin \theta$, $\cos \theta$.

Example 9.2.   Because $\cos 2\theta + i \sin 2\theta = (\cos \theta + i \sin \theta)^2 = \cos^2 \theta - \sin^2 \theta + (2 \cos \theta \sin \theta)i$, it follows that $\cos 2\theta = \cos^2 \theta - \sin^2 \theta$ and $\sin 2\theta = 2 \sin \theta \cos \theta$, showing that $\cos 2\theta$ and $\sin 2\theta$ are polynomials in $\cos \theta$, $\sin \theta$.

Remark 2

Every trigonometric polynomial is periodic with period 2π; that is, if f is a trigonometric polynomial, then $f(x + 2\pi) = f(x)$ for all real x. Proof is left to the reader.

Suppose that f is a trigonometric polynomial defined by (9.13). How can c_m, m an integer, $-n \leq m \leq n$, be determined? A straightforward calculation shows that

$$\frac{1}{2\pi} \int_{-\pi}^{\pi} e^{ikx} \, dx = \begin{cases} 1, & \text{if } k = 0, \\ 0, & \text{if } k = \pm 1, \pm 2, \cdots. \end{cases}$$

It follows that if we multiply $f(x)$ by e^{-imx} and integrate, we get

$$\int_{-\pi}^{\pi} f(x)e^{-imx} \, dx = \int_{-\pi}^{\pi} \sum_{k=-n}^{n} c_k e^{i(k-m)x} \, dx = \sum_{k=-n}^{n} c_k \int_{-\pi}^{\pi} e^{i(k-m)x} \, dx = 2\pi c_m;$$

in other words, we have shown that if

$$f(x) = \sum_{k=-n}^{n} c_k e^{ikx} \quad \text{for all } x,$$

then

$$c_m = \frac{1}{2\pi} \int_{-\pi}^{\pi} f(x)e^{-imx} \, dx, \qquad m = 0, \pm 1, \pm 2, \cdots, \pm n.$$

But if we examine the equality

$$c_m = \frac{1}{2\pi} \int_{-\pi}^{\pi} f(x)e^{-imx} \, dx, \tag{9.14}$$

we see that if f is any integrable function, then $f(x)e^{-imx}$ is also integrable and the expression (9.14) giving c_m is meaningful. This suggests the following.

Definition 9.2. If f is an integrable function on $[-\pi, \pi]$ having period 2π, the *Fourier coefficients of f* are the numbers c_k, $k = 0, \pm 1, \pm 2, \cdots$, defined by

$$c_k = \frac{1}{2\pi} \int_{-\pi}^{\pi} f(x)e^{-ikx} \, dx. \qquad (9.15)$$

The sequence whose nth term is the function s_n defined by

$$s_n(x) = \sum_{k=-n}^{n} c_k e^{ikx} = \sum_{k=-n}^{n} \left[\frac{1}{2\pi} \int_{-\pi}^{\pi} f(t)e^{-ikt} \, dt \right] e^{ikx}$$

or

$$s_n(x) = \frac{1}{2\pi} \sum_{k=-n}^{n} \int_{-\pi}^{\pi} f(t)e^{ik(x-t)} \, dt \qquad (9.16)$$

is called the *Fourier series of f*. We introduce the notation

$$f(x) \sim \sum_{k=-\infty}^{\infty} c_k e^{ikx} \qquad (9.17)$$

and read this: The Fourier series of f is $\sum_{k=-\infty}^{\infty} c_k e^{ikx}$ where c_k is given by (9.15) and the symbol $\sum_{k=-\infty}^{\infty} c_k e^{ikx}$ stands for the sequence $\{s_n(x)\}$ given by (9.16). When the limit of this sequence exists we sometimes use the symbol $\sum_{k=-\infty}^{\infty} c_k e^{ikx}$ to stand for this limit. The context in which the symbol appears will remove any ambiguity. We emphasize that the notation (9.17) will be used without regard for convergence or divergence of $\{s_n(x)\}$. We use it even in case $\{s_n(x)\}$ converges but not to $f(x)$.

Remark 3

If we take Remark 1 under Definition 9.1 into account, it is easy to see that if $f(x) \sim \sum_{k=-\infty}^{\infty} c_k e^{ikx}$, then $f(x) \sim A_0 + \sum_{k=1}^{\infty} (A_k \cos kx + B_k \sin kx)$; for our purposes, however, it is more convenient to use the exponential form for the Fourier series, and this is why we lay the emphasis there.

Remark 4

It was shown above that if $f(x) = \sum_{k=-n}^{n} c_k e^{ikx}$, then

$$c_m = \frac{1}{2\pi} \int_{-\pi}^{\pi} f(x)e^{-imx} \, dx.$$

Since $f(x)$ is real iff $f(x) = \overline{f(x)}$ (see Section 3.10, Exercise 6), it follows that the trigonometric polynomial f is real iff $c_{-m} = \overline{c_m}$, $m = 0, 1, 2, \cdots, n$. Details are left to the reader (Section 9.3, Exercise 10).

Example 9.3. Find the Fourier series of the function f defined by

$$f(x) = x, \qquad -\pi < x < \pi.$$

By definition,

$$c_k = \frac{1}{2\pi} \int_{-\pi}^{\pi} xe^{-ikx}\,dx, \qquad k = 0, \pm 1, \pm 2, \cdots.$$

If $k = 0$, we find

$$c_0 = \frac{1}{2\pi} \int_{-\pi}^{\pi} x\,dx = 0.$$

If $k \neq 0$, we may integrate by parts to get

$$c_k = \frac{1}{2\pi} \int_{-\pi}^{\pi} xe^{-ikx}\,dx = \frac{1}{2\pi}\left[\frac{xe^{-ikx}}{-ik}\Big|_{-\pi}^{\pi} - \int_{-\pi}^{\pi} \frac{e^{-ikx}}{-ik}\,dx\right]$$

$$= -\frac{1}{2\pi ki}\left[\pi e^{-ik\pi} - (-\pi)e^{-ik(-\pi)}\right]$$

(the last integral above vanishes)

$$= -\frac{1}{2ki}\left[(-1)^k + (-1)^k\right] \quad (\text{since } e^{ik\pi} = e^{-ik\pi} = (-1)^k)$$

$$= \frac{(-1)^k i}{k}.$$

Therefore, the Fourier series of f is

$$\sum_{k=-\infty}^{\infty} c_k e^{ikx} = i \sum_{\substack{k=-\infty \\ k \neq 0}}^{\infty} \frac{(-1)^k}{k} e^{ikx}.$$

Adding pairs of terms with $k = n$ and $k = -n$, we have as an alternative expression

$$\sum_{k=-\infty}^{\infty} c_k e^{ikx} = i \sum_{n=1}^{\infty} \left[\frac{(-1)^n}{n} e^{inx} + \frac{(-1)^{-n}}{-n} e^{-inx}\right]$$

$$= i \sum_{n=1}^{\infty} \frac{(-1)^n}{n}\left[e^{inx} - e^{-inx}\right]$$

$$= 2 \sum_{n=1}^{\infty} \frac{(-1)^{n+1}\sin nx}{n} \quad \left(\text{since } \sin nx = \frac{1}{2i}\left[e^{inx} - e^{-inx}\right]\right)$$

$$= 2\left[\sin x - \frac{\sin 2x}{2} + \frac{\sin 3x}{3} - \frac{\sin 4x}{4} + \cdots\right].$$

Using the convention introduced by (9.17), we write

$$x \sim i \sum_{\substack{k=-\infty \\ k \neq 0}}^{\infty} \frac{(-1)^k}{k} e^{ikx}$$

or, alternatively,

$$x \sim 2 \sum_{n=1}^{\infty} (-1)^{n+1} \frac{\sin nx}{n}.$$

Example 9.4. Show that if f is an integrable odd function and if $f(x) \sim \sum_{k=-\infty}^{\infty} c_k e^{ikx}$, then $c_k = -c_{-k}$.

If f is an odd function, that is, if $f(-x) = -f(x)$, then

$$c_k = \frac{1}{2\pi} \int_{-\pi}^{\pi} f(x)e^{-ikx}\, dx = -\frac{1}{2\pi} \int_{\pi}^{-\pi} f(-u)e^{iku}\, du$$

$$= -\frac{1}{2\pi} \int_{-\pi}^{\pi} f(u)e^{iku}\, du = -c_{-k}.$$

Now suppose we are given an integrable function f. We form its Fourier series and raise two questions:

(1) Does the Fourier series of f converge?

(2) If the Fourier series of f converges for some x, does it converge to $f(x)$? We certainly cannot expect the Fourier series of the function f to converge to the value $f(x)$ of the function at *every* point of the domain of f for changing the value of the function at a point will affect neither its integrability nor the value of the integral, and hence two integrable functions which differ at a point (actually on a set of measure zero) will have the same Fourier series (see Section 9.3, Exercise 12).

To indicate the degree of difficulty of the questions raised above, it was not known until recently whether or not for a given continuous function f there exists a point x such that the Fourier series of f converges. L. Carleson solved this problem.* He proved that if f is periodic with period 2π and if $|f|^2$ is integrable on $[0, 2\pi]$ in the sense of Lebesgue, then the Fourier series of f converges to f almost everywhere. Since continuity of f on $[0, 2\pi]$ implies integrability of $|f|^2$ in the sense of Lebesgue, Carleson's result implies that the Fourier series of a continuous periodic function f converges almost everywhere to f.

Our immediate goal in the theory is, by comparison, a very modest one. We want to prove that *if the function f satisfies a Lipschitz condition at a point x of its domain, then the Fourier series of f converges at x to $f(x)$.* In order to achieve this goal, we can divide our plan of proof into four parts:

(1) In Section 9.4 we will find a convenient form for the expression giving $s_n(x)$ (remember we want to show that "f Lipschitzian at x implies $|s_n(x) - f(x)|$ can be made small provided n is large enough").

(2) We will prove that the Fourier coefficients c_k of any (integrable) function tend to zero as $|k| \to \infty$ (Section 9.4).

(3) We will prove Riemann's localization theorem (Section 9.4). Roughly

---

* See *Acta Mathematicae*, 116 (1966), 135–157, "On convergence and growth of partial sums of Fourier series."

speaking, this theorem says that the convergence at a point x of the Fourier series of f is determined by the behavior of f in an arbitrarily small neighborhood of x.

(4) Using the results in (1) to (3) above, in Section 9.5 we reach our immediate goal.

9.3 EXERCISES

1. Show that if u is defined by

$$u(r, \theta) = r^{|m|}e^{im\theta}$$

where m is an arbitrary integer, then u satisfies conditions (9.2) to (9.4) of Dirichlet's problem (Section 9.1).

2. Show that if u is the complex-valued function with real and imaginary parts α and β so that

$$u(r, \theta) = \alpha(r, \theta) + i\beta(r, \theta),$$

and if u is a solution of Dirichlet's problem, then each of α, β furnishes a solution to Dirichlet's problem.

3. Show that if each of $u_1, u_2, \cdots, u_n$ is a function of (r, θ) satisfying (9.2) to (9.5) in Dirichlet's problem, and if $c_k, k = 1, 2, \cdots, n$ are arbitrary complex numbers, then the function $v = \sum_{k=1}^{n} c_k u_k$ defined by

$$v(r, \theta) = \sum_{k=1}^{n} c_k u_k(r, \theta)$$

also satisfies (9.2) to (9.5).

4. Show that

$$\frac{1}{2\pi} \int_{-\pi}^{\pi} e^{ikx}\, dx = \begin{cases} 1, & \text{if } k = 0, \\ 0, & \text{if } k = \pm 1, \pm 2, \cdots. \end{cases}$$

5. Prove that every trigonometric polynomial is periodic with period 2π.

6. Taking the open interval $(-\pi, \pi)$ as domain, find the Fourier series of the functions defined by:

(a) $f(x) = |x|$.

(b) $f(x) = e^{\alpha x}$, α real.

(c) $f(x) = x^2$.

(d) $f(x) = \begin{cases} -1, & \text{if } -\pi < x < 0 \\ 0, & \text{if } x = 0 \\ 1, & \text{if } 0 < x < \pi. \end{cases}$

(e) $f(x) = \begin{cases} 0, & \text{if } -\pi < x < 0 \\ 1, & \text{if } 0 \le x < \pi. \end{cases}$

(*f*) $f(x) = 1$.

(*g*) $f(x) = |\sin x|$.

7. Show that if *f* is an even function [that is, $f(-x) = f(x)$], then $c_{-k} = c_k$ for all integers *k*.

8. (*a*) Show that if *f* is an even function and *g* is an odd function, then the product is an odd function.

   (*b*) Show that if *f*, *g* are both even functions or if both are odd, then the product is even.

9. Let *f* be a given function with domain $[-\pi, \pi]$. Define

$$g(x) = f(x) + f(-x)$$

$$h(x) = f(x) - f(-x).$$

   (*a*) Show that *g* and *h* are even and odd, respectively.

   (*b*) Show that *f* is the sum of an even function and an odd function.

10. Show that the trigonometric polynomial *f* given by

$$f(x) = \sum_{k=-n}^{n} c_k e^{ikx}$$

   is real iff $c_{-m} = \overline{c_m}$, $m = 0, 1, 2, \cdots, n$ (see Remark 4 following Definition 9.2).

11. Give an example of functions *f* and *g* with the following properties: $f = g$ almost everywhere, *f* is Riemann integrable but *g* is not.

12. (*a*) Show that if *f*, *g* are integrable on $[a, b]$ and if $f = g$ almost everywhere, then $\int_a^b f(x)\, dx = \int_a^b g(x)\, dx$.

   $\left[\text{HINT:} \quad \text{Consider } h(x) = f(x) - g(x). \text{ Show that } \int_a^b h(x)\, dx = 0. \right]$

   (*b*) Show that two integrable functions which differ only on a set of measure zero have the same Fourier series.

13. Consider the relation *S* defined by

$$S = \{(f, g) \,|\, f, g \text{ are functions with domain } [a, b] \text{ and}$$

$$f = g \text{ almost everywhere}\}.$$

   Show that *S* is an equivalence relation.

9.4 TWO KEY THEOREMS IN FOURIER SERIES

In this section we prove two basic theorems in our investigation of Fourier series: the Riemann-Lebesgue lemma and Riemann's localization theorem. In order to arrive at the latter, we shall need a more tractable form for $s_n(x)$ (see Definition 9.2), and this is the content of the next theorem.

■ **Theorem 9.1.**   The geometric series $\sum_{k=-n}^{n} e^{ik\alpha}$ can be written in closed form:

$$\sum_{k=-n}^{n} e^{ik\alpha} = \frac{\sin (n + \frac{1}{2})\alpha}{\sin (\alpha/2)}.$$

Proof: An easy consequence of the definition $e^{i\alpha} = \cos \alpha + i \sin \alpha$ is the following:

$$\sin \alpha = \frac{1}{2i} (e^{i\alpha} - e^{-i\alpha}), \qquad \cos \alpha = \frac{1}{2} (e^{i\alpha} + e^{-i\alpha}).$$

Once we have this result and we recall the elementary formula

$$a + ar + ar^2 + \cdots + ar^{n-1} = \frac{a - ar^n}{1 - r},$$

the rest is easy:

$$\sum_{k=-n}^{n} e^{ik\alpha} = \frac{e^{-in\alpha} - e^{i(n+1)\alpha}}{1 - e^{i\alpha}} \cdot \frac{e^{-i\alpha/2}}{e^{-i\alpha/2}} = \frac{e^{-i(n+1/2)\alpha} - e^{i(n+1/2)\alpha}}{e^{-i\alpha/2} - e^{i\alpha/2}} \frac{1/2i}{1/2i}$$

$$= \frac{\sin (n + \frac{1}{2})\alpha}{\sin \alpha/2}. \quad ■$$

It is now a matter of computation to prove the following.

■ **Theorem 9.2.**   If $f \sim \sum_{k=-\infty}^{\infty} c_k e^{ikx}$, then

$$s_n(x) = \sum_{k=-n}^{n} c_k e^{ikx} = \frac{1}{2\pi} \int_{-\pi}^{\pi} f(t) \frac{\sin [(n + \frac{1}{2})(x - t)]}{\sin [(x - t)/2]} dt.$$

Proof:

$$s_n(x) = \sum_{k=-n}^{n} c_k e^{ikx} = \sum_{k=-n}^{n} \left[\frac{1}{2\pi} \int_{-\pi}^{\pi} f(t)e^{-ikt} dt \right] e^{ikx}$$

$$= \frac{1}{2\pi} \int_{-\pi}^{\pi} f(t) \sum_{k=-n}^{n} e^{ik(x-t)} dt$$

$$= \frac{1}{2\pi} \int_{-\pi}^{\pi} f(t) \frac{\sin [(n + \frac{1}{2})(x - t)]}{\sin [(x - t)/2]} dt. \quad ■$$

At this point it is convenient to introduce the following.

Definition 9.3.   *Dirichlet's kernel D_n is the trigonometric polynomial* defined by

$$D_n(x) = \sum_{k=-n}^{n} e^{ikx} = \frac{\sin (n + \frac{1}{2})x}{\sin (x/2)}.$$

Remark

According to Theorem 9.2 and Definition 9.3, we may write

$$s_n(x) = \frac{1}{2\pi} \int_{-\pi}^{\pi} f(t) D_n(x - t)\, dt.$$

But if we make the change of variable $u = x - t$ and take into account the periodicity of f, we get

$$s_n(x) = \frac{1}{2\pi} \int_{-\pi}^{\pi} f(x - t) D_n(t)\, dt.$$

The reader is asked to supply the details in Section 9.6, Exercise 1.

Thus the Fourier series generated by f will converge at the point x iff the

sequence $\left\{ \dfrac{1}{2\pi} \displaystyle\int_{-\pi}^{\pi} f(x - t) D_n(t)\, dt \right\}$ of integrals converges.

Our next task is to show that the Fourier coefficients c_k of any integrable function tend to zero as k tends to infinity. As we shall see, this is implied by the more general Riemann-Lebesgue lemma. In proving that lemma, we use the notions of characteristic function and step function.

Definition 9.4.   Let S be any set. By the *characteristic function f_S* of S is meant the function defined by

$$f_S(x) = \begin{cases} 1, & \text{if } x \in S, \\ 0, & \text{if } x \notin S. \end{cases}$$

Definition 9.5. f is a *step function* on $[a, b]$ iff f is a linear combination of a finite number of characteristic functions of subintervals of $[a, b]$; that is, iff f is a function of the form

$$\sum_{m=1}^{n} a_m f_{I_m},$$

where $a_1, a_2, \cdots, a_n$ are complex numbers and f_{I_m} is the characteristic function of the interval $I_m \subset [a, b]$ (the bounded interval I_m may be open, closed, or half-open). Of course, the value of f at $x \in [a, b]$ is given by

$$f(x) = \sum_{m=1}^{n} a_m f_{I_m}(x).$$

Example 9.5.   Consider the function f defined by

$$f(x) = x^2, \qquad 0 \le x \le 1.$$

Let n be a positive integer. Consider the partition $P = \{0, 1/n, 2/n, \cdots,$ $(n - 1)/n, 1\}$. This partition determines the intervals I_m described by

$$I_m = \left\{ x \;\middle|\; \frac{m-1}{n} < x \le \frac{m}{n} \right\}, \qquad m = 1, 2, \cdots, n.$$

(See Fig. 9.1.) Put

$$a_m = \sup \{ f(x) \mid x \in I_m \}, \qquad m = 1, \cdots, n$$

[in other words, $a_m = M_m(f)$ in the notation of Chapter 7]. The graphs of f and the step function

are shown in Fig. 9.1. Note that the integral of this step function is simply the Darboux upper sum $U(P, f)$.

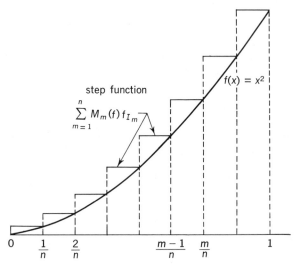

Fig. 9.1   Graphs of f and a step function whose integral approximates the integral of f.

■ **Theorem 9.3.** (Riemann-Lebesgue lemma). If f is integrable on $[a, b]$ and if $[c, d] \subset [a, b]$, then $\lim_{|\lambda| \to \infty} \int_c^d f(x) e^{-i\lambda x}\, dx = 0$.

Proof: (The plan of the proof is to first show that the theorem holds when f is the characteristic function of $[c, d]$; then to verify the theorem for any step function f on $[a, b]$, and finally to extend the result to an arbitrary integrable function.)

If f is the characteristic function of $[c, d]$, then

$$\left| \int_a^b f(x) e^{-i\lambda x} \, dx \right| = \left| \int_c^d e^{-i\lambda x} \, dx \right| = \left| \frac{1}{\lambda} \right| |e^{-i\lambda d} - e^{-i\lambda c}|$$

$$\le \frac{1}{|\lambda|} \left[|e^{-i\lambda d}| + |e^{-i\lambda c}| \right] \le \frac{2}{|\lambda|}.$$

This proves the theorem for the characteristic function of any subinterval $[c, d]$ of $[a, b]$. We observe that if $f(x) = 1$ for x in the open interval (c, d) and f is defined arbitrarily at the endpoints c, d, then the result above still holds since two functions which differ only at the endpoints of an interval have the same Riemann integral over that interval (see Section 9.3, Exercise 12(a)).

Now consider any step function f defined on $[a, b]$ by

$$f(x) = \sum_{m=1}^n a_m f_{I_m}(x), \qquad I_m \subset [a, b]. \tag{9.18}$$

To prove the theorem for the step function f given by (9.18), we write

$$\left| \int_a^b f(x) e^{-i\lambda x} \, dx \right| = \left| \int_a^b \sum_{m=1}^n a_m f_{I_m}(x) e^{-i\lambda x} \, dx \right| = \left| \sum_{m=1}^n a_m \int_a^b f_{I_m}(x) e^{-i\lambda x} \, dx \right|$$

$$\le \sum_{m=1}^n |a_m| \left| \int_a^b f_{I_m}(x) e^{-i\lambda x} \, dx \right| \le \frac{2}{|\lambda|} \sum_{m=1}^n |a_m|$$

where, in the last step, we used the above proof of the theorem for the characteristic function f_{I_m}. But $\sum_{m=1}^n |a_m|$ is a fixed number and, consequently, the theorem is proved for any step function.

Now we pass to an arbitrary *real-valued* integrable function f. Let $\epsilon > 0$. Since f is integrable on $[a, b]$, f satisfies Riemann's condition; that is, $\exists$ partition $P_\epsilon = \{a = x_0, x_1, \cdots, x_n = b\}$ of $[a, b]$ such that

$$U(P_\epsilon, f) - L(P_\epsilon, f) < \frac{\epsilon}{2}.$$

We have

$$U(P_\epsilon, f) = \sum_{k=1}^n M_k(f) \, \Delta x_k,$$

from which we may define a step function M by setting

$$M(x) = M_k(f), \text{ if } x \in (x_{k-1}, x_k), \qquad k = 1, 2, \cdots, n,$$

and assigning values to M arbitrarily at the points of P_ϵ. We may then write

$$U(P_\epsilon, f) = \int_a^b M(x) \, dx.$$

Similarly, we define a step function m so that

$$L(P_\epsilon, f) = \int_a^b m(x) \, dx.$$

Then

$$\int_c^d |f(x) - m(x)|\, dx \le \int_a^b |f(x) - m(x)|\, dx \le \int_a^b |M(x) - m(x)|\, dx$$

$$= U(P_\epsilon, f) - L(P_\epsilon, f) < \frac{\epsilon}{2},$$

and

$$\left| \int_c^d f(x) e^{-i\lambda x}\, dx \right| = \left| \int_c^d [f(x) - m(x)] e^{-i\lambda x}\, dx + \int_c^d m(x) e^{-i\lambda x}\, dx \right|$$

$$\le \frac{\epsilon}{2} + \left| \int_c^d m(x) e^{-i\lambda x}\, dx \right|.$$

But this last integral has an absolute value dominated by $\epsilon/2$ for all λ with $|\lambda|$ greater than some integer, say L, since the theorem has been proved for step functions. The proof is therefore complete for all real-valued integrable functions.

Now let $f = u + iv$ where u and v are the (integrable) real and imaginary parts, respectively, of f. Then

$$\left| \int_c^d [u(x) + iv(x)] e^{-i\lambda x}\, dx \right| \le \left| \int_c^d u(x) e^{-i\lambda x}\, dx \right| + \left| \int_c^d v(x) e^{-i\lambda x}\, dx \right|.$$

But we have just shown that

$$\exists L_1 \ni \lambda > L_1 \Longrightarrow \left| \int_c^d u(x) e^{-i\lambda x}\, dx \right| < \frac{\epsilon}{2}$$

and

$$\exists L_2 \ni \lambda > L_2 \Longrightarrow \left| \int_c^d v(x) e^{-i\lambda x}\, dx \right| < \frac{\epsilon}{2}.$$

If $L = \max(L_1, L_2)$, then $\lambda > L \Longrightarrow \left| \int_c^d f(x) e^{-\lambda i x}\, dx \right| < \epsilon$. This proves the theorem for complex-valued f. ∎

Corollary 1. If $f \sim \sum_{k=-\infty}^{\infty} c_k e^{ikx}$, then $\lim_{|k|\to\infty} c_k = 0$.

(NOTE: $\lim_{|k|\to\infty} c_k = 0$ implies $\lim_{k\to\infty} c_k = 0$ and $\lim_{k\to-\infty} c_k = 0$.)

Proof: $\lim_{|k|\to\infty} c_k = \lim_{|k|\to\infty} (1/2\pi) \int_{-\pi}^{\pi} f(x) e^{-ikx}\, dx = 0$, where we have used the definition of the Fourier coefficients c_k and have simply invoked Theorem 9.3. ∎

Corollary 2. If f is integrable on $[a, b]$, then

$$\lim_{\lambda\to\infty} \int_a^b f(x) \cos \lambda x\, dx = 0 \quad \text{and} \quad \lim_{\lambda\to\infty} \int_a^b f(x) \sin \lambda x\, dx = 0.$$

Proof: If f is integrable on $[a, b]$, then

$$\int_a^b f(x)e^{-i\lambda x}\, dx = \int_a^b f(x)[\cos \lambda x - i \sin \lambda x]\, dx$$

$$= \int_a^b f(x) \cos \lambda x\, dx$$

$$- i \int_a^b f(x) \sin \lambda x\, dx.$$

Now invoke Theorem 9.3 to complete the proof. ∎

We now turn to a result with a curious consequence.

■ **Theorem 9.4.** (Riemann's localization theorem.) Let f be integrable on $[-\pi, \pi]$ and suppose $0 < \delta < \pi$. Then

$$\lim_{n \to \infty} \left[\int_{-\pi}^{-\delta} f(x - t)D_n(t)\, dt + \int_\delta^\pi f(x - t)D_n(t)\, dt \right] = 0.$$

Proof: Fix x and define

$$g(t) = \begin{cases} 0, & \text{if } |t| < \delta, \\ \dfrac{f(x - t)}{\sin (t/2)}, & \text{if } \delta \le |t| \le \pi. \end{cases}$$

Then

$$\int_{-\pi}^{-\delta} f(x - t)D_n(t)\, dt + \int_\delta^\pi f(x - t)D_n(t)\, dt = \int_{-\pi}^\pi g(t) \sin (n + \tfrac{1}{2})t\, dt$$

$$= \int_{-\pi}^\pi g(t) \cos \tfrac{1}{2}t \sin nt\, dt + \int_{-\pi}^\pi g(t) \sin\tfrac{1}{2}t \cos nt\, dt.$$

Applying Corollary 2 of Theorem 9.3 to the integrable functions $g(t) \cos \tfrac{1}{2}t$ and $g(t) \sin \tfrac{1}{2}t$, we conclude that each of the last two integrals tends to 0 as n tends to infinity. ∎

The full impact of the theorem above is reflected in the following.

Corollary. Let f be integrable on $[-\pi, \pi]$. The Fourier series of f converges for a given value of x iff $\exists \delta > 0$, $\delta < \pi$ such that

$$\lim_{n \to \infty} \frac{1}{2\pi} \int_{-\delta}^\delta f(x - t)D_n(t)\, dt$$

exists; moreover, when this limit exists it is the sum of the Fourier series of f evaluated at x.

Proof: Since

$$s_n(x) = \frac{1}{2\pi} \int_{-\pi}^\pi f(x - t)D_n(t)\, dt$$

(see remark following Definition 9.3), we may write in obvious notation

$$s_n(x) = \left[\int_{-\pi}^{-\delta} + \int_{\delta}^{\pi} \right] + \int_{-\delta}^{\delta} \left[\text{integrand: } \frac{1}{2\pi} f(x-t) D_n(t) \right]. \quad (9.19)$$

From Theorem 9.4, we conclude that $\lim_{n \to \infty} s_n(x)$ exists iff

$$\lim_{n \to \infty} \int_{-\delta}^{\delta} \frac{1}{2\pi} f(x-t) D_n(t) \, dt$$

exists for some δ, $0 < \delta < \pi$. If this last limit exists, then again by (9.19) and Theorem 9.4

$$\lim_{n \to \infty} s_n(x) = \lim_{n \to \infty} \frac{1}{2\pi} \int_{-\delta}^{\delta} f(x-t) D_n(t) \, dt. \quad \blacksquare$$

Now we see the reason for calling Theorem 9.4 Riemann's localization theorem: It asserts that the behavior of the Fourier series of f at the point x is determined by the behavior of f in some neighborhood of x. This is a surprising situation since the Fourier coefficients

$$c_k = \frac{1}{2\pi} \int_{-\pi}^{\pi} f(t) e^{-ikt} \, dt$$

clearly depend on the behavior of f on the entire interval $[-\pi, \pi]$.

9.5 LIPSCHITZIAN FUNCTIONS HAVE SELF-CONVERGENT FOURIER SERIES

We are now ready to prove one of the main theorems of this chapter.

■ **Theorem 9.5.** If f is integrable on $[-\pi, \pi]$ and satisfies a Lipschitz condition at $x \in [-\pi, \pi]$ and if $f(t + 2\pi) = f(t)$ for all real numbers t, then the Fourier series of f at x converges to $f(x)$.

Proof: Since f satisfies a Lipschitz condition at x,

$$\exists M \text{ and } \exists N(x;r) \ni |t| < r \Rightarrow |f(x-t) - f(x)| \leq M|t|. \quad (9.20)$$

Let $\epsilon > 0$. Since we know from elementary calculus that

$$\lim_{t \to 0} \frac{t/2}{\sin(t/2)} = 1,$$

it follows that

$$\exists r' \ni |t| < r' \Rightarrow \left| \frac{t/2}{\sin(t/2)} - 1 \right| < \epsilon;$$

in particular with $\epsilon = 1$,

$$|t| < r' \Rightarrow \left| \frac{t/2}{\sin(t/2)} \right| < 1 + \epsilon = 2. \quad (9.21)$$

Define

$$\delta = \min \{r, r', \pi/2\}. \tag{9.22}$$

We will show that for this δ,

$$\lim_{n \to \infty} \int_{-\delta}^{\delta} [f(x - t) - f(x)] D_n(t) \, dt$$

$$= \lim_{n \to \infty} \int_{-\delta}^{\delta} \left[\frac{f(x - t) - f(x)}{\sin (t/2)} \right] \sin \left[\left(n + \frac{1}{2} \right) t \right] dt = 0 \,.$$

According to Corollary 2 of Theorem 9.3, to accomplish this it is sufficient to show that the function G defined by

$$G(t) = \frac{f(x - t) - f(x)}{\sin (t/2)}$$

is integrable on $[-\delta, \delta]$. Using Lebesgue's criterion for integrability, this is equivalent to showing that G is bounded and continuous almost everywhere on $[-\delta, \delta]$. Boundedness of G follows from (9.20) and (9.21):

$$|G(t)| = \left| \frac{f(x - t) - f(x)}{\sin (t/2)} \right| \le 2M \left| \frac{t/2}{\sin (t/2)} \right| < 4M.$$

The set of points of discontinuity of $G(t)$ on $[-\delta, \delta]$ has measure zero, since f has this property, by hypothesis, and $\sin (t/2)$ vanishes at a finite set of points of $[-\delta, \delta]$. This proves that

$$\lim_{n \to \infty} \int_{-\delta}^{\delta} [f(x - t) - f(x)] D_n(t) \, dt = 0.$$

Now we invoke the corollary to Theorem 9.4, concluding that the Fourier series (evaluated at x) of the function g, where $g(x - t) = f(x - t) - f(x)$ (see Section 9.9, Exercise 8), converges to $g(x) = 0$. But the Fourier series of g is given by

$$\sum_{k=-\infty}^{\infty} d_k e^{ikt}$$

where

$$d_k = \frac{1}{2\pi} \int_{-\pi}^{\pi} g(u) e^{-iku} \, du = \frac{1}{2\pi} \int_{-\pi}^{\pi} [f(u) - f(x)] e^{-iku} \, du$$

$$= \frac{1}{2\pi} \int_{-\pi}^{\pi} f(u) e^{-iku} \, du - \frac{1}{2\pi} \int_{-\pi}^{\pi} f(x) e^{-iku} \, du$$

$$= c_k - \frac{1}{2\pi} f(x) \int_{-\pi}^{\pi} e^{-iku} \, du,$$

c_k denoting the Fourier coefficients of f. Thus

$$d_0 = c_0 - f(x)$$

and if $k \neq 0$

$$d_k = c_k - \frac{1}{2\pi} f(x) \frac{e^{-iku}}{-ik} \Big|_{-\pi}^{\pi} = c_k.$$

It is now clear that the convergence to $g(x) = 0$ of the Fourier series of g evaluated at x implies the convergence of the Fourier series of f evaluated at x to $f(x)$, for

$$\lim_{n \to \infty} \sum_{k=-n}^{n} d_k e^{ikx} = 0 \Rightarrow \lim_{n \to \infty} \left[c_0 - f(x) + \sum_{\substack{k=-n \\ k \neq 0}}^{n} c_k e^{ikx} \right] = 0$$

$$\Rightarrow \lim_{n \to \infty} \sum_{k=-n}^{n} c_k e^{ikx} = f(x). \quad \blacksquare$$

Corollary. If f is differentiable at x, then the Fourier series of f at x converges to $f(x)$.

Proof: Differentiability of f at x implies f is Lipschitzian at x (Theorem 6.3), hence the conclusion follows from Theorem 9.5. $\blacksquare$

Example 9.6.   Find the Fourier series of the function f defined by

$$f(x) = \begin{cases} 0, & \text{if } x = -\pi \\ -1, & \text{if } -\pi < x < 0 \\ 0, & \text{if } x = 0 \\ 1, & \text{if } 0 < x < \pi \\ 0, & \text{if } x = \pi \end{cases}$$

and discuss its convergence.

We note that

$$c_0 = \frac{1}{2\pi} \int_{-\pi}^{\pi} f(x) \, dx = 0;$$

and if $k \neq 0$,

$$c_k = \frac{1}{2\pi} \int_{-\pi}^{\pi} f(x) e^{-ikx} \, dx = \frac{1}{2\pi} \int_{-\pi}^{0} -e^{-ikx} \, dx + \frac{1}{2\pi} \int_{0}^{\pi} e^{-ikx} \, dx$$

$$= \frac{i}{\pi k} [(-1)^k - 1]$$

(the reader should check the missing details here). Thus $c_{2m} = 0$ while

$$c_{2m+1} = -\frac{2i}{\pi(2m+1)}.$$

It follows that

$$f(x) \sim -\frac{2i}{\pi} [e^{ix} - e^{-ix} + e^{3ix} - e^{-3ix} + e^{5ix} - e^{-5ix} + \cdots].$$

But

$$\sin k\theta = \frac{1}{2i}(e^{ik\theta} - e^{-ik\theta})$$

therefore

$$f(x) \sim \frac{4}{\pi}\left[\sin x + \frac{\sin 3x}{3} + \frac{\sin 5x}{5} + \cdots\right]$$

or

$$f(x) \sim \frac{4}{\pi}\sum_{k=0}^{\infty}\frac{\sin (2k+1)x}{2k+1}.$$

It is obvious that if $x = -\pi$ or 0 or π, the series converges to 0. Since f satisfies a Lipschitz condition at all other points of its domain (since it is differentiable there), we actually have

$$f(x) = \frac{4}{\pi}\sum_{k=0}^{\infty}\frac{\sin (2k+1)x}{2k+1}, \qquad -\pi \le x \le \pi.$$

9.6 EXERCISES

1. Show that

$$\int_{-\pi}^{\pi}f(t)D_n(x-t)\,dt = \int_{-\pi}^{\pi}f(x-t)D_n(t)\,dt$$

where $f(x+2\pi) = f(x)$ and f is integrable.

2. Show that

$$\frac{1}{2\pi}\int_{-\pi}^{\pi}D_n(t)\,dt = 1.$$

(See Theorem 9.1.)

3. Discuss the convergence of the Fourier series found in Section 9.3, Exercise 6.

4. Show that if the series $\sum_{k=-\infty}^{\infty}c_k e^{ikx}$ converges uniformly to f, for all x, then c_k, k an integer, are the Fourier coefficients of f.

5. Find the Fourier series of the function f defined by

$$f(x) = \begin{cases} -1, & \text{if } -1 < x < 0, \\ 1, & \text{if } 0 < x < 1. \end{cases}$$

Differentiate the resulting series term by term and show that it diverges for all x.

9.7 FEJÉR'S THEOREM

It can be shown that there are continuous functions whose Fourier series diverge at points of continuity.* If, however, instead of looking at the sequence $\{s_n\}$ of partial sums of the Fourier series of f, we consider the sequence $\{\sigma_n\}$ of arithmetic means where

$$\sigma_n(x) = \frac{s_0(x) + s_1(x) + \cdots + s_n(x)}{n + 1}, \tag{9.23}$$

then the situation is remarkably improved: If f is continuous and periodic with period 2π, then

$$\lim_{n \to \infty} \sigma_n(x) = f(x)$$

uniformly for all x (see Definition 8.2). This is Fejér's theorem. In order to prove it, we begin with certain preliminaries. Recall that

$$s_k(x) = \frac{1}{2\pi} \int_{-\pi}^{\pi} f(x - t) D_k(t) \, dt$$

and consequently

$$\sigma_n(x) = \frac{1}{n + 1} \sum_{k=0}^{n} \frac{1}{2\pi} \int_{-\pi}^{\pi} f(x - t) D_k(t) \, dt$$

$$= \frac{1}{2\pi(n + 1)} \int_{-\pi}^{\pi} f(x - t) \sum_{k=0}^{n} D_k(t) \, dt.$$

Let us introduce, for convenience, the following definition.

Definition 9.6. *Fejér's kernel*, denoted by K_n, is given by

$$K_n(t) = \frac{1}{n + 1} \sum_{k=0}^{n} D_k(t).$$

We may therefore write

$$\sigma_n(x) = \frac{1}{2\pi} \int_{-\pi}^{\pi} f(x - t) K_n(t) \, dt. \tag{9.24}$$

Next we recall that $(1/2\pi) \int_{-\pi}^{\pi} D_n(t) \, dt = 1$, and so

$$\frac{1}{2\pi} \int_{-\pi}^{\pi} K_n(x) \, dx = \frac{1}{2\pi} \int_{-\pi}^{\pi} \frac{1}{n + 1} \sum_{k=0}^{n} D_k(x) \, dx$$

$$= \frac{1}{2\pi(n + 1)} \sum_{k=0}^{n} \int_{-\pi}^{\pi} D_k(x) \, dx = 1.$$

---

* See, for example, G. H. Hardy's and W. W. Rogosinski's *Fourier Series*, No. 38 of Cambridge Tracts in Mathematics and Mathematical Physics, Cambridge University Press, 1950, p. 50.

Using this result, (9.24), and the fact that $f(x) = (1/2\pi)f(x) \int_{-\pi}^{\pi} K_n(t)\, dt =$ $(1/2\pi) \int_{-\pi}^{\pi} f(x)K_n(t)\, dt$:

$$\sigma_n(x) - f(x) = \frac{1}{2\pi} \int_{-\pi}^{\pi} [f(x - t) - f(x)]K_n(t)\, dt. \tag{9.25}$$

There is one final result of a technical nature that we need before proving Fejér's theorem. It is contained in the following lemma.

Lemma.   The Fejér kernel has the following properties:

$$K_n(x) = \frac{1}{n+1} \cdot \frac{1 - \cos(n+1)x}{1 - \cos x}, \qquad n = 0, 1, 2, \cdots.$$

Hence, $K_n \geq 0$, and if $0 < \delta \leq |x| \leq \pi$,

$$K_n(x) \leq \frac{2}{(n+1)(1 - \cos \delta)}. \tag{9.26}$$

Proof: By definition,

$$K_n(x) = \frac{1}{n+1} \sum_{m=0}^{n} D_m(x).$$

Therefore,

$$K_n(x) = \frac{1}{n+1} \sum_{m=0}^{n} \sum_{k=-m}^{m} e^{ikx} = \frac{1}{n+1} \sum_{m=0}^{n} \frac{e^{-imx} - e^{i(m+1)x}}{1 - e^{ix}},$$

or

$$(n+1)(1 - e^{ix})K_n(x) = \sum_{m=0}^{n} e^{-imx} - \sum_{m=0}^{n} e^{i(m+1)x}$$

$$= \frac{1 - e^{-i(n+1)x}}{1 - e^{-ix}} - \frac{e^{ix} - e^{i(n+2)x}}{1 - e^{ix}}.$$

Multiplying both sides by $(1 - e^{-ix})$ and noting that $(1 - e^{-ix})/(1 - e^{ix}) = -e^{-ix}$, we have

$$(n+1)(1 - e^{ix})(1 - e^{-ix})K_n(x) = 1 - e^{-i(n+1)x} + e^{-ix}(e^{ix} - e^{i(n+2)x})$$

$$= 2 - e^{-i(n+1)x} - e^{i(n+1)x}.$$

But $\cos \alpha = \frac{1}{2}(e^{i\alpha} + e^{-i\alpha})$; therefore

$$K_n(x) = \frac{1}{n+1} \cdot \frac{1 - \cos(n+1)x}{1 - \cos x}, \tag{9.27}$$

proving the first part of the lemma.

Since $|\cos \alpha| \leq 1$, it is obvious from (9.27) that $K_n \geq 0$. Moreover, if $0 < \delta \leq |x| \leq \pi$, then since $1 - \cos(n+1)x \leq 2$ and $1 - \cos x \geq 1 - \cos \delta$, it follows from (9.27) that (9.26) is valid. ∎

■ **Theorem 9.6.** (Fejér) If f is continuous and periodic with period 2π, then the sequence $\{\sigma_n\}$ of arithmetic means of the partial sums of the Fourier series of f converges uniformly to f; that is,

$$\lim_{n \to \infty} \sigma_n(x) = f(x) \quad \text{uniformly for all } x.$$

Proof: Since f is continuous on the closed interval $[-\pi, \pi]$, f has a maximum M; that is,

$$|f(x)| \le M, \qquad -\pi \le x \le \pi. \tag{9.28}$$

Let $\epsilon > 0$. Continuity of f on the closed interval implies uniform continuity of f so that

$$\exists \delta > 0 \ni |x - y| < \delta \Rightarrow |f(x) - f(y)| < \frac{\epsilon}{2}. \tag{9.29}$$

Using (9.29) and the fact that $K_n(t) \ge 0$ (see lemma), we have for all n

$$\int_{-\delta}^{\delta} |f(x - t) - f(x)| \, |K_n(t)| \, dt < \frac{\epsilon}{2} \int_{-\pi}^{\pi} K_n(t) \, dt = \epsilon\pi. \tag{9.30}$$

Invoking the inequality (9.26) of the lemma, we see that

$$\exists N \ni n > N \quad \text{and} \quad \delta \le |t| \le \pi \Rightarrow K_n(t) \le \frac{\epsilon}{4M}. \tag{9.31}$$

It follows from (9.28) that $|f(x - t) - f(x)| \le |f(x - t)| + |f(x)| \le 2M$. Thus from (9.31), if $n > N$,

$$\int_{-\pi}^{-\delta} |f(x - t) - f(x)| K_n(t) \, dt + \int_{\delta}^{\pi} |f(x - t) - f(x)| K_n(t) \, dt$$

$$\le \frac{\epsilon}{4M} \left[\int_{-\pi}^{-\delta} 2M \, dt + \int_{\delta}^{\pi} 2M \, dt + \int_{-\delta}^{\delta} 2M \, dt \right]$$

$$\le \frac{\epsilon}{4M} \int_{-\pi}^{\pi} 2M \, dt = \pi\epsilon. \tag{9.32}$$

Consequently, (9.25), (9.30) and (9.32) yield: $\forall \epsilon > 0, \exists N \ni n > N \Rightarrow$

$$|\sigma_n(x) - f(x)| = \left| \frac{1}{2\pi} \int_{-\pi}^{\pi} [f(x - t) - f(x)] K_n(t) \, dt \right| < \frac{1}{2\pi} (\pi\epsilon + \pi\epsilon) = \epsilon$$

for all x. ■

Corollary 1. If f and g are continuous functions having the same Fourier series, then $f(x) = g(x)$ for all x.

Proof: Let $\{\sigma_n\}$ be the sequence of arithmetic means of the partial sums of the common Fourier series. Then, by Theorem 9.6,

$$\sigma_n(x) \to f(x) \text{ uniformly for all } x$$

and

$$\sigma_n(x) \to g(x) \text{ uniformly for all } x.$$

It follows that

$$\lim \sigma_n(x) = f(x) = g(x) \text{ for all } x. \quad \blacksquare$$

Conversely, it is clear that if $f(x) = g(x)$ for all x and if we are dealing with continuous (even just integrable) functions f, g, then the Fourier series of f and g coincide.

Corollary 2. If f is continuous and if $\int_{-\pi}^{\pi} f(x)e^{-inx}\, dx = 0$ for every integer n, then $f(x) = 0$ for all x. (To put this another way: If all the Fourier coefficients of a continuous function vanish, then the function itself vanishes.)

Proof: By hypothesis, every Fourier coefficient c_n of f is 0 since

$$c_n = \frac{1}{2\pi} \int_{-\pi}^{\pi} f(x)e^{-inx}\, dx = 0.$$

But the function g which is identically 0 is continuous and all its Fourier coefficients are also 0. From Corollary 1, we conclude $f = g$; that is, we deduce $f(x) = 0$ for all x. $\quad \blacksquare$

Although we obtain the next result as a consequence of Fejér's theorem, it is of such importance that we call it

■ **Theorem 9.7.** (Weierstrass approximation theorem.) If f is a continuous function on $[a, b]$, then there exists a sequence $\{p_n\}$ of polynomials such that

$$\lim p_n(x) = f(x)$$

uniformly on $[a, b]$.

(To paraphrase the result: Every continuous function on $[a, b]$ can be uniformly approximated by a polynomial.)

Proof: Having been given the continuous function f on $[a, b]$, our first step is to define a new function g on $[-\pi, \pi]$ by

$$g(t) = f\left(\frac{(b-a)t}{2\pi} + \frac{a+b}{2}\right). \tag{9.33}$$

It will be noted that the change of variable effected by putting

$$x(t) = \frac{(b-a)t}{2\pi} + \frac{a+b}{2}$$

simply represents a straight line passing through the two points $(-\pi, a)$ and (π, b) of the tx plane; continuity of x as a function of t, together with the assumed continuity of f, allows g to inherit continuity by virtue of its definition as a continuous function of a continuous function. Thus g is a continuous function on $[-\pi, \pi]$.

Let $\epsilon > 0$. By Fejér's theorem, there exists a trigonometric polynomial $\sigma(t)$ such that

$$|\sigma(t) - g(t)| < \frac{\epsilon}{2} \qquad \text{for all } t \in [-\pi, \pi]. \tag{9.34}$$

But the trigonometric polynomial $\sigma(t)$ is a finite sum of terms of the form $A_k e^{ikt}$ and since each term can be approximated uniformly by a polynomial in t, so can the sum (see Section 9.9, Exercises 1 to 3). Thus, there exists a polynomial p in t such that

$$|\sigma(t) - p(t)| < \frac{\epsilon}{2} \qquad \text{for all } t \in [-\pi, \pi]. \tag{9.35}$$

From (9.34) and (9.35) we have

$$|g(t) - p(t)| < \epsilon \qquad \text{for all } t \in [-\pi, \pi]. \tag{9.36}$$

In view of (9.33) it follows from (9.36) that with $x = (b - a)t/2\pi + (a + b)/2$,

$$|f(x) - q(x)| < \epsilon \qquad \text{for all } x \in [a, b],$$

where $q(x)$ is the polynomial defined by

$$q(x) = p(t) = p\left(\frac{\pi(2x - a - b)}{b - a}\right). \quad \blacksquare$$

Fejér's theorem lends strong support to considering, in lieu of the Fourier series $\{s_n\}$ of a continuous function, the sequence $\{\sigma_n\}$ of arithmetic means:

$$\sigma_n(x) = \frac{s_0(x) + s_1(x) + \cdots + s_n(x)}{n + 1}. \tag{9.37}$$

Additional emphasis on this method of summation (called Cesàro-1 summability or $(C, 1)$ summability) is furnished by our next result which says, roughly speaking, that nothing is lost in $(C, 1)$ summability in the sense that if a series converges to begin with, the arithmetic means of its partial sums will not only converge, but to the same value.

■ **Theorem 9.8.**   If the sequence $\{s_n\}$ converges to s, then the sequence

$$\{\sigma_n\} = \left\{\frac{s_0 + s_1 + \cdots + s_n}{n + 1}\right\}$$

of arithmetic means converges to s.

Proof: Observe that

$$|\sigma_n - s| = \left| \frac{s_0 + s_1 + \cdots + s_n}{n+1} - s \right|$$

$$= \frac{1}{n+1} |(s_0 - s) + (s_1 - s) + \cdots + (s_n - s)|. \qquad (9.38)$$

Let $\epsilon > 0$. Since every convergent sequence is bounded, $\exists M \ni |s_k - s| \leq M$, for all positive integers k. Since $s_n \to s$, $\exists N \ni n > N \Rightarrow |s_n - s| < \epsilon/2$. Let $n > \max \{[2(N+1)M]/\epsilon, N\}$ and split $|\sum_0^n (s_k - s)|$ in (9.38) into two sums: one from $k = 0$ to $k = N$ and the other from $k = N+1$ to $k = n$. Then, by the triangle inequality,

$$|\sigma_n - s| \leq \frac{1}{n+1} [|s_0 - s| + |s_1 - s| + \cdots + |s_N - s|]$$

$$+ \frac{1}{n+1} [|s_{N+1} - s| + \cdots + |s_n - s|]$$

$$< \frac{1}{n+1} (N+1)M + \frac{1}{n+1} (n - N) \frac{\epsilon}{2}$$

$$< \frac{1}{n} (N+1)M + \frac{n}{n+1} \frac{\epsilon}{2} \qquad \text{(since } n < n+1 \text{ and } n > n - N)$$

$$< \frac{\epsilon}{2} + \frac{\epsilon}{2} = \epsilon. \quad \blacksquare$$

Our next example is final evidence of the superiority of Cesàro summability over ordinary summability since it shows that Cesàro summability is indeed a generalization of ordinary summability.

Example 9.7.   The series $1 - 1 + 1 - 1 + \cdots$ diverges since its partial sums are $1, 0, 1, 0, 1, 0, \cdots$. Nevertheless, if we consider the sequence of arithmetic means of these partial sums, we have (for convenience put $\sigma_n = (s_1 + \cdots + s_n)/n$):

$$\sigma_1 = 1, \sigma_2 = \frac{1+0}{2} = \frac{1}{2}, \sigma_3 = \frac{1+0+1}{3} = \frac{2}{3}, \sigma_4 = \frac{1+0+1+0}{4} = \frac{2}{4}, \cdots$$

$$\sigma_{2n} = \frac{1}{2}, \sigma_{2n+1} = \frac{n+1}{2n+1}.$$

Thus $\lim_{k \to \infty} \sigma_k = \frac{1}{2}$.

9.8 SOLUTION OF THE DIRICHLET PROBLEM

Recall that the Dirichlet problem (Section 9.1) was defined as follows: Find a function u of (r, θ) such that

$$\frac{\partial^2 u}{\partial r^2} + \frac{1}{r}\frac{\partial u}{\partial r} + \frac{1}{r^2}\frac{\partial^2 u}{\partial \theta^2} = 0, \qquad r \neq 0, \tag{9.39}$$

$$u \text{ is a continuous function of } (r, \theta), \qquad 0 \leq r \leq 1, \qquad \theta \text{ real}, \tag{9.40}$$

$$u(r, \theta) = u(r, \theta + 2\pi), \tag{9.41}$$

$$u(1, \theta) = f(\theta), \tag{9.42}$$

where f is a prescribed function.

In Section 9.1, the following approach to the Dirichlet problem was suggested:

(1) The Fourier series of the given function f is determined:

$$f(\theta) \sim \sum_{k=-\infty}^{\infty} c_k e^{ik\theta} \tag{9.43}$$

(here, of course, we must assume integrability and periodicity of f).

(2) A proposed solution u is then constructed as the limiting form of (9.9), Section 9.1 (assuming the infinite sum indicated below exists):

$$u(r, \theta) = \sum_{k=-\infty}^{\infty} c_k r^{|k|} e^{ik\theta}. \tag{9.44}$$

(NOTE: (9.44) results from (9.43) by introducing the factor $r^{|k|}$.) We now investigate the feasibility of this plan. We shall prove that the procedure is successful if we assume that f is continuous. Our plan of proof runs as follows:

There are two main difficulties here: We must prove under suitable conditions that the series (9.44) converges and secondly that (9.42) is valid.

If we assume for the moment that (9.44) does indeed define a function u; that is, the series (9.44) converges, then (9.39) will be satisfied if the partial differentiations of u called for in (9.39) can be carried out term by term since u is simply the limit of a linear combination of functions each of which satisfies (9.39) (see Section 9.3, Exercises 1 to 3). But termwise differentiation is permissible here since the coefficients c_k are Fourier coefficients and hence by Corollary 1 to Theorem 9.3 (Riemann-Lebesgue lemma) $\lim_{|k|\to\infty} c_k = 0$ which implies the existence of a common bound for the c_k, and this, in turn, implies uniform convergence of the series (9.44) in the interior of every circle with radius $r < 1$ (see Section 9.9, Exercises 9 and 10).

Condition (9.40) follows from the fact that u is the limit of a uniformly convergent sequence of continuous functions, hence u is continuous.

Condition (9.41) is obviously valid for (9.44).

So there are two things left to do:

(1) Impose conditions on f which will guarantee the convergence of (9.44).

(2) Check the validity of (9.42).

We have pointed out that there are continuous functions whose Fourier series diverge so certainly continuity of f does not imply that the symbol $\sim$ in (9.43) can be replaced by the symbol "$=$"; however, continuity of f does imply (Fejér's theorem) that the sequence of arithmetic means of the partial sums of the Fourier series of f converges to f uniformly; that is,

$$\lim_{n\to\infty} \sigma_n(\theta) = f(\theta), \qquad \text{uniformly in } \theta.$$

This fact is coupled with a theorem of Frobenius (to be proved shortly): Let $\sum_{k=0}^{\infty} u_k$ be a given infinite series. Put

$$s_n = u_0 + u_1 + \cdots + u_n,$$

$$\sigma_n = \frac{s_0 + s_1 + \cdots + s_n}{n+1}.$$

If $\lim \sigma_n$ exists, then $\lim_{r\to 1^-} [u_0 + u_1 r + u_2 r^2 + \cdots]$ also exists and the two limits are equal.

Now observe that with the identification $u_0 = c_0$, $u_k = c_k e^{ik\theta} + c_{-k} e^{-ik\theta}$, $k = 1, 2, \cdots$ in Frobenius's theorem we must identify σ_n with the arithmetic means of the partial sums of the Fourier series of f; Fejér's theorem yields the convergence of these arithmetic means thereby fulfilling the hypothesis of Frobenius's theorem and, finally, Frobenius's theorem admits the conclusion that

$$\lim_{r\to 1^-} u(r, \theta) = f(\theta), \qquad \text{uniformly in } \theta.$$

Thus we can obtain the condition (9.42) required in Dirichlet's problem by restricting u as defined in (9.44) to $0 < r < 1$ and then extending the domain to $r = 1$ and $r = 0$ by defining $u(1, \theta) = \lim_{r\to 1^-} u(r, \theta)$ and $u(0, \theta) = c_0$, respectively.

■ **Theorem 9.9.** (Frobenius.) Let the series whose nth partial sum is $s_n = u_0 + u_1 + \cdots + u_n$ be given. Define

$$\sigma_n = \frac{s_0 + s_1 + \cdots + s_n}{n+1}$$

and assume $\lim \sigma_n = \sigma$ exists. Then

$$\lim_{r\to 1^-} [u_0 + u_1 r + u_2 r^2 + \cdots]$$

exists and is equal to $\lim \sigma_n$.

Proof: We make the preliminary observation that (see Example 8.12) if
$$|r| < 1,$$
then
$$\sum_{k=0}^{\infty} r^k = (1 - r)^{-1}.$$

Moreover, this power series can be differentiated termwise: if
$$|r| < 1,$$
then
$$\sum_{k=1}^{\infty} k r^{k-1} = (1 - r)^{-2}. \tag{9.45}$$

In particular, the series $\sum_{k=0}^{\infty} (k + 1)r^k = \sum_{k=1}^{\infty} k r^{k-1}$ converges. By hypothesis, $\lim \sigma_k$ exists and therefore there exists a number M such that $|\sigma_k| \le M$ for all positive integers k. Since the convergent series $\sum_{k=0}^{\infty} (k + 1)M r^k$, $0 \le r < 1$, majorizes the series $\sum_{k=0}^{\infty} (k + 1)\sigma_k r^k$ (that is, $|(k + 1)\sigma_k r^k| \le (k + 1)M r^k$ for all k), it follows that $\sum_{k=0}^{\infty} (k + 1)\sigma_k r^k$ converges. This establishes the following:

if $\exists \lim \sigma_k$ and if $0 \le r < 1$, then $\displaystyle\sum_{k=0}^{\infty} (k + 1)\sigma_k r^k$ converges absolutely. (9.46)

[Of course, $\sum_{k=0}^{\infty} (k + 1)\sigma_k r^{k+1}$ also converges since it is obtained from the convergent series in (9.46) by multiplication by r.]

Our goal is to show that $|\sum_{n=0}^{\infty} u_n r^n - \sigma|$ is meaningful (when $|r| < 1$) and is less than any $\epsilon > 0$. To this end, we write
$$u_n = s_n - s_{n-1}$$
so that if we define $s_{-1} = 0$, and assume temporarily that $\sum_{n=0}^{\infty} s_n r^n$ converges,
$$\sum_{n=0}^{\infty} u_n r^n = \sum_{n=0}^{\infty} (s_n - s_{n-1})r^n$$
$$= \sum_{n=0}^{\infty} s_n r^n - \sum_{n=0}^{\infty} s_n r^{n+1}$$
$$= (1 - r) \sum_{n=0}^{\infty} s_n r^n. \tag{9.47}$$

In order to bring the sequence $\{\sigma_n\}$ into the picture, we note that
$$(n + 1)\sigma_n = \sum_{k=0}^{n} s_k,$$
$$n\sigma_{n-1} = \sum_{k=0}^{n-1} s_k,$$
so by subtraction,
$$(n + 1)\sigma_n - n\sigma_{n-1} = s_n. \tag{9.48}$$

Substituting (9.48) into (9.47) and putting $\sigma_{-1} = 0$:

$$\sum_{n=0}^{\infty} u_n r^n = (1 - r) \sum_{n=0}^{\infty} [(n + 1)\sigma_n - n\sigma_{n-1}]r^n$$

$$= (1 - r)\left[\sum_{n=0}^{\infty} (n + 1)\sigma_n r^n - \sum_{n=0}^{\infty} (n + 1)\sigma_n r^{n+1} \right]. \quad (9.49)$$

Making use of (9.46), we see from (9.49), (9.48), and (9.47) that $\sum_{n=0}^{\infty} u_n r^n$ converges and

$$\sum_{n=0}^{\infty} u_n r^n = (1 - r) \sum_{n=0}^{\infty} (n + 1)\sigma_n(r^n - r^{n+1}),$$

or

$$\sum_{n=0}^{\infty} u_n r^n = (1 - r)^2 \sum_{n=0}^{\infty} (n + 1)\sigma_n r^n. \quad (9.50)$$

But we know from (9.45) that

$$(1 - r)^2 \sum_{n=0}^{\infty} (n + 1)r^n = 1, \quad (9.45)$$

hence

$$(1 - r)^2 \sum_{n=0}^{\infty} (n + 1)r^n\sigma = \sigma. \quad (9.51)$$

Subtracting σ from both members of (9.50) and utilizing (9.51), we get

$$(1 - r)^2 \sum_{n=0}^{\infty} (n + 1)r^n(\sigma_n - \sigma) = \sum_{n=0}^{\infty} u_n r^n - \sigma. \quad (9.52)$$

Let $\epsilon > 0$. Since

$$\lim \sigma_k = \sigma, \qquad \exists K \ni k > K \Rightarrow |\sigma_k - \sigma| < \frac{\epsilon}{2}.$$

Then from (9.52),

$$\left| \sum_{n=0}^{\infty} u_n r^n - \sigma \right| \leq (1 - r)^2 \sum_{n=0}^{K} |(n + 1)r^n(\sigma_n - \sigma)|$$

$$+ (1 - r)^2 \sum_{n=K+1}^{\infty} |(n + 1)r^n(\sigma_n - \sigma)|$$

$$\leq (1 - r)^2 \sum_{n=0}^{K} (n + 1)r^n(|\sigma_n| + |\sigma|) + (1 - r)^2 \frac{\epsilon}{2} \sum_{n=0}^{\infty} (n + 1)r^n$$

$$\leq (1 - r)^2(M + |\sigma|)(K + 1) \sum_{n=0}^{K} r^n + \frac{\epsilon}{2} \quad \text{[by (9.45)]},$$

$$\leq (1 - r)^2(M + |\sigma|)(K + 1)^2 + \frac{\epsilon}{2} \quad (\text{since } 0 \leq r < 1).$$

Put

$$\delta = \left[\frac{\epsilon}{2(M + |\sigma|)(K + 1)^2} \right]^{1/2}.$$

Then

$$|1 - r| < \delta, \qquad 0 \le r < 1 \Rightarrow \left| \sum_{n=0}^{\infty} u_n r^n - \sigma \right| \le \frac{\epsilon}{2} + \frac{\epsilon}{2} = \epsilon.$$

Therefore,

$$\lim_{r \to 1^-} \sum_{n=0}^{\infty} u_n r^n = \sigma. \quad \blacksquare$$

Let us summarize our result.

■ **Theorem 9.10.** If f is a continuous function with period 2π and

$$f(x) \sim \sum_{k=-\infty}^{\infty} c_k e^{ikx},$$

then the function u with $u(1, 0) = \lim_{r \to 1^-} u(r, \theta)$, $u(0, \theta) = c_0$, and

$$u(r, \theta) = \sum_{k=-\infty}^{\infty} c_k r^{|k|} e^{ikx}, \qquad \text{if } 0 < r < 1,$$

is a solution of Dirichlet's problem.

There is another form in which the solution of the Dirichlet problem can be expressed. Because of its simplicity and elegance, we would be remiss if attention was not called to it.

We begin with the solution (9.44) for continuous f and the definition of c_k to arrive at

$$u(r, \theta) = \sum_{k=-\infty}^{\infty} r^{|k|} e^{ik\theta} \frac{1}{2\pi} \int_{-\pi}^{\pi} f(x) e^{-ikx} \, dx$$

$$= \sum_{k=-\infty}^{\infty} \frac{1}{2\pi} \int_{-\pi}^{\pi} r^{|k|} e^{ik(\theta-x)} f(x) \, dx.$$

If $0 < r < 1$, this series may be integrated termwise since it converges uniformly in θ so that

$$u(r, \theta) = \frac{1}{2\pi} \int_{-\pi}^{\pi} \sum_{k=-\infty}^{\infty} r^{|k|} e^{ik(\theta-x)} f(x) \, dx. \tag{9.53}$$

But $|r| < 1$ implies

$$\sum_{k=0}^{\infty} r^k e^{ik(\theta-x)} = \frac{1}{1 - re^{i(\theta-x)}}.$$

and

$$\sum_{k=-1}^{-\infty} r^{-k} e^{ik(\theta-x)} = \frac{re^{i(\theta-x)}}{1 - re^{-i(\theta-x)}},$$

hence (9.53) becomes, if $r < 1$,

$$u(r, \theta) = \frac{1}{2\pi} \int_{-\pi}^{\pi} \frac{1 - r^2}{1 - 2r \cos (\theta - x) + r^2} f(x) \, dx. \tag{9.54}$$

This neat form for $u(r, \theta)$ is called *Poisson's integral*.

Definition 9.7.   The function P of (r, θ) defined by

$$P(r, \theta) = \frac{1}{2\pi} \frac{1 - r^2}{1 - 2r \cos \theta + r^2}$$

is called *Poisson's kernel*.

Some of the properties of this function will be found in the exercises.

9.9 EXERCISES

1. Show that the trigonometric polynomial σ_n where

$$\sigma_n(t) = \frac{1}{n+1} \sum_{m=0}^{n} s_m(t)$$

and

$$s_m(t) = \sum_{k=-m}^{m} c_k e^{ikt},$$

can be written as

$$\sigma_n(t) = \sum_{k=-n}^{n} \left(1 - \frac{|k|}{n+1}\right) c_k e^{ikt}.$$

2. Show that if f_m, $m = 1, 2, \cdots, n$ is a complex-valued function of t, $a \le t \le b$, which can be approximated uniformly on $[a, b]$ by the polynomial (in t) p_m, $m = 1, 2, \cdots, n$, then the linear combination

$$F = \sum_{m=1}^{n} A_m f_m$$

(A_m, $m = 1, 2, \cdots, n$ complex constants) can be approximated uniformly on $[a, b]$ by the polynomial $P = \sum_{m=1}^{n} A_m p_m$.

3. Show that the function f defined by $f(t) = A e^{ikt}$, $a \le t \le b$, where A is a complex constant and k is an integer, can be approximated uniformly on $[a, b]$ by a polynomial in t.

4. Consider the series $1 - 2 + 3 - 4 + 5 - 6 + \cdots$.
   (a) Show that $\sigma_{2n} = (n + 1)/(2n + 1) \to \frac{1}{2}$ and $\sigma_{2n+1} = 0$. Hence $\lim \sigma_n$ does not exist.
   (b) On the other hand, for $|r| < 1$,

   $$1 - 2r + 3r^2 - 4r^3 + \cdots = \sum_{n=0}^{\infty} (n + 1)(-r)^n = (1 + r)^{-2},$$

   hence $\lim_{r \to 1^-} (1 + r)^{-2} = \frac{1}{4}$.
   (c) Is the converse of Frobenius's theorem true or false?
5. Prove the following properties of the Poisson kernel $P(r, \alpha)$ (see Definition 9.7):
   (a) $P(r, -\alpha) = P(r, \alpha)$.
   (b) The maximum of $P(r, \alpha)$ is $(1 + r)/2\pi(1 - r)$ and this value is assumed at $\alpha = 0$.
   (c) With r fixed, $P(r, \alpha)$ is monotonic decreasing for $0 \le \alpha \le \pi$. The minimum value, $(1 - r)/2\pi(1 + r)$, is assumed at $\alpha = \pi$.
   (d) $P(r, \alpha) > 0$.
   (e) $\int_{-\pi}^{\pi} P(r, \alpha) \, d\alpha = 1$.
6. Show that for $0 < r < 1$, the series (9.44) in Section 9.8 converges uniformly in θ and hence may be integrated term by term.
7. By considering the Fourier series of $f(x) = |x|$, $-\pi \le x \le \pi$, and its convergence at 0, deduce

   $$\frac{1}{1^2} + \frac{1}{3^2} + \frac{1}{5^2} + \cdots = \frac{\pi^2}{8}.$$

8. In the proof of Theorem 9.5, we used the following: If f is integrable on $[-\pi, \pi]$ and if $f(t + 2\pi) = f(t)$ for all real numbers t, then the function g with $g(x - t) = f(x - t) - f(x)$ where x is a fixed real number, is integrable on $[-\pi, \pi]$. We needed this fact in order to insure that g has a Fourier series. Prove the statement.

   [HINT: Let $h(u) = x - u$ and let D_m denote the set of points of discontinuity of the function m. Show that $D_{fh} \subset h^{-1}(D_f) = \{u \mid u = x - t, t \in D_f\}$ and the latter set has measure zero.]
9. Show that if c_k, $k = 0, \pm 1, \pm 2, \cdots$ are the Fourier coefficients of some integrable function f, and if $0 < r < 1$, and if the series

   $$u(r, \theta) = \sum_{k=-\infty}^{\infty} c_k r^{|k|} e^{ik\theta}$$

   converges, it may be differentiated termwise twice with respect to r.

   [HINT: See Example 8.12.]

10. Using the same hypotheses as in Exercise 9, show that the series there may be differentiated termwise twice with respect to θ.

11. Prove that if f is continuous on $[-\pi, \pi]$ and $f(x) \sim \sum_{k=-\infty}^{\infty} c_k e^{ikx}$, and if $x, \xi \in [-\pi, \pi]$, then $\int_{\xi}^{x} f(t)\, dt = \sum_{k=-\infty}^{\infty} \int_{\xi}^{x} c_k e^{ikt}\, dt$; that is, the Fourier series of f can be integrated termwise.

[HINT: Define $F(x) = \int_{\pi}^{-x} [f(t) - c_0]\, dt$. Show that the Fourier series of F converges uniformly to F, using Theorems 9.6 and 9.8. Let $F(x) \sim \sum_{k=-\infty}^{\infty} C_k e^{ikx}$. Then integrate by parts to see that if $k \neq 0$,

$$C_k = \frac{1}{2\pi} \int_{-\pi}^{\pi} F(t) e^{ikt}\, dt = -\frac{c_k}{ik}.$$]

Appendix

Ordered Field

A. THE CONCEPT OF A FIELD

Definition 1. A *binary operation* on a set F is a function with domain $F \times F$ and range contained in F.

Definition 2. A *field* is a set F with more than one element, together with two binary operations on F, called addition and multiplication, subject to the following conditions:

I. *Addition*
With every ordered pair (a, b) of elements of F is associated a unique element of F called the *sum* of a and b, written $a + b$, such that

239

(i) $(a + b) + c = a + (b + c)$. [Addition is associative.]

(ii) $a + b = b + a$. [Addition is commutative.]

(iii) There exists a (unique) element 0 such that $a + 0 = 0 + a = a$, for all $a \in F$. [Additive Identity.]

(iv) $a \in F \Rightarrow \exists x \in F \ni a + x = 0$. [Additive Inverse.]

II. Multiplication

With every ordered pair (a, b) of elements of F is associated a unique element of F called the *product* of a and b, written ab, such that

(i) $(ab)c = a(bc)$. [Multiplication is associative.]

(ii) $ab = ba$. [Multiplication is commutative.]

(iii) There exists a (unique) element 1 such that $a(1) = 1(a) = a$, for all $a \in F$. [Multiplicative Identity.]

(iv) $a \in F, a \neq 0 \Rightarrow \exists x \in F \ni ax = 1$. [Multiplicative Inverse for non-zero elements.]

III. The Distributive Law

$$a(b + c) = ab + ac \text{ for all } a, b, c \in F.$$

The following consequences of these axioms are proved in abstract algebra. We assume them here:

(1) $a, b \in F \Rightarrow \exists x \in F \ni a + x = b$. [Subtraction is always possible.]

We define $x = b - a$ to be the solution of the equation $a + x = b$.

(2) $a \neq 0, b \in F \Rightarrow \exists x \in F \ni ax = b$. [Division by nonzero elements is always possible.]

We define $x = b/a$ to be the solution of the equation $ax = b, a \neq 0$.

(3) $a + b = a + c \Rightarrow b = c$.

(4) $ab = ac, a \neq 0 \Rightarrow b = c$.

(5) $a, b \in F \Rightarrow (-a)(-b) = ab$ and $(-a)b = -ab$.

(6) $ab = 0$ and $a \neq 0 \Rightarrow b = 0$.

(7) $a(b - c) = ab - ac$.

We point out that any nonempty set with an operation satisfying I(i), (iii), and (iv) is called a *group* (the operation need not be called "addition"; it simply must have the indicated properties). If, beside I(i), (iii), and (iv) we assume that I(ii) also holds, we call the group a *commutative group* or *Abelian group*. If, beside all of I, we have II(i) and III, plus $(b + c)a = ba + ca$, we speak of a *ring*. If, in addition to being a ring, II(ii) holds, we have a *commutative ring*.

EXERCISES A1

Consider the following systems (that is, sets of elements with the operations indicated) and tell which of the properties of a field hold:

1. The natural numbers with the usual addition and multiplication.
2. The integers with the usual addition and multiplication.
3. The rational numbers with usual addition and multiplication.
4. The complex numbers with rational real and imaginary parts, that is, numbers of the form $a + bi$ where a, b are rational numbers and $i^2 = -1$. (Usual addition and multiplication.)
5. All real numbers of the form $a + b\sqrt{2}$ with a, b rational. (Add and multiply as usual.)
6. All real numbers of the form $a + b\sqrt{p}$ where p is a prime, and a, b are rational numbers.
7. The symbols $\bar{1}$ and $\bar{0}$ with addition and multiplication defined as though $\bar{1}$ corresponds to an odd integer, $\bar{0}$ corresponds to an even integer; that is, since even + odd = odd, we define $\bar{0} + \bar{1} = \bar{1}$, and so on.
8. The symbols $\bar{0}, \bar{1}, \bar{2}, \bar{3}, \bar{4}$, with addition and multiplication defined "modulo 5," that is, since $4 + 3 = 7 \equiv 2(5)$, we define $\bar{4} + \bar{3} = \bar{2}$.
9. The symbols $\bar{0}, \bar{1}, \bar{2}, \bar{3}, \bar{4}, \bar{5}$ with addition and multiplication defined "modulo 6." (See Exercise 8.)
10. Can you generalize Exercises 7, 8, and 9? [Hint: 2 and 5 are prime numbers; 6 is not prime.]
11. The set of all real-valued functions defined on $[a, b]$ with addition and multiplication defined "point-wise"; for example, if f and g are real-valued functions, then $f + g$ is defined by $(f + g)(x) = f(x) + g(x)$ for all $x \in [a, b]$ and fg is defined by $(fg)(x) = f(x)g(x)$.

B. AN ORDERED FIELD

An ordered field is a field in which a relation of "less than" ($a < b$) is defined satisfying the familiar rules for operating with inequalities. More precisely,

Definition 3. An *ordered field* is a field F together with a relation $<$ ("less than") satisfying:
  (i) $a, b \in F \Rightarrow$ one and only one of $a = b, a < b, b < a$ holds. (*The trichotomy law.*)
  (ii) $a < b$ and $b < c \Rightarrow a < c$. (*The transitive law.*)
  (iii) $a < b \Rightarrow a + x < b + x$ for all $x \in F$. ($<$ is preserved under addition.)
  (iv) $a > 0, b > 0 \Rightarrow ab > 0.$* (The product of two "positive" elements is positive.)

---

* The symbol $>$ is defined by $x > y$ iff $y < x$. An element a for which the relation $a > 0$ holds is called a *positive* element.

EXERCISES A2

1. The reader should convince himself that the definition of ordered field could have been framed in terms of our formal notion of a relation as follows:

   Definition. An *ordered field* is a field F, together with a subset S of $F \times F$, satisfying the following:
   - (i) $a, \ b \in F \Rightarrow$ one and only one of $a = b$, $(a, b) \in S$, $(b, a) \in S$ holds.* (*The trichotomy law.*)
   - (ii) $(a, b) \in S, (b, c) \in S \Rightarrow (a, c) \in S$. (*The transitive law.*)
   - (iii) $(a, b) \in S, x \in F \Rightarrow (a + x, b + x) \in S$. (*The relation "less than" is preserved under addition.*)
   - (iv) $(0, a) \in S, (0, b) \in S \Rightarrow (0, ab) \in S$. (*The product of two "positive elements" is positive.*)

2. Show that if F is an ordered field and if the set of all positive elements is specified, then the relation "$<$" is determined completely.
   [Hint: To determine whether $a < b$ or not, subtract a from both sides of the tentative relation $a < b$ and invoke property (iii) in the definition of an ordered field.]

3. Which of the fields in the previous set of exercises are converted to ordered fields by introducing appropriate definitions of "$<$"?

---

* What we have in mind is that $(a, b) \in S$ iff $a < b$.

Bibliography

Ahlfors, L., *Complex Analysis.* New York: McGraw-Hill Book Co., 1953.

Apostol, T., *Mathematical Analysis: A Modern Approach to Advanced Calculus.* Reading, Massachusetts: Addison-Wesley Publishing Co., 1957.

Ritt, J. F., *Theory of Functions.* New York: King's Crown Press, 1947.

Rudin, W., *Principles of Mathematical Analysis.* New York: McGraw-Hill Book Co., 1964.

Seeley, R., *Introduction to Fourier Series and Integrals.* New York: W. A. Benjamin, 1966.

Symbols and Notation

$\in$	belongs to, is a member of
$\{x \mid P\}$	the set of all x having property P
$\subset$	subset of
$\subsetneq$	proper subset of
$A \cup B$	union of A and B
$A \cap B$	intersection of A and B
cA	complement of A
$A \times B$	Cartesian product of A and B
$A \bigtriangleup B$	symmetric difference of A and B
$\varnothing$	the empty set
$\Rightarrow$	implies
$\Leftrightarrow$	if and only if; iff
$\exists$	there exists

$\forall$	for every; for all
$\ni$	such that
S^{-1}	inverse of the relation S
∎	the end of proof of a statement
$\sim$	is equivalent to (used between elements of an equivalence relation) or "has the Fourier series" (used in Chapter 9)
$\aleph_0$	aleph-null (cardinal number of the set of positive integers)
$\underline{\underline{c}}$	continuum (cardinal number of the set of real numbers)
$\overline{\overline{A}}$	cardinal number of A
$f(A)$	image of A under f
$f^{-1}(A)$	inverse image of A under f
A'	derived set of A; set of accumulation points of A
$\overline{xy}$	closed interval with endpoints x and y
$\downarrow$	monotonic nonincreasing
$\uparrow$	monotonic nondecreasing
$\sup A$	supremum of A
$\inf A$	infimum of A
$N(x)$	neighborhood of x
$N(x; r)$	neighborhood of x, radius r
$N'(x)$	deleted neighborhood of x
$\bar{z}$	conjugate of the complex number z
$f't$	derivative of f at t (also $f'(t)$)
$M_k(f)$	supremum of f on kth interval of a partition
$m_k(f)$	infimum of f on kth interval of a partition
$U(P,f)$	upper Darboux sum
$L(P,f)$	lower Darboux sum
$\Omega_k(f)$	oscillation of f on the kth interval of a partition
$\omega(x)$	oscillation of a function at point x
D_f	set of points of discontinuity of f

Index

247

DATE

M